RESEARCH METHODS

IN HEALTH, PHYSICAL EDUCATION, AND RECREATION

RESEARCH METHODS

IN HEALTH, PHYSICAL EDUCATION, AND RECREATION

3rd revised edition

Edited by
Alfred W. Hubbard

AMERICAN ASSOCIATION FOR HEALTH, PHYSICAL EDUCATION, AND RECREATION

Washington, D. C.

1973

GV
14.5
.H82
1973

COPYRIGHT © 1949, 1959, 1973 BY
AMERICAN ASSOCIATION FOR HEALTH,
PHYSICAL EDUCATION, AND RECREATION

Printed in the United States of America. All rights reserved. This book, or parts thereof, may not be reproduced in any form without permission of the publisher. For information, address the Association, 1201 Sixteenth Street, N.W., Washington, D.C. 20036.

FIRST EDITION — 1949
    FIRST EDITION, REVISED — 1952
    SECOND PRINTING — 1956

SECOND EDITION — 1959
    SECOND PRINTING — 1961
    THIRD PRINTING — 1964
    FOURTH PRINTING — 1965
    FIFTH PRINTING — 1966
    SIXTH PRINTING — 1967
    SEVENTH PRINTING — 1968
    EIGHTH PRINTING — 1969
    NINTH PRINTING — 1970
    TENTH PRINTING — 1972

THIRD EDITION — 1973

Order from: AAHPER Publications — Sales,
1201 Sixteenth Street, N.W.,
Washington, D.C. 20036

PREFACE

The need for a fresh, up-to-date view of research methods in health, physical education, and recreation areas is the principal reason for this third edition of *Research Methods*. New ideas and approaches in research techniques are constantly being introduced, and it is important for the research worker (whether he is a beginning graduate student or an experienced researcher) to be aware of the latest techniques. This book is intended to continue the tradition of the two previous editions in presenting the newest approaches as reported by leading experts.

The steering committee for this third edition of *Research Methods* was appointed late in 1967; a January 1968 survey evaluated the 1949 and 1959 editions and provided suggestions for the new publication. The committee met in February 1968 for a three-day planning session with staff representatives of the American Association for Health, Physical Education, and Recreation, and it was decided that the third edition would concentrate on factors and principles underlying research methodology. The committee arranged the topics into homogeneous groups, selected chapter titles, nominated possible authors, and assigned to the chairman the responsibility for arranging authorship and supervising production.

To the authors go our sincere appreciation for explaining the principles and processes of scholarly research.

Alfred W. Hubbard

Steering Committee
    Research Council
        Marguerite Clifton
        William W. Huesner
        Alfred W. Hubbard, chairman
        Henry J. Montoye
        M. Gladys Scott
        Arthur H Steinhaus
        Wayne D. Van Huss

CONTENTS

PART I: INTRODUCTION

1. Why This Research? 3
   Arthur H Steinhaus

2. Overview of Research: Basic Principles 21
   Benjamin H. Massey

PART II: PREPARATIONS

3. Selecting and Defining a Research Problem 45
   Marion R. Broer and Dorothy R. Mohr

4. Searching the Literature 57
   Vern Seefeldt

PART III: INSTRUMENTATION, DATA COLLECTION AND ANALYSIS

5. Introduction to Instrumentation 77
   Marlene J. Adrian

6. Instrumentation: Software 89
   M. Gladys Scott

7. Instrumentation: Hardware 113
   W. D. Van Huss

8. Collecting Data 143
   Henry J. Montoye

9. Understanding Statistics 179
   Alfred W. Hubbard

PART IV: BASIC RESEARCH METHODS AND RESEARCH REPORTING

10 Experimental Research 239
Robert N. Singer

11 Descriptive Research 271
Anna S. Espenschade and G. Lawrence Rarick

12 The Historical Method 289
D. B. Van Dalen

13 The Philosophic Method of Research 305
Richard B. Morland

14 Writing Proposals, Theses, Dissertations, Research Articles 323
Hope M. Smith

15 Oral Research Reports 331
Perry B. Johnson

PART V: APPENDICES

A. Selected List of Abstracts, Bibliographies, Digits and Indices 347
Vern Seefeldt

B. Selected Bibliography: Laboratory Instrumentation 357
W. D. Van Huss

Index 361

PART I

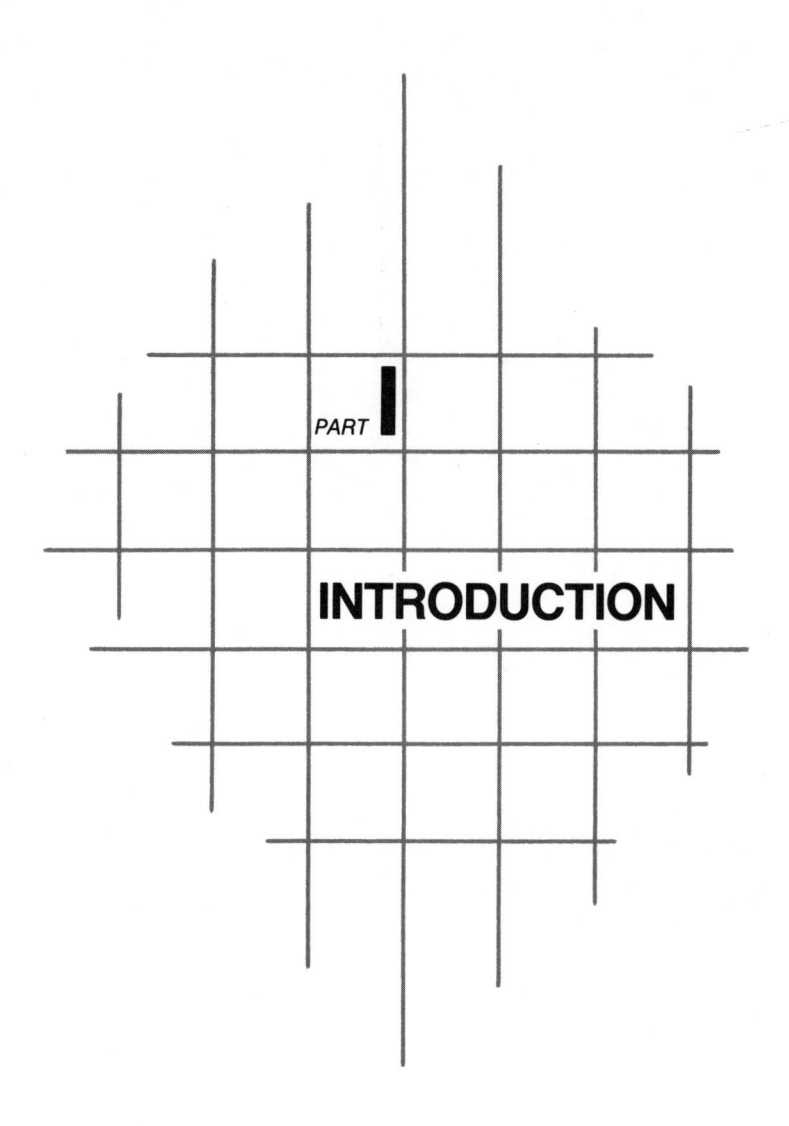

INTRODUCTION

CHAPTER 1

WHY THIS RESEARCH?

Arthur H Steinhaus †
George Williams College
Chicago, Illinois

THE EMPLOYMENT OF EDUCATIONAL methods to achieve better health, greater fitness, and the fuller enjoyment of life is an art, not a science. When this is done in the interest of humanity with reasonable likelihood of meeting certain needs of mankind it constitutes the practice of a profession. Those practices which we have come to include under the headings of health education, physical education, and recreation constitute an important specialty or branch of education, the oldest of the professions.

Education and Medical Professions

In this area where education becomes interested in health it borders most closely on another great profession, namely, the art of the practice of medicine. In fact, on this border there sometimes has been understandable but needless confusion. It is understandable because both professions have the same goal—the improvement of man's physical, mental, and social well-being; and both professions draw their factual information from the same pools of knowledge—the basic physical, biological, and social sciences. It is, however, a needless confusion because these professions should not differ in their ultimate goals nor in their sources of knowledge, but should differ only in the practices they employ to bring these knowledges into the service of mankind.

---

† Deceased.

We in education employ the methods of education. Our colleagues in the medical services employ the methods of medicine. At the risk of oversimplification may it be suggested that medicine in common with other services to mankind, such as public health and engineering, does things for people; whereas education, strictly speaking, does nothing for people, but instead helps people to do things for themselves. Consequently, the methods of education are as different from those of medicine as are the practices of farming or tree culture different from those of bread making or carpentering.

Research in our fields may appropriately interest itself (a) in basic research which aims to enlarge the pools of knowledge common to all professions, or (b) in applied research which aims to discover the best ways of using this knowledge in the practice of our professional art. Sometimes the distinction between basic and applied research is not as simple as this sounds. It is safe to assume that most of us will do applied research.

Science and Professions

The thermometer records temperature; the thermostat does something about temperature. Every thermostat needs a good temperature recording device. It needs also many other accurately designed, carefully fitted parts and, in addition, some source of power to move valves. When this power is properly released and controlled in accord with predefined objectives of desirable temperature, the thermostat performs its function.

The sciences and scientists, like thermometers, observe, measure, and record. The professions employ the findings of science to do something for mankind. Always, the professions must draw on many sciences for the best available facts lest they fail mankind. In 1927 the great St. Francis Dam near Los Angeles gave way. The commission that probed the cause of this catastrophe reported that the perfectly constructed, modern concrete structure had been built on a rock bed of mica schist in an area of geologic faults. Any geologist could have predicted the disaster. Because the science of geology had not been permitted to contribute its pertinent facts, the engineering profession's efforts at St. Francis were a disservice to mankind. The commission strongly urged the inclusion of geology in the curriculums of engineering schools.

The profession of education and its specialty, physical education, may be of far greater significance to man than is engineering; but few people realize this—which is fortunate for us. What would become of us if people attributed to education all the great disasters for which it is responsible? The list would include depressions, congressional filibusters, an assortment of world wars, and diplomatic failures at Lake Success, as well as their backyard counterparts: ignorance, delinquency, prejudice, ill health, and foul play. What do we lack?

Research

If this seems but a pompous beginning for a manual on research, let its intention be clear. The greatest danger that besets the professional worker who engages in research is that while absorbed in examining details, he may lose his professional perspective, and even worse, his orientation that gives purpose and direction to all his endeavors.

This is not to deprecate the complete mastery of detail. It is rather to give purpose to detail. The easier airplane view will never master the problems of the forest. Too few of us are willing to toil the hard hours in the depths of detail which alone will produce solid foundation for a strong profession. Such constitute the sad array of lazy, unprepared workers. A more pathetic figure, however, is the nearsighted fusser with statistics who substitutes mere toil for directed effort and is so engrossed in each figure that he does not read the score.

The purpose of this manual is to encourage and assist intelligent research directed toward worthy goals. Such activity will at once advance the profession and the professional worker.

In its early beginnings a profession must draw its personnel from related professions and its principles from related fields. In time it will generate more and more of its own personnel and guiding principles. This desirable evidence of growing maturity is, however, not without danger. Confined to its own sources the profession may stagnate. Always some of our best graduate students should find their ways into the graduate divisions of the natural and social sciences of our great universities, there to search the latest findings and the crispest methods of pure research in the older disciplines. They should go well prepared and alert to "pick the minds" of the master workers in these fields in order to bring back to physical education that which is new, stimulating, and helpful. Such students should find challenges in what this manual leaves unsaid as well as in the bare spots of our knowledge that it points out. For techniques of research they will look elsewhere. For the larger number of our graduate students, whose interest is rightly in applied research as a way of becoming more intelligent and productive professional workers, this manual is "tailor made." For those who face a research task as the final obstacle before that higher degree and the promotion that depends on it, this manual is a "godsend." It might direct even such unwilling steps to useful ends.

But let nothing be said to cause this latter group to take on greater feelings of inferiority. Research is important; it is imperative; but it is not all! The majority of our most inspiring teachers and most efficient administrators are miserable researchers. This is true also in medicine and the other professions. If all of us were thermometers, who would operate the valves? Even more crucial, who would say, "It's too hot here, let us reset the thermostat"? Finally, who would dare stick out his neck to say, "Let us create a new thermostat"? Obviously such functions are as essential for the creation and operation of useful programs for a city system as they are for the attainment of a suitable room temperature.

The best thermostat, speaking for our profession, is one in which each part is conversant with the ways of working and purposes of the other, and is appropriately influenced by the special contribution of the other. An illustration will serve to clarify this point. All of us at sometime have had to learn the basic laws of health and many of the games and skills that constitute sports and recreation activities. We have also gained some understanding of children and adults. Some of us have become expert performers, some expert teachers. Others of us must supervise or administer a diverse range of programs and rarely operate at the performing or teaching level. Nevertheless, we are better workers because we know that which must be taught and those who must be taught, and we understand the tasks and the tribulations of the teacher. Still others of us may come into a situation where we must completely revamp a program or an entire system.

Disciple, Practical Worker, Student

In this illustration one thing is missing. How do we know that we are teaching the right things in the right way to the right people at the right time? In fact, how do we know anything is right or best? People answer these questions in different ways. Some say it is right because they themselves were taught that way. Such people who tacitly accept the authority of a leader are *disciples*. Others say it is right because it works. These are the *practical workers*. Maybe these persons are right, but without some measurement of their results they have only their own intuition and perhaps the approval of others to guide them. Often they tend to be dogmatic. For much of our practice this may be as far as we can go at present.

Still others seek the largest base of experience by which to test all practice. They discover what others have found and practiced; they devise ways of examining the results of their practice by methods that will exclude their own prejudices; they find ways to study themselves and others as objectively as possible; they learn to judge the degree of accuracy of their findings to know how seriously to accept them; and when they must make decisions that reach out beyond the facts they have been able to establish, they employ reasoning disciplined by all the available facts.

Even then, they do not take their projected judgments or hypotheses too seriously. They know the difference between a hunch or guess; a good working hypothesis; a well-supported theory, law, or doctrine; and an established fact. Such people are *students* of their profession; their practices are scientifically based; they are imbued with the scientific spirit. They are all this whether their day's work finds them leading play in the nursery, coaching a football team, classifying pupils for intramural competition, making an administrative decision, sitting on a community council, or baking a cake. When such "on the job" practical searching and experimentation is subjected to disciplined record keeping and rigorous control of procedure, perhaps in a sample or pilot-type situation under actual working conditions, it is often called clinical or *action research*. Needless to say, such activity demands a high level of research leadership lest it degenerate into a mere proving of prejudices under the exercise of politically held powers.

Any person who accepts the public trust implicit in the position of a professional worker is morally bound to true up his practices with the findings of our best researches and his methods of working with the recognized habits of modern science. These he can learn best by intelligently exploring the researches of others and consciously practicing their methods.

THE METHODS OF RESEARCH

The methods of research, though endlessly different in their specific application, are fundamentally simple. Essentially they comprise four steps: observation; recording, organizing, and treating the observed data; generalization to the formulation of a theory; and testing the new formulation with further observations.

Historical Research

Many things have happened before the researcher comes on the scene. In such instances he must depend on observations made by others who lived before him, and variously recorded in personal files, letters, minutes of meetings, and other contemporary documents of all kinds—even in the memories of friends or relatives. This is *historical research*. If it centers on the life of an individual it is sometimes called *biographic research*. It is obviously limited by the availability of materials, and begins with their discovery. The historian has refined the methods of discovery and validating the authenticity of his raw data, but essentially his activity is confined to the second step in the above list, i.e., the recording, organizing, and treating of his data, which are the observations made by others. Often such research covering the development of concepts over a long period of time provides clues to the formulation of new generalizations, which lend themselves to further testing. This bringing together and reworking of older ideas and findings is itself a form of research sometimes called *collation or integration.* It is also called *library research* and should in fact be an early step in every research program.

Philosophical Research*

Problems where the basic purpose is to derive principles, build models, or to examine theoretical presuppositions obviously cannot be solved by looking exclusively into history. The researcher is engaged in philosophical analysis. His principal concern may be to ferret out various meanings from descriptive data, to project possible alternatives that would flow from the implementation of experimental findings, to analyze conflicting points of view, or to determine the apparent influence that one educator has had on another. Research of this type—where the focus is on values, the worth of experiences, or other qualitative factors—calls for the philosophic method. "Should we reset the thermostat?" (change the curriculum) or "Do we need the thermostat?" (justification of the program) are questions that are best answered by the objective and in-depth analysis of a number of different variables, conditions, and possibilities. The philosophic method is the tool to employ in the critical investigation of propositions that do not lend themselves to experimental designs or to other methods contingent on the quantification of data.

Observational Research

Many phenomena such as the movement of stars, the weather, and the behavior of our fellow human beings are occurring contemporaneously, often in our very midst, subject to regular and even continuous observations. Often these phenomena are entirely outside our control. We must take them as they come and sometimes it is a long wait. Thus, the sun's corona has been under observation by astronomers for less than two hours all in all. The late Professor David Todd of Amherst probably witnessed more solar eclipses than any other scientist, yet his number totalled only eleven and during seven of these, clouds obstructed his view. Phenomena such as the weather, the growth of children, and the behavior of nations, though much more commonly observed, are nevertheless almost as completely outside our control. We may count, weigh,

---

* Addition on philosophical research by R. B. Morland.

measure, average, and chart them. We may submit the findings to endless mathematical treatment but always we must wait for the phenomena to happen.

This is known as *observational research*. It employs questionnaires to gather factual data, or "opinionnaires," as some have called them, to gather opinions, often by mail and from a great number of persons or institutions. This would be called a *broad survey*. At other times, such data are gathered by visitations and interviews employing interview schedules, checklists, testing, measurements, or other more intensive case study procedures. It is then called *analytical survey*. Sometimes the data so observed and collected are used in the development of scales for rating and scoring achievement and for comparing individuals or groups. Such normative procedures may be called *normative surveys*. At times data are subjected to other statistical procedures to determine the extent to which two or more kinds of observations made on an individual or a group have a tendency to be related or found together (*correlation*); to determine the extent to which one or several observed items may be causally related to another and therefore usable to predict the other (*casual analysis*); and finally to determine the nature, number, and relative importance of several causes known or unknown, that together produce one result (*factor analysis*).

The validness of conclusions drawn from any series of observations depends on the representativeness of the raw data. Sometimes it is possible to place all members of a group under observation. This is the nature of any *census* study. More commonly, for practical reasons, this is impossible. Then it becomes important to get a truly representative *sampling*. The determination of such a sample population for study is itself a critical procedure for which special methods are available. There are also statistical procedures which give an indication of the degree of certainty that the results derived from computations based on one sample are likely to be identical with results gained from similar observations on another sample (*probable error*).

Thus statistics in essence provides a mathematical control over an uncontrollable experiment being carried out by nature. This ingenious use of mathematics is the quintessence of abstraction from concrete observations. Just as whipped cream, no matter how bulky its billows of foam, is never better than the cream of which it is made; so the abstractions of statistics, no matter how impressive they seem, are never better than the initial raw data that went into the formulas. Many other pitfalls beset the user of statistics, so that often such departures from raw data—the terra firma of accurate observations—sink in the quicksands of bemuddled thinking, far below the level that sound abstraction should allow.

Experimental Research

Thus far we have considered research in which man's efforts are limited to observing phenomena when and if they occur about him, and taking them as they come. Fortunately some phenomena can be made to happen at the will of the observer. Thus the chemist, by mixing the proper ingredients at the right temperature, etc., in his test tube, can reproduce endlessly and at will what nature may do only rarely and in remote corners. Similarly, by completely controlling the diet and other environmental factors of an animal, the physiologist is able to study at will the effect of a single vitamin or amino acid on growth. By observing thousands of flies in scores of generations of predetermined and forced matings, the geneticist establishes the laws that govern the mixing and resorting of the genes that determine what we inherit. This management of the several components which together cause or determine a phenomenon under observation is the mark of the *controlled experiment* in *experimental research*. It is the latest accomplishment of science. Though best developed in physics and chemistry, it has also been profitably employed in the biological field beginning with Harvey in 1628.

Not all phenomena are subject to study by all three of these methods, i.e., the historical, observational, and experimental. Nor is this necessary in order to have an accurate science. For example, astronomy, one of the accurate sciences, will never become an experimental science in the complete sense of the term as here used until solar eclipses can be produced at will. Psychology has only recently entered the experimental field. It is most doubtful if the social sciences will ever become truly experimental in the sense of the controlled experiment. This is no reflection on social scientists; it is a comment on the extreme complexity and uncontrollability of all but the simplest social phenomena.

PREDICTABILITY AS REAL MEASURE

The real measure of a science is its ability to predict. Predictability is based on the assumption that ours is a world of "law and order." This is the fundamental *belief* of scientists and is inspired by a *faith* in the inescapable relation between cause and effect. These may be called doctrines, or better, the charter or *sine qua non* of science. Without them there would be no science, and research would be an organized wild goose chase.

This needs illustration. Aristotle said, "Jupiter rains not to grow corn but of necessity." Even Jupiter cannot help it. Once all the preliminary causes and sequences have transpired he must rain. Today we explain the cause of rain in terms of sudden cooling of warm moist air. Cooling is due to wind currents moving cold air into warm air or warm air into a cold spot. Wind is caused by the unequal expansion of gases under the influence of sun, etc. When the proper combination of conditions prevails the water vapor condenses (perhaps around tiny particles of dust whose presence is also accountable) and it rains. It can't help itself. Man has learned to observe many of these preliminary steps. His hundreds of meteorological stations make and record thousands of observations. His high and low pressure maps chart these findings into a composite picture of the atmosphere's behavior. If man is sensitive to a sufficiently complete number of factors and if he has the skill, acquired from previous experience, to interpret their interactions accurately, he predicts the weather.

In astronomy, where measurements have reached greater perfection, man is able with split-second precision to predict solar eclipses, the time of sunrise, and the time schedule of the evening star. Man has not yet learned to change the weather very much and probably never will be able to hurry an eclipse. But if he were able to change them, it would be man the *engineer*, not man the *scientist*, who did it. The final test of science is not its ability to change phenomena, but its ability to predict them—not to control the universe, but to know it. Such knowledge may then be used by man to serve his ends. If he cannot change this world, he may change himself like Mark Twain's Yankee in King Arthur's Court who saves his life by awing angry savages into worshiping him when he "invokes" a solar eclipse at the psychologic moment which he himself created, after consulting his almanac and wrist watch.

Ofttimes we are convinced of predictability even though we are unable to predict. In this sense, predictability expresses a faith which authorizes the expenditure of research energies to uncover relationships that may guide professional practices short of complete predictability. Imagine, for example, a raindrop several hundred feet above the earth's surface. Can you predict the spot on which it will land—let us say to within an inch? You may say, "No, and no one cares." But let us see. Do you agree that its course is determined by gravity and many other more variable factors, and that if you knew the strength of every gust of wind, its exact direction and its duration, if you knew how the drop was deformed and therefore the resistance it would offer to the next gust from another direction, and so on and on, will you agree that if you could take the time and had the facilities for measuring all this, then you could predict where it would land? If so, then you agree that the raindrop's course is *predictable* and *researchable* whether or not anyone will ever predict exactly where any one drop will land.

Concerning the effects of sports on the body of man, we have at present sufficient data and fairly defined principles to permit some prediction. Concerning the effects of sports on the mind and spirit of man, we have beliefs and convictions but few facts. We are here in the predicament of the raindrop analogy. There are effects, and there is rhyme and reason about them which justifies the assumption of predictability. Our difficulty stems from the fact that we do not as yet have sufficiently adequate devices for observing and measuring changes in all areas; and where we can measure we are confronted by a terrifically complex array of possible causes. To illustrate, it is easy to determine whether a season of football or weight lifting under specified conditions has resulted in increased body weight or caused muscles to grow. It is possible to predict that the increase in muscle size will be roughly proportional to the intensity of work, i.e., the amount of work done in a unit of time. Further, we know that this will be true, though in varying degree, depending on body type, of all healthy persons so engaged. This begins to sound scientific. In contrast, who is able to predict just what interracial attitudes, what standards of honesty, or what appreciation of infinite values will develop in consequence of a season of sport? Even though most of us are convinced that such changes do occur, who knows their direct causes? Is it the smile of a competitor, the odor of his perspiration, or his dogged perseverance that turns the trick? And does it turn the trick in the same direction for each participant —or for each spectator? Obviously, in these areas we cannot predict even though we are convinced of the existence of the kind of law and order that permits the assumption of predictability. It is our inability to comprehend and measure all of the multitudinous variants which here act and interact, in different combinations for each person, that has to date delayed the research necessary to gain scientific mastery.

Also in these areas it is not man the scientist who will bring about change in body size, contour, skill, or personality of people; but man the teacher, coach, or counselor who, using the best available facts from research and tested experience, will work with people to produce changes. The skills, interests, temperament, and even motivations demanded of the discoverer of facts and those demanded of the user of facts are far from alike. This probably explains why the best research scientist may not be a good teacher; and conversely, why many a topnotch teacher is poor at research. A sincere respect for truth and the highest level of integrity, however, must be qualities common to both.

FACTS AND THEORIES

Research is the scientific method for finding answers to questions. When we are insufficiently informed we often find it convenient to formulate tentative answers based on the available facts. Such tentative answers or generalizations are called hunches, guesses, hypotheses, theories, laws, or principles depending on how sure we are of them. They are important tools of thought because they help to place the known facts in proper relation to each other, show up the limitations of available facts, and most important they provide something to test or shoot at, the doing of which may uncover further facts, and thus hasten the finding of the true answer to the question.

A homely illustration will serve to clarify the interrelation of facts and theory and the special importance of each. Let us say that for some reason it is imperative that you know the whereabouts of Mr. Brown. Your question is: Where is Mr. Brown? From the observations and recordings made by others before you, you are in possession of Mr. Brown's street address and a city guide containing a city map, a register of streets, and street car directions. Library research in the telephone directory discloses that Mr. Brown has no listed telephone; consequently, you use the available records to find your way to his home. You knock on the front door which you observe stands ajar. There is no reply. You push the door open and look around the hall. Though the night is cold, you see Mr. Brown's coat on the hall tree—the hat is missing. Through another door you see the dining room table covered with dishes. Closer examination discloses warm coffee in the cups and plates but half emptied. The chairs are pushed back, one is lying on its side. These are all facts. You say to yourself, "Mr. Brown left the house in a hurry." That is your first generalization or guess concerning the whereabouts of Mr. Brown. You look around and your glance falls on another door half open leading into a bedroom. On the bed, you see a woman apparently unconscious. She groans. Now you theorize: "Aha, Mr. Brown went to the theater"—do you? Perhaps you will want to assure yourself that the unconscious woman is Mrs. Brown before you decide—but very likely you will conclude that taking all the facts so far gathered into account, the best guess concerning the whereabouts of Mr. Brown is that he has hurried out to get a doctor. That is your theory. But it is only a theory, no matter how plausible it sounds; and it must remain a theory until it is verified. True, it may be a fact. *The point is you don't know whether or not it is a fact.*

There are now two courses open to you in your search for Mr. Brown. You may decide to sit down and wait for his return; or you may adopt your guess as a working theory and start out for the nearest doctor's office. You are energetic and a little impatient and therefore start out in search of the nearest drug store. Here you inquire concerning doctors' offices, Mr. Brown, Mr. Brown's doctor, etc. You are told that the doctor upstairs is on a hunting trip so you start for the one who is said to live a block down the street. Before reaching the next corner you run into Mr. Brown who is carrying a prescription slip and in a moment of conversation your theory is confirmed. Further, your theory has helped you find Mr. Brown several minutes before you would have found him had you waited at his home. But let us say that you had not met Mr. Brown but instead you had run into a crowd of people just dispersing and the police patrol wagon starting away from the scene. The crowd is talking about a drunk Mr. Brown who had got into a fight. Their description of Mr. Brown tallies with that of your friend. Here are new facts. You cannot now go on unquestioningly holding your theory that Mr. Brown has gone to fetch a doctor. In your confusion you bump into a mutual friend who definitely settles the identity of this Mr. Brown as the one you are looking for. Should you now continue to claim that Mr. Brown went to a doctor's office, the world would call you a fool and say that you lacked judgment. Someone might say you were unscientific.

Actually, you are failing to consider all of the available facts in the formulation of your theory. You have a closed mind. You are a stand-patter refusing to adjust to more recently established facts. This is even worse than had you jumped to the conclusion that Mr. Brown had gone to the theater when you first entered his home! The theory as well as the facts has its place. Without a theory one merely sits and waits. The skill exhibited in developing a theory is called judgment. *We must not minimize the importance of the theory.* On the other hand we must not be fooled into confusing a theory with facts. Someone has said the facts represent the maps, charts, and logs of our journey. Theory is the compass which guides us in the seeking of further facts. Together they guide us over the high seas of human experience to our destination.

Now let us ask another question: How is muscular strength developed? Although it sounds almost as simple as "Where is Mr. Brown?" there is much more to it. Even after ruling out the diverting questions usually raised—"What do you mean by strength?" and "Why is strength necessary?"—more pertinent ones remain:

1. How can strength be measured in animals and man?

2. How is strength related to muscle size?

3. What happens in a muscle when it becomes larger and stronger?

4. What kinds of exercise will most rapidly develop muscular strength?

5. Is there a limit to the amount of strength that can be developed in a person?

6. If so, what factors determine the limit?

7. Are differences in the ability to develop strength related to constitutional type?

8. Are the commonly observed sexual differences in strength biologically or socially conditioned, or both?

9. Given two people with the same size of muscle why can one generate more strength than the other?

10. Why is a person often able to exert much more strength under hypnosis and in acute emergencies than ordinarily?

11. What series of tests will give the best picture of a person's over-all strength?

12. To what extent can a person's success in different sports or playing positions be predicted from measures of strength?

13. What strength criteria shall be used in the selection of military personnel for various responsibilities?

14. How much strength shall be required in the training of soldiers?

15. Is there correlation between physical strength and
    (a) resistance to disease?
    (b) mental health?
    (c) personality adjustment?

16. Is strength more readily developed in the young or in the mature organism?

17. Does strength developed in childhood persist throughout life?

18. How long does it last?

Anyone can think up many more questions and subquestions, each of which may be as large or larger than "Where is Mr. Brown?" In going through this list the reader may have found himself formulating answers to each question. Whether these answers were guesses, well-substantiated principles, or rank falsehoods based on superstition depends only in part on the preparation of the reader. Some of the questions even in this relatively simple field are completely unanswerable in today's state of knowledge, and the rest are answerable with greatly varying degrees of certainty.

Thus, questions 1 to 4 can be answered with reasonable certainty because of observations made under controlled, experimental conditions in physiological and histological laboratories. Answers for 2 and 4 are anticipated by historical research and supported by clinical research.

Answers for 5 and 6 are broad generalizations based on histologic observations of the limits of hypertrophy, the diffusion rate of oxygen, and the inability of highly differentiated muscle fibers to multiply.

Answers for 7 and 8 are based on statistical treatment of clinical observations with some verification for 8 from controlled experimentation.

Answers for 9 and 10 are at the stage of working hypotheses or mere guesses based on observations made in psychologic laboratories and psychiatric clinics.

Answers for 11 to 14 are based on extensive observation under clinical conditions that have been treated statistically to determine which scores correlate with success. This is likely to culminate in a series of correlation indices, which are really theories or working hypotheses, of how important strength is to this or that. Unfortunately research too often stops here, without testing its theories. Only rarely does one find a study that tests its claimed ability to predict, for example, a man's time in the 440-yard run from certain measurements, by subsequently determining how closely other runners' actual times compare with the times predicted for them from various measurements and test scores. That the development of strength in the training camp will help ensure a soldier's success partakes of the nature of *predictability* in the same sense as does the path of a falling raindrop cited in an earlier analogy, and is obviously even more difficult to prove by actual prediction.

The answer for 15a is based on widely accepted generalities or principles from related professions, but inadequately tested by controlled experiment. Answers for 15b and 15c are, at best, good hunches based on isolated clinical observations.

Number 16 is answered only with moderate certainty from experimental observations on animals, insufficiently corroborated on man.

Numbers 17 and 18 can be answered with reasonable certainty from controlled studies on animals and from careful observations on man made in laboratories, gymnasiums, and hospitals.

From the hundreds of studies that contribute in one way or another to the answering of the above questions, three broad principles or laws have emerged. These may be designated the overload principle; hypertrophy of use and atrophy of disuse, or the principle of reversibility; and the principle of individual and sex differences. Such principles guide the formulation of a philosophy of physical education that is scientifically grounded when it advocates some segregated activities for older boys and girls, strenuous programs for the development of strength, the necessity of continuing an exercise program throughout life, negation of absolute standards of strength in favor of standards related to individual type and adapted to the everyday requirements of life, and a high degree of expectancy of prompt results from a carefully planned program of strength building.

REMAINING TASKS

The history of research in any field has some similarities to picking apples. The early pickers can get fruit without reaching very high. Because the lower branches are now bare some may think there is nothing left to pick. The facts are otherwise in our field. There remain more problems unsolved than any of us can imagine. True, some are on rather inaccessible branches. It may help to mention just a few.

At what stage in the development of an individual do muscle cells cease to multiply? Does exercise in any way modify the timing of this? Does the fact that all body proteins in man are renewed at least once in 160 days have any significance for training programs or training diets? Does a strenuous training program shorten this "turn over" period? Do any of the metabolites of exercise modify the colloid states of cell protoplasm in a way that might give basis for prolonging the general flexibility of youth? In what ways do exercise and the endocrine glands interact? Are there any observable changes in the composition of blood constituents in consequence of a period of recreational activity? Are there any objective measures of the amount of inner tension in a person that might be used to observe the progress of recovery from so-called "nervous states," and thus be used to justify recreational activities? What objective evidence, if any, can be found to throw light on the good or bad effects of highly emotionalized competition on the female organism? Is this in any way different from its effect on the male? What is the relationship, if any, between mechanical and chemical stresses exerted on muscles, cartilage, and ligaments in youth and the incidence of fibrositis, arthritis, and related conditions in later life? Is there any relationship between swimmers' cramps and the recency of alimentation, or blood sugar, or temperature, or state of fatigue? What effect does "drying out" to lose weight have on vital body functions. What habits of living such as diet, exercise, and emotional disturbance modify the clotting time of blood, modify other blood ingredients that may predispose to vascular diseases? What changes discernible by mental testing programs follow punishment inflicted to the head as in boxing? What effects of boxing may be revealed through intensive case studies of individual boxers? How do the vitamin and protein needs in strenuous training differ from those of more sedentary living?

Even such a list as this is in no sense more than indicative of the vastness of the field for research. Obviously, some of the answers must first be sought in animal experiments. To the student who is thoroughly trained in biology and experimental psychology, experimentation on lower animals makes sense even though he does not assume that all findings are entirely applicable to man. The person who denies the validity of animal experimentation reveals a shallow understanding of the fundamental unity of living matter and the attendant implications for experimentation.

This list also points to the necessity for working more closely together with scholars in the fundamental sciences, such as biology, chemistry, and physics.

WHY THIS RESEARCH?

"Why This Research?" is answered in the analogy of woodchopping. Woodchopping produces both useful wood and a better woodchopper. Research must give to our fields the building materials of accurate facts and principles with which to construct sound practice and wise philosophy. It must supply ideas to kindle enthusiasm in our professional ranks and, in the public mind, a warm reception for our programs.

Research must also create for us a professional personnel that is expert in its attack on new problems, keenly alert to new opportunities, wisely guided in the efficient application of its energies, and disciplined with a fine humility that is fathered by confidence in one's power and mothered by an appreciation of one's limitations.

THE RESEARCHER

In the last analysis no work is better than the worker and the quality of research depends entirely on the knowledge, wisdom, and personal integrity of the investigator.

* * *

If you are well informed of advances in your field, and yet endowed with a curiosity that breeds dissatisfaction with the present state of this knowledge,

If you can ask significant questions and also formulate crucial methods for discovering honest answers,

If you have imagination to conceive a dozen hunches, and at once the industry to explore each until disciplined wisdom points to the one of choice,

If you can concentrate on an issue, and yet be alert to happenings on the periphery,

If you stick tenaciously to the rightness of your best hunch, yet possess the objectivity to treat it with detachment as though it were another's and stand ready to give it up when it becomes untenable,

If enthusiasm and industry drive you to collect much data and you record with equal respect that which supports and that which negates your theory,

If you are possessed of a fantastic memory for facts yet are willing to record them systematically as though you could not trust your memory,

If your mind works with speed and accuracy, and yet you double check your calculations,

If you are justly proud of your theory, yet humble enough to be led by facts,

If you are "hell-bent" on proving your theory, and yet satisfied that disproving it is just as great a contribution to knowledge,

If you have the courage to persist in the face of disagreement, and at once the patience to listen to the opposition,

If you are endowed with energy for long hours of searching and have enough left to organize, tabulate, analyze, and publish your findings,

If your mind is capable of holding the profoundest ideas and you have the understanding and restraint to express them in simple words even though you also know the big words,

If you are eager to forge a reputation for yourself, and at once willing to acknowledge generously your indebtedness to the labors of others,

If you are really capable of research, and your activity persists beyond your doctorate to the time when you must yourself supply both the time and motivation,

If to all of the above you can give honest affirmation, you are better than most of your contemporaries and predecessors but you are none too good for service to health, physical education, and recreation.

* * *

Let no reader of this book be unduly impressed. Though it is written by many of today's best minds in our fields, the writers will be the first to admit shortcomings. He would be a poor reader who could find no flaws in these pages. Such discovery will not discourage the authors, but will be welcomed by them as the mark of an intelligent rising generation. But if such a generation will not be capable in time to produce a much better successor to this volume, we of the present generation have cause to mourn. For where, more than on the research front, must there be progress! And how can there be progress if students do not excel their teachers—each generation standing on the shoulders of its predecessors, thus fulfilling the aspirations of the generation that begat it.

CHAPTER 2
PRINCIPLES OF PROBLEM SOLVING

Benjamin H. Massey
University of Illinois
Urbana, Illinois

"Each generation must seek its own answers to the hitherto unanswerable and define new problems for the next generation to explore."—Anonymous

RESEARCH IS DILIGENT and systematic inquiry—an investigation to discover or revise facts, theories, and applications (3). Basically, it is a matter of *problem solving* through application of the scientific method of inquiry. The purpose of this chapter is to present concepts basic to problem solving. Other chapters deal with the techniques specifically appropriate to the experimental, descriptive, and historical approaches. The principles set forth in this chapter are general and for the most part are fundamental to all forms of research.

A *problem* in the research sense is not merely a perplexity or frustration of the kind encountered in daily living or in the course of one's work. Rather, it is any proposition or question set forth for study and inquiry. The word comes from the Greek *proballein*, meaning "to set forth," a contraction of *pro*, "forward," and *ballein*, "to throw." Any proposition advanced for examination constitutes a problem for research.

The scientific method of inquiry represents a special kind of inquiry. This method is not restricted solely to the basic sciences; rather, it is a method appropriate to all fields of study. The principles involved are as applicable to research in history and philosophy as they are to research in physics and chemistry. The word "science" comes from a Latin word meaning "to know" (*scire*) and any systematized body of knowledge gained through systematic study with due regard for facts and principles constitutes a science.

THE SCIENTIFIC METHOD

The scientific method represents the melding of two approaches to understanding logic and practical experience. The Greeks and medieval scholastics placed emphasis upon logical deduction. Starting with *axioms*, accepted but nonverifiable propositions, the Greeks worked through a series of logical steps to a conclusion. This procedure is illustrated by the deductive process commonly used in mathematics. For centuries, conclusions reached in this way were considered immutable facts. The scientific awakening of the sixteenth and seventeenth centuries changed all this. Logic continued to be important, but men like Copernicus, Galileo, Newton, and Harvey, to name a few, could not accept the status quo. It seemed to them nonsense to accept as immutable truths knowledge derived through mental gyrations based on suppositions which in reality were nothing more than someone's fallible opinion. These pioneers wanted proof for everything. Proof to them meant testing a proposition against practical experience through planned, systematic observation and experimentation. Today, scientific inquiry involves both logic and the empirical testing of propositions. Three basic steps are always involved: 1) identification of a problem through formulation of a specific question, 2) advancement of a tentative answer to the question —hypothesis—in the form of a stated proposition derived through inductive and/or deductive reasoning, and 3) empirical testing of the validity of the hypothesis, proving it, through planned observation and experimentation. The third step involves the basic research methods referred to in Chapter 1, p. 7: observation, data accumulation and treatment, generalization, and further testing of the derived theory.

Research

The Rationale of Research

The basic rationale underlying all scientific inquiry is man's sense of obligation to understand himself and his environment. He is driven to problem solving through his innate curiosity and the desire to explore, control, and predict the ways of the universe in which he lives. The scientist has faith that the universe is orderly, if not purposeful, and as such it can be described, understood, and predicted. The scientist believes that if he asks a direct question of nature he can obtain, through observation and experimentation, a direct answer. Causation is a matter of concern, but recognizing that causation can never be substantiated, he is content with the idea that cause exists if one phenomenon is always associated with, and preceded by, another in time. The scientist has faith that man is mentally suited to, and capable of, understanding the universe and that any apparent aberration in the orderly processes of nature is a figment of his own thinking and inability to grasp the total picture. He believes that his first and primary obligation is to bring conceptual order out of chaos, and that this can be accomplished by the continuous process of fragmenting phenomena into their many parts and studying each fragment systematically and intensively. The scientist considers it his obligation to simplify and give order to phenomena so that each aspect can be better understood. It is his job to establish facts, structure theories, and develop operational principles applicable to practical ends.

The Myth of Orderliness

There is a popular conception that research is accomplished in a nice, orderly fashion. This is a misconception. Science strives for orderliness, but this is more an ideal than a reality. The scientific method, as conceptualized, is quite orderly. An investigator should strive for orderliness in thinking and in practice, otherwise research experience can terminate in fantastic confusion and frustration. However, despite the scientist's efforts toward orderliness, investigation and the acquisition of knowledge are something less than an orderly process. They proceed by fits and starts with periods of tedious observation and frustration interspersed with sudden understanding and insight.

Two factors operate to obstruct the orderly process: 1) extraneous circumstances beyond the control of the investigator, and 2) the way in which man thinks. With respect to extraneous circumstances, there is an overriding rule in research—if something can go wrong, it will. This is especially true in studies involving humans. The cooperation of the individuals being studied, environmental influences, and research protocol are all difficult to control. There are ways of minimizing frustrations, but no way of removing them. Investigators, past and present, have been challenged to devise methods to cope with such frustrations. As a result, ever better methods of problem solving have evolved, so that today we have a well-established method of scientific inquiry. The researcher willing to adhere to accepted methodology will avoid many pitfalls and frustrations.

The second obstruction to the orderly process of scientific inquiry, the way man thinks, is not easily regulated. Man's attempt to regulate thinking has led to the discipline of logic. Despite rules and guidelines, each man thinks in his own unique ways. Rules for problem solving suitable to one man may be entirely unsuited to another. The essential feature in thinking is an unshackled mind. Preconceived notions and arbitrary rules for problem solving must not obstruct the researcher's thinking and creativity. Mental alertness, ingenuity, and initiative are at a premium in research. Insight, the fundamental purpose of research, is as much a matter of chance and intuition as the outgrowth of logical processes. An anecdote in the life of Henri Poincaré, the mathematician, illustrates this:

> For fifteen days I strove to prove that there could not be any functions like those I have since called Fuchsian functions. I was then very ignorant; every day I seated myself at my work table, stayed an hour or two, tried a great number of combinations and reached no results. One evening, contrary to my custom, I drank black coffee and could not sleep. Ideas rose in crowds; I felt them collide until pairs interlocked, so to speak, making a stable combination. By the next morning I had established the existence of a class of Fuchsian functions, those which come from the hypergeometric series; I had only to write out the results, which took but a few hours.
>
> Then I wanted to represent these functions by the quotient of two series; this idea was perfectly conscious and deliberate, the analogy with elliptic functions guided me. I asked myself what properties these series must have if they existed, and I succeeded without difficulty in forming the series I have called theta-Fuchsian.
>
> Just at this time I left Caen, where I was then living, to go on a geologic excursion under the auspices of the school of mines. The changes of travel made me forget my mathematical work. Having reached Coutances, we entered an omnibus to go some place or other. At the moment when I put my foot on the step the idea came to me, without anything in my former thoughts seeming to have paved the way for it, that the transformations I had used to define the Fuchsian functions were identical with those of non-Euclidean geometry. I did not verify the idea; I should not have had time, as, upon taking my seat in the omnibus, I went on with a conversation already commenced, but I felt a perfect certainty. On my return to Caen, for conscience's sake I verified the result at my leisure. (2: 36–37)

James D. Watson, one of the discoverers of the structure of DNA, commented on the illusion of orderliness in research as follows:

> ... science seldom proceeds in the straightforward logical manner imagined by outsiders. Instead, its steps forward (and sometimes backward) are often very human events in which personalities and cultural traditions play major roles. (4)

The Role of the Investigator

The critical element in problem solving is the investigator. This is not surprising, since research is essentially a matter of *thinking*. The successful researcher brings to his task three qualifications: 1) motivation, 2) skill in research procedures, and 3) a familiarity with the relevant body of knowledge.

Motivation is a tricky matter. Mixed motives are the rule rather than the exception. Often one is moved to research by such considerations as professional advancement, impressing colleagues, adding another publication to the list, or leaping the thesis hurdle. Such motives are acceptable but should not dominate the researcher's thinking. The dominant motive must be a sincere desire to obtain the correct answer to a question. The researcher must be motivated by curiosity if his efforts are to have focus and purpose.

Skill in research is acquired only through experience. Reading about research and the study of methodology is important, but actual involvement in research is even more important. The more one engages in the research process, the more competent one becomes. Failure to become involved insures ineptness. Involvement is essential.

The importance of familiarity with the existing body of relevant knowledge cannot be overemphasized. One cannot select a meaningful problem without background information, nor can he conduct a significant study. Researchers, particularly inexperienced researchers, all too often attempt to formulate and carry out an investigation without first searching out what others have reported. Time is wasted and the findings more often than not contribute little to man's store of knowledge.

Significant Research

Any number of equally attractive problems are available to an investigator. The task confronting him is to select one which has particular significance. No professional is interested in wasting time seeking solutions to problems of negligible importance or to those that have been already solved. Identifying a truly significant problem, however, is no easy task.

The object of research is to establish a verifiable finding, a *fact*. A fact, in scientific terms, is any verified or verifiable observation. Facts at random lead nowhere, but when "ordered" and "conceptualized" provide the basis for a *theory*. Theories are the bases for structuring a body of knowledge. Theories are broad conceptualizations which are believed to be true in the light of the best available evidence. They can never be fully substantiated. Theories provide the grounds for developing principles—guidelines to decision making. Facts are limited in scope and relatively fixed. Theories continually change and evolve. As new facts come to light, theories change consistently with, and for the purpose of explaining, the new facts. Theories make it possible for us to move from situation to situation with some confidence in our ability to make correct decisions. Without theories, one moves from crisis to crisis hoping that the decision made is reasonably correct. A significant problem for study is one which will lead to the establishment of a fact which has implications for modifying an existing theory or structuring a new theory.

Unfortunately, the selection of a problem for study often is based on considerations other than its potential contribution to man's store of knowledge. The immediate needs of the researcher and the problem's applicability to an immediate situation often take precedence. Such problems are too local to have broad and significant implications. Such problems unquestionably are important in a transitory sense, but have little permanence. Concerned with this point, Francis Bacon wrote:

> Again, even in the great plenty of mechanical experiments, there is yet a great scarcity of those which are of most use for the information of the understanding. For the mechanic, not troubling himself with the investigation of truth, confines his attention to those things which bear upon his particular work, and will not either raise his mind or stretch out his hand for anything else. But then only will there be good ground of hope for the future advance of knowledge, when there shall be received and gathered together into natural history a variety of experiments, which are of no use in themselves, but simply serve to discover causes and axioms; which I call *experimenta lucifera*, experiments of *light*, to distinguish them from those which I call *fructifera*, experiments of *fruit*.
>
> Now experiments of this kind have one admirable property and condition; they never miss or fail. For since they are applied, not for the purpose of producing any particular effect, but only of discovering the natural cause of some effect, they answer the end equally well whichever way they turn out; for they settle the question. (1: 134–35)

A significant problem is one which contributes, even minutely to man's total store of knowledge and understanding (see Chapter 3, pp. 45–47). Too often old discoveries pass for new. Too often researchers merely define, embellish, or couple together that which is already known. Too often, devoid of the initiative and courage to respond to the challenge of the unknown, they delight in repetitious data collecting, content with a safe, well-planned measurement study which leads nowhere.

Reasoning

Auguste Comte wrote that "reasoning and observation, duly combined, are the means of . . . knowledge" (1: 224). Careful and valid observation is important, but unless one proceeds to make sense out of the observation, it is useless. The ability to reason correctly with the facts at hand is important in problem solving. Thinking is an intangible process. How it takes place and its determinants are not well understood. We do know it is hard work and most of us avoid it at all costs. It is easier to make observations than to interpret them. Native intelligence, past experiences, interest, and focus of attention contribute to the process of thought. Descartes concluded that the primary reason that individuals reach different conclusions was, " ... that we conduct our thoughts along different ways and do not fix our attention on the same objects." He went on to observe, "For to be possessed of a vigorous mind is not enough; the prime requisite is rightly to apply it" (1: 163).

Traditionally, reasoning has been classified into two categories, *deductive* and *inductive* (see also Chapter 10, pp. 267–268). These represent different approaches, but are not opposite extremes of one continuum. The two may be used in combination. They represent mental constructs of how man proceeds in ordering his thoughts and in drawing conclusions. They are useful conceptual models designed to help us think more definitively about the process of reasoning. The *deductive* method starts with general axioms and leads to specific corollaries—conclusions considered settled and beyond question. It is the method of certainty. The *inductive* method starts with many particulars and proceeds toward axioms and theories, moving along a course during which intermediary propositions and principles are developed. It is the method of probability.

The deductive method, used so effectively by Aristotle, is the method of "cold reason." It is the method of the logician: "If this, then that." The process starts with a self-evident, accepted truth—an axiom—and through a series of steps argues to a conclusion. It is a method particularly useful in deducing principles from established theories, which, incidentally, have been inductively formulated from observation. The deductive method is the method of certainty, for its conclusions must be true if the original premise is true, and reasoning proceeds step-by-step according to the established rules of logic. Every schoolboy has encountered the method in geometry. The following is an example of the deductive method of reasoning:

a. Participation in varsity sports builds character.
b. Football is a varsity sport.
c. Therefore: participation in football builds character.

A number of schemes have been established by logicians for reasoning deductively. These are described in standard textbooks on logic. The prospective researcher could profit from taking at least one course in logic, for reasoning deductively requires experience and training. In the hands of the inexperienced, the method can lead to erroneous conclusions with all of the confidence of certainty. If an original premise is incorrect, or if any step in the argument is incorrect, the conclusion will be incorrect. The novice, attempting to reason deductively, is apt to arrive at an incorrect conclusion. The trained logician will not do so.

Inductive reasoning is the method which leads from observation of a number of specific cases to an overall conclusion. It is the method leading from particulars to generalized concepts.

In this method, particular events are observed, and the observations are ordered, organized, and classified. A search is made for a pattern of uniformity from which a generalization can be drawn and stated in terms of probability, not certainty. Through the years, elaborate statistical procedures have evolved, making it possible to draw inferences from data at specified levels of probability. Without such statistical formulae, it would be impossible to organize and draw rational conclusions from the masses of data now made available through modern instrumentation. The inductive method requires that data be ordered and analyzed in a concise, direct fashion.

Certainty and Probability

Sooner or later every researcher must come to grips with the problem of "knowing." How can he be certain that his conclusions are correct?

To the nonresearcher, the findings of an investigator are absolute, especially if the findings support a prejudice. "Research shows this," or, "research shows that," are familiar phrases. Articles in popular journals frequently relate with certainty scientific findings which, in the original report, were stated in the most tenuous terms. This simplistic approach to the interpretation of findings may do irreparable harm. Not only is the public misled but also research is stifled. Why study a problem which has already been solved? Even mature professionals sometimes are so naive as to believe that a single study will answer a question. To them repeated studies seem unwarranted and, academically speaking, "not cricket." This view discourages sustained study of a problem. Consequently, all too often only the surface of important problems is scratched, while professors and students search frantically for new problems to investigate. Studies in series permit clarification and crystallization of one's thinking, which leads ultimately to a reasonably certain answer.

The modern scientist does not attempt to deal in certainty. *Knowing* is a matter of probability rather than certainty. The findings of a study are expressed at some selected level of probability. This is not a serious limitation, for as Sir Arthur Stanley Eddington has pointed out, "When the probabilities are large the substitution of probability for certainty makes little difference; it adds only a negligible haziness to the world" (1 : 439).

Probability as a research concept is not difficult to grasp, even though some have a mental block to anything statistical. Probability has the same meaning in research as it does at the racetrack or when playing cards, throwing dice, or gambling in any form. In fact, it was from the gambling halls of central Europe that scientists got the idea of using probabilities in research. Probability merely is a matter of estimating what will happen in the future from what has happened in the past. For example, in throwing dice the six faces of a die can be expected to show equally often—the six face, one-sixth of the time; the five face, one-sixth of the time; the four face, one-sixth of the time; etc. The probability for any specific face turning up is one-sixth, or about 17 times in 100 casts. We have learned to expect this from having thrown perfectly formed cubes many times. When this probability does not occur, the conclusion is reached that the die is loaded. In a loaded die the probability is changed and we can learn what the new probability is only by casting the die many times.

In research, if condition X always follows condition Y, or at least 99 times out of 100 condition X follows condition Y, in future trials X is expected to follow Y approximately 99 times out of 100. This is the level of probability. Practical experience has demonstrated this to be the expected result. Research is practical. The scientist observes and establishes on the basis of observation an experiential basis for predicting future events at a given level of probability. Findings often are expressed in terms of probability. Despite the importance of repeating studies, it is not always feasible to repeat them over and over, hundreds of times. Consequently, elaborate statistical methods for inferring probability have been developed. To utilize these tools, an investigator must become well schooled in statistical theory.

In some areas of research, history for example, the findings are a matter of subjective interpretation. To date, no easy way has been discovered to quantify and express historical findings in terms of probability. The conclusions of the historian must be based on his subjective interpretation of the data. He must select the explanation he believes to be most tenable. Statistical procedures applicable to historical research will, it is hoped, be developed.

It might be inferred from what has been stated that the scientist rejects the concept of any ultimate absolutes. This, however, is not the case. But the scientist is practical. He recognizes that human limitations do not permit exact knowledge of any phenomenon, even an absolute. Further, he recognizes that man is incapable of proving anything to the satisfaction of all concerned. Consequently, he is content to live and function in the realm of probability, leaving arguments regarding reality and absolutes to the philosopher.

Cause

Cause represents to the researcher a special kind of problem. Historically, the ultimate aim of research was to discover cause. The premise was that if the cause of a phenomenon could be identified, the basis would be established for the prediction and control of resultant events. The difficulty with cause as a scientific concept, however, is that of establishing its certainty. The term *cause* implies that, in a very direct way, one phenomenon initiates and determines a second. Two events must occur in exactly the same relationship, one giving rise to the other in every eventuality, if the relationship is to be accepted as a causal one. It is not feasible, in fact it is impossible, to test every eventuality. Such a venture would continue indefinitely. Consequently, the scientist has found it impracticable to attempt to establish cause. Rather than discarding the term, however, he has chosen to define it in a special way: a recurring chronological relationship between two phenomena. If, in the course of experience, phenomenon A is observed to occur systematically in association with, and to precede, phenomenon B, then A may be accepted as the cause of B, without further proof. This solution to the scientist's dilemma might sound like "nit-picking," but it does provide a precise, workable definition of cause on a simple, descriptive basis, and eliminates the obligation to prove the impossible, namely, the existence of a true causal relationship between phenomena.

Terminology

Problem solving requires clarity of communication as well as clarity of thought. It is doubtful if one can exist without the other. The importance of *thinking* logically in research is well accepted, but the importance of clarity in communication is not always associated in one's mind with the research process.

Our thoughts are of little value to anyone but ourselves unless we can communicate them to others. Through communication we submit them for review and evaluation. The solution of a problem cannot be accepted as fact until it has been verified. Obviously, a study cannot be repeated and the findings verified unless it has been reported in clear, concise language.

The scientific method demands that each word and symbol have a precise meaning. The words used must refer to definite, identifiable objects and concepts. Each noun must have an absolute referent. Frequently, in exploratory work, a concept arises for which a word or symbol does not exist. A word or symbol must be coined. More often, however, a frequently used word has too many referents. The investigator in such an instance is obligated to define the particular word as specifically as possible, to give it the meaning he wishes it to have. The emphasis placed on the use of specific definitions and the coining of terms has led to the development in each discipline of a jargon peculiar to that area of inquiry. The result has been that communication for "in-groups" has improved, but language barriers have arisen between disciplines. Such barriers may be undesirable; however, no good way of avoiding them without sacrificing precision in terminology has yet been devised. To communicate with scholars in a particular field requires one to become conversant in the terminology of that field. It is a matter of learning a new language. Every beginning researcher must learn the language of his area of inquiry and learn to respect the words and use them correctly.

Basic Assumptions

An investigator undertaking a study has to make certain *basic assumptions*. These assumptions are the starting point for an investigation. A basic assumption, or *postulate*, is a proposition which is not testable but is accepted as true in the light of the best available evidence. This act of faith is important, for without basic assumptions, each investigation would have to begin at the very earliest stage of knowledge. Each investigator, like René Descartes, would have to prove first his own existence and from that point test each subsequent proposition. Such a procedure would be ridiculous. Alfred North Whitehead (1: 351) has said, " .... the very groundwork of a fruitful methodology is to start from those clear postulates which must be held to be ultimate so far as concerns the occasion in question."

Some basic assumptions are so basic and so much a part of the philosophy of the scientific process that their existence may not be recognized. An example is the assumption that the universe is orderly, systematic, and predictable. Circumstantial evidence indicates this to be true, but man has no adequate method of testing this proposition. Another assumption fundamental to the research process is that the human mind is capable of sensing and interpreting the world about it. A third underlying assumption is that anything which exists must exist in some measurable quantity. These unstated and often unrecognized assumptions are, in essence, unprovable value judgments so basic and so universally accepted that we proceed with our research without giving them a second thought.

There is another category of basic assumptions implicit in the research process, not quite as subtle as the group mentioned, and normally accepted as a matter of convenience and common sense without being verbalized. These are the assumptions underlying research methodology. Normally, for example, it is assumed that other researchers are basically honest, competent individuals and that the findings reported in the literature are valid. Further, in historical research it is normally assumed that although the primary source materials utilized may individually contain error, when taken in toto they present a reasonably valid picture of the past. Another example of this kind of assumption concerns the use of statistics. It is assumed that the statistical formulae utilized have been appropriately derived, based on sound theoretical concepts, and are valid for the task at hand. Obviously, these kinds of assumptions are essential to the research process, but like those underlying the philosophy of scientific inquiry, they may not be recognized and seldom are verbalized.

A third class of assumptions which must be made are those specific to the study at hand. Such assumptions must be clearly stated or explicitly implied. They may relate to the total field of inquiry on which a study rests or may pertain to a single aspect of the study. An investigator studying the effects of an exercise routine on physical fitness must assume, for example, that physical fitness is a real, identifiable entity subject to definition and measurement. In the absence of exhaustive validative evidence he will have to assume that the test being used to measure physical fitness does measure it, that the exercise routine which has been selected for use is sufficiently intense to induce a change in fitness, that the training period selected is sufficiently long to effect a change, that the factor(s) selected for measurement represent fitness, that the factors selected can be adequately measured (quantified), that the units selected to quantify the phenomenon are suitable for that purpose, and that the instruments to be used will adequately reflect the variables measured in the units selected. All of the items listed may be accepted as basic assumptions by one investigator, while a second may be skeptical and unwilling to accept any as assumptions.

Any proposition not supported by circumstantial evidence and logic as being highly probable should not be accepted as a basic assumption on which to base an investigation. Every investigator must ask and satisfactorily answer two questions: 1) What are the assumptions upon which this study rests? 2) Is each assumption logical in the light of existing knowledge?

A Researchable Question

Earlier, it was indicated that problem solving by the scientific method involves three overt steps: 1) asking a specific question; 2) advancing a logical hypothesis representing a tentative answer to the question; and 3) testing the hypothesis, proving or disproving it, through direct observation. Each step is important but the first is basic, setting the pattern for the entire research effort.

A researchable question does not come by chance. It is usually the result of reading, reflective thinking, and practical experience. The beginning researcher can read and think reflectively, but experience in the field and in research is necessary to formulate a substantive question. For the graduate student, assistance may be required from the thesis adviser or committee.

A good question is one stated in simple, direct, clear terms. It should be free from ambiguity, with each term and phrase clearly defined with respect to a specific referent. It should lead to a clear, well-stated, testable hypothesis.

Developing a question from a generalized idea is not easy. It is an art demanding a great deal of experience and skill. Too frequently investigations are begun without a specific question asked or a basic thesis developed. Such investigations are little more than superficial looks or haphazard collections of data dignified by statistical analysis.

Ideas for research can originate anywhere—through observation, reading, or conversation. Initially such ideas are usually nebulous and too generalized to be researched. Initial ideas must be pared down to manageable, researchable size and form. The task requires imagination, ingenuity, skill, and concentrated effort.

The Hypothesis

A question, by its very nature, demands an answer. A researchable question may have any number of potentially good answers which appear equally feasible. The task confronting an investigator is to identify the one most seemingly correct and to check it through systematic, controlled observation. This procedure is straightforward and effective. The tentative answer selected for investigation can best be checked if set forth as a proposition to be proved tenable or untenable. The word *proved*, in the language of science, does not mean to support or justify one's preconceived opinion. Rather, it signifies the objective testing of a proposition. The proposition set forth represents the investigator's belief as to the most logical answer to the question. It is called the *hypothesis* from the Greek words, *hypo*, meaning "under," and *thesis*, "to put or set down" and, in essence, it is a scientific guess. By definition, any proposition put forth for consideration is a thesis, and any thesis upon which an investigation rests, that is, is set forth to be proved, is a hypothesis.

Formulating a rational hypothesis pertinent to the question asked is the most efficient way to proceed in obtaining an answer. If something is lost, there are an infinite number of places to look. An intelligent person, however, does not begin to search blindly, in a haphazard manner.

First, he will think back and decide where the article most likely was left. He will then proceed to look in that location. Similarly, in research, the most feasible hypothesis available in the light of existing information should be the proposition set forth for testing. If the proposition stands up under careful observation and proves tenable at a high level of probability, it can be considered, for all practical purposes, as the right answer. If the hypothesis, however, does not prove tenable, then grounds have been established for selecting another hypothesis for testing. In testing a hypothesis, it is important to remember two things: 1) failure to substantiate a hypothesis as tenable at a high level of probability does not prove the hypothesis wrong, rather it merely indicates that the hypothesis has not been demonstrated to be tenable at a level of probability approaching certainty; 2) if the hypothesis is a good one, it is just as important to find that it is not tenable as it is to find it tenable. In other words, negative findings are important, and the researcher should not feel obligated to substantiate the hypothesis he selected for testing.

Every rational study involves a verbalized or implied hypothesis. In some, the specific hypothesis to be tested is clearly stated. In others, the hypothesis is implicit in the stated purpose of the study and is not verbalized. The more that is known about a problem, the easier it is to state a hypothesis. If there is little existing knowledge, the development of a specifically worded proposition is difficult to accomplish. An investigator does not know in which direction to look for the answer. In an exploratory, descriptive study, for example, so little information is available that a concrete hypothesis is difficult to formulate. In fact, the purpose of such a study normally is to gain enough information to establish hypotheses leading to more definitive research. In such instances, the nonverbalized hypothesis on which the investigation rests is that there exists an underlying uniformity sufficiently distinct to make meaningful description of the phenomenon possible. If the investigator did not expect to find a describable pattern, the investigation would not be undertaken. Only the most foolish individual would waste time observing and describing random variation. Historical and social research often is descriptive, so hypotheses to be tested are not stated. The investigator expects to find some trend or pattern of events which will serve to answer the question researched and proceeds to make appropriate observations.

Background information is essential for selecting and formulating a significant hypothesis. Consequently, one should acquire as much information as possible concerning the question under consideration before attempting to establish the hypothesis. Fortified with adequate knowledge, a definitive, meaningfully worded hypothesis can be structured which will give focus and direction to the study. This will prevent needless waste in energy and time in the collection of useless data. Further, it will lead to specific findings and make possible definitive conclusions.

Testing the Hypothesis

The third step in problem solving, proving the hypothesis, involves testing through practical experience the validity of the thesis advanced. This, to many, is what the word *research* signifies. The step includes planning, making, and recording the observations (data), analyzing the data, and drawing conclusions. This step uniquely characterizes the scientific method of problem solving. It reflects the skepticism of the practical mind. Irrespective of how feasible something may sound, it must be tried out before being accepted. This we do in the daily course of human affairs, and it is equally as reasonable to follow this course of action in dealing with ideas and theories.

Hypothesis testing is a sensible, straightforward process. The investigator is testing his logic. He wishes to discover if the proposition postulated is, in fact, correct. If it has been logically derived from the best available information, it matters little whether it is proved tenable or untenable. Either finding is important and when an investigator places extreme emphasis upon supporting a hypothesis one suspects immaturity as a scholar.

The approach to testing a hypothesis is determined by the nature of the problem, with the demands of the historical, descriptive, and experimental methods all differing. Irrespective of differences, all require that there be careful selection of the observations to be made, careful recording of the observations, intelligent analysis of the data, and the drawing of definite conclusions.

The practical steps in testing a hypothesis are as follows:

1. *Clear identification of the phenomena to be observed*—The phenomena to be observed must be clearly identified and described. Observations may be of any type as long as they are relevant to the purposes of the study. Court documents, personal letters, monument inscriptions, statements by individuals, human behavior of all sorts, and physical characteristics are kinds of phenomena to be observed.

2. *Recording observations*—Observations must be recorded in usable, retrievable form. It is one thing to observe a phenomenon, quite another to recall it accurately. An observation first must be reduced to manageable terms, then recorded in a relatively permanent, readily accessible form. The variety of forms in which observations can be recorded are infinite. They may appear in short, concise summary statements, as alphabetical letters signifying categories, or perhaps reduced to some standard unit of measure, e.g., pounds, meters, yards, or microns. The objective always is to simplify and facilitate conceptualization of the thing observed. Since observations, when recorded, constitute the data to be analyzed, they must reflect accurately the quality and quantity of the thing observed.

It would be absurd to try to report distance in pounds or the height of boys in miles. Inappropriate units lead to hazy, nebulous findings.

3. *Selection of appropriate methods of observation*—All observation, in the final analysis, is a matter of sensory input. This is readily apparent when the observation is made *directly* with the eyes, ears, or some other sense modality. It is equally true when the observation is accomplished *indirectly*, utilizing complex, sophisticated instrumentation. Instruments amplify and enhance the powers of natural observation. Consequently, an observation utilizing high fidelity equipment can be much more accurate than an observation accomplished through ordinary sensory input. Meter sticks, force gauges, microscopes, telescopes, electronic recorders, questionnaires, and checklists are instruments which have been devised to enhance the powers of observation. They objectify and/or amplify that which is observed. Scientific progress through the ages has directly coincided with improved instrumentation. The scientific breakthroughs associated with electron miscroscopy, carbon labeling, and laser beams illustrate this point.

4. *Identifying the inference base*—The findings of a study, to be meaningful, have to be applicable to a definable group of individuals or objects. Such a group constitutes what is known as the *inference base*. In statistical studies, the inference base is the *population* or *universe* from which the sample to be studied has been drawn. In historical studies, it is a selected period of time and selected groups of people. The importance to a study of having a clearly defined inference base is inestimable. It extends the relevance of the findings beyond the immediate scope of the study, makes sampling feasible, and gives focus to the research.

The value of an inference base becomes clear when one realizes that no one investigator, in one lifetime, can possibly hope to collect all the data relevant to a significant problem, nor, in many instances, can he hope to measure all possible relevant eventualities in a single study. He is forced to select and choose the specific phenomena on which he wishes to focus. One interested in the jumping ability of jackrabbits cannot possibly hope to measure the capabilities of all jackrabbits living at any given time. Rabbits come and go too fast to make this possible. Defining a potential population and sampling it is the only feasible recourse. A study of the attitude of educators toward intercollegiate athletics likewise could go on indefinitely unless the investigator identified precisely what constituted an educator according to his purposes. He could, for example, define educators as all teachers who had ever lived, but this would make an unmanageable situation. More feasibly, he could direct his attention to all college professors teaching at four-year institutions in the United States during the 1975–76 academic year. Findings based on an appropriately drawn sample legitimately can be generalized to the entire population when the inference base has been clearly established.

5. *Controlled observation*—Observations can be distorted through numerous extraneous influences. A single unknown factor can lead to erroneous conclusions. For example, persons interested in examining changes in body size through weight training should not use a linen tape. Cloth tapes will shrink and an apparent increase in arm size will seem to have occurred when none actually took place. Systematic influences of this sort introduce bias which leads to faulty findings. Systematic error can infiltrate in many ways, e.g., an investigator's attitude, inferior instrumentation, and environmental changes are common sources of error.

Not all extraneous influences, however, cause systematic errors. At times the result is random error. Random errors fluctuate in an unpredictable plus and minus fashion. These variable types of errors reduce the precision of data, making findings difficult to interpret, and lead to confused, indefinite conclusions. Inaccuracy in data because of systematic error (bias) or variable error (random fluctuations) tends to invalidate a study.

6. *Proof of data reliability*—One cannot assume from the work of others, or from one's own work, irrespective of the care exerted, that a given instrument or procedure provides accurate data. Each investigator must check and present evidence of the reliability of his own observations. Data reliability can be checked in a number of ways. This is accomplished normally by repeating the observations and then checking the degree to which the measures deviate, one from the other. The true measure of a phenomenon can never be known. Hence, the average of repeated measurements usually is accepted as representing the correct value. This average can be used as the basis for estimating the error of fluctuation observed in the repeated measures and gives some idea of the accuracy of the data. Probably the most frequently used method of checking data reliability in educational circles is to test a group of subjects twice and then to correlate the results. There are other methods also available for checking data reliability. Irrespective of method, however, the objective is the same, that is, to discover if the measurements obtained are reproducible. The reliability of data must be demonstrated before the data can be considered valid, and valid data are prerequisite to hypothesis testing. The care shown by an investigator in checking the reliability of his observations reflects his thoroughness as a researcher.

7. *Validation of observations*—Data, to be valid, must be reliable, but reliable data are not necessarily valid. If, with repeated observation,

one obtains the same results, it usually is assumed that the observations are accurate. The reproducibility of observations, however, only guarantees that the method of observation is consistent. It does not assure that one is truly measuring what he thinks he is measuring. Repeatedly looking through a telescope at what one thinks is Mars, carefully aligning the telescope and equally carefully recording the observations insures reliable data. It does not insure that the observer actually is viewing Mars. In reality he may be seeing Venus. The observations are reliable, but not valid. Knowing whether data are valid or not is extremely important but very difficult to check. Consequently, data are often assumed valid without adequate proof.

Ways have been devised to test the validity of data. One method which often is thought of as a check on reliability, but which in reality is also a check on validity, is to have two or more observers, independently, observe a phenomenon. If the same thing is seen and recorded, it is assumed that the observations are both reliable and valid. This procedure is suitable in those studies involving direct observation of a phenomenon. When instruments are utilized, validity must be assessed in other ways. Frequently, the report of reputable investigators who have studied the validity of an instrument or technique can be accepted as sufficient evidence of validity. Such proof is considered especially strong if several independent investigators report the same findings. If, however, an instrument has not been validated by others, an investigator has two choices: he can discard that instrument and select one which has been validated, or he can test the validity of the instrument for himself before proceeding with the study.

8. *The calibration of instruments*—A matter related to the reliability and validity of data is the matter of instrument calibration. Mechanical and electronic instruments, in particular, must be carefully calibrated before data collection begins and repeatedly calibrated throughout the course of a study. Calibration is accomplished by checking the measurements obtained with a particular instrument against more precise measures of the same phenomenon. Dynamometers used in measuring strength, for example, can be calibrated by suspending known amounts of weight from the dynamometer. Investigators often show considerable originality in devising methods of calibration. In a study utilizing rebounding tennis balls, the investigator calibrated the balls daily by dropping each an established distance and measuring the height of rebound. Any ball failing to rebound to the proper height was replaced with a new ball.

The method of calibration selected must be appropriate to the instrument and the purposes of the study. Repeated calibration contributes to the accuracy of data and eliminates one factor which can invalidate a study—faulty observation. Any method of calibration is suitable which produces accurate information. (For a detailed discussion of calibration, see Chapter 7, pp. 115–121.)

9. *Recording data*—Data ultimately have to be interpreted. The form in which they are recorded and the level of precision achieved limit the preciseness and accuracy of findings. Recorded data should be reduced to the simplest possible form and stored in some permanent fashion. They might be written legibly on a specially prepared record sheet, stored on tape for later playback, or located on computer cards. Modern computer systems make the storage and analysis of vast sums of data practicable. The protocol for making observations should be planned in advance and carefully followed with modification made only in extreme circumstances. A basic rule to avoid data error is simplicity of procedure and frugality in handling. The less complex the procedure and the fewer times it is handled, the less likelihood of error.

10. *Data analysis*—Descartes set the pattern for analyzing data when he proposed that a problem, to be solved effectively, must be broken down into its basic parts and each segment dealt with separately, proceeding from the simplest to the most complex. Data summarized and organized into logical segments are conceptually manageable. Appropriately used mathematical and statistical formulae help in accomplishing this task. Inappropriately used formulae complicate rather than simplify, confuse rather than clarify. At completion, the analysis should provide a conceptually clear basis for decision making.

11. *Decision making*—The objective in research is to obtain a *yes* or *no* answer regarding the tenability of a hypothesis, recognizing, of course, that an answer in absolute terms is impossible. The answer can be correctly couched only in terms of probability. The decision made should be reached objectively, based upon sound data. The temptation to twist, modify, and overgeneralize must be resisted. Conclusions ought to be restricted to the data actually on hand. Analyzing data is principally a matter of common sense and experience. It requires reflective thought with an open mind and a willingness to forego pet, preconceived opinions.

The hardest step in hypothesis testing is forming a definitive conclusion, that is, drawing a conclusion without unnecessary equivocation. At this point in an investigation the skill of the investigator as a researcher is placed on the line. Some individuals attempt to avoid the obligation of clear-cut decision making by presenting a summary of observations and leaving the reader to interpret them. The rationale for this is that no one has the right to impose his thinking on others. Let each interpret the data as he likes. The fact is, however, that research is an art and the the most important function occurring during data collection and analysis is the development of insights. Consequently the investigator, and he alone, is in a position to draw valid conclusions. A study is not complete until a conclusion based upon the best available evidence has been drawn and clearly stated.

Criteria for Good Research

There is more to successful research than following a series of prescribed steps by rote. The approach, the way of doing things, is very important. Through the years the works of successful scientists have been characterized by the following:

1. *Intrinsically interesting problems*—A problem for study must be interesting, at least to the investigator. It must hold significance for the researcher even though it may be only a matter of satisfying curiosity. Ulterior motives, e.g., impressing colleagues, satisfying a thesis requirement, or listing another publication are not sufficient to guarantee good research. Conducting a thorough study requires long, tedious hours of collecting, sifting, and analyzing data, and of engaging in hard, concentrated thought. Extraneous rewards alone will not provide the motivation necessary to study a problem thoroughly. Only genuine curiosity ensures full commitment to obtaining the answer to a question. Often studies fall by the wayside from a lack of genuine interest on the part of the investigator or, if completed, are so poorly done that the findings are questionable.

2. *Objectivity*—*Truth* begets *truth* and *error* begets *error*. Objectivity is the key to arriving at the truth. An investigator must strive at every step to eliminate personal bias, to be intellectually honest, and to put aside prejudices and opinions. A correct answer is the end result of rigorous, objective enquiry.

3. *Simplicity*—Problem solving requires moving from the complex approach to the simple. Complicated approaches serve only to confuse, not elucidate. A first principle of the scientific method is *simplicity*. When two or more choices are open to an investigator, whether they concern instrumentation or the selection of a statistical formula, all else being equal the simpler of the two is the correct choice.

4. *Fragmentation*—Concomitant with simplicity is the scientist's penchant for fragmenting. "Each in its own turn" is the rule. The scientist does not attempt to attack all fronts at once. He does not deal with a problem globally, but breaks it down into its parts, focusing attention on each in turn, moving from subproblem to subproblem until the whole problem is solved.

5. *Orderliness*—Inherent in the scientific method is the principle of order. From Aristotle's time to the present, the scientist has been com-

pulsive in his commitment to order. He feels compelled to organize, categorize, and classify. Good research is characterized by orderliness in planning, data analysis, and reporting.

6. *Quantification*—There is a basic scientific premise that if a phenomenon exists, it can be measured and if it can be measured, it can be understood. Anything which cannot be measured can scarcely be conceptualized and for all practical purposes does not exist. Not all phenomena lend themselves to easy quantification. The researcher has an obligation, however, to attempt to measure that in which he is interested. With effort, an understanding of the phenomenon gradually evolves.

7. *Verification*—Paramount in research is commitment to verification. Each step in an investigation should be subject to verification through checking and rechecking. The thorough investigator checks the validity of his instruments, the reliability of the data, the adequacy and correctness of the statistical procedures employed, the legitimacy of his conclusions, and, above all, the accuracy of the written report. The written report is particularly important, since it makes possible verification of the findings by other investigators.

8. *Precision*—There is no tolerance in science for haziness. Within the limits of one's ability, and consistent with the objectives of a study, precision is expected. One should strive to be as precise as the nature of the problem requires—no more, no less. An appropriate level of precision is essential in the use of words, planning protocol, making observations, recording observations, analyzing data, and interpreting findings. The report should be precise, with direct, clear wording and a minimum of complex terminology.

9. *Patience*—A good research question cannot be answered easily. If it could be, it would have already been answered. It is the difficult questions which require research and the answers come only with intense effort and patient, reflective thought. An answer, at least the correct answer, cannot be hurried.

10. *Involvement*—There is an adage that if you want something to be done well, do it yourself. This is particularly true in research. In fact, it is the only way in which research can be accomplished. Research can be a cooperative venture by several persons, but it is not something that one person can do for another. The essence of research is *thinking*, and one person cannot think for another. The uninvolved researcher, removed from the research process, has little feel for or understanding of the data. The research process requires that one actually engage in planning and making the observations. Without such involvement it is virtually impossible to gain the insights necessary to decision making.

The most important single outcome of a study is not the listed findings, but rather the insights and crystallization of thought growing out of actual involvement.

The Successful Researcher

Irrespective of all that has been said about research up to this point, the final key to successful research is the researcher. He must bring to the task the attributes of creativity, independence of thought, and complete honesty. He must be skeptical to a reasonable degree, alert, self-disciplined, and both willing and capable of engaging in intense mental effort. He must be receptive to new ideas and ways of thinking, but at the same time have convictions. He must be patient and persevering, with confidence in his own ability. Other qualifications of the successful researcher are discussed in Chapter 3, pp. 48–49.

REFERENCES

1. Commins, Saxe and Linscott, Robert N., eds. *The World's Great Thinkers*, vol. 4. New York: Random House, 1947.
2. Ghiselin, Brewster, ed. *The Creative Process*. New York: New American Library of World Literature, 1952.
3. *Random House Dictionary of the English Language*. Unabridged ed. New York: Random House, 1966.
4. Watson, James D. *The Double Helix*. New York: Atheneum Press, 1968.

SELECTED READINGS

Barzun, Jacques and Graff, Henry F. *The Modern Researcher*. Rev. ed. New York: Harcourt, Brace & World, 1957.

Cohen, Morris R. and Nagel, Ernst. Hypothesis and scientific method. In *An Introduction to Logic and Scientific Method*. New York: Harcourt, Brace & World, 1934.

Fitts, Paul M. and Posner, Michael I. *Human Performance*. Belmont, Calif.: Brooks/Cole Publishing Co., 1967.

Goode, William J. and Hatt, P.K. *Methods in Social Research*. New York: McGraw-Hill Book Co., 1952.

Hempel, Carl G. *Philosophy of Natural Science*. Englewood Cliffs, N.J.: Prentice-Hall, 1966.

Metheny, E. Philosophical methods. In *Research Methods in Health, Physical Education, and Recreation*, 2d ed., pp. 482–501. Washington, D.C.: American Association for Health, Physical Education, and Recreation, 1959.

On thinking things through. *The Royal Bank of Canada Monthly Letter* 49, no. 12: 1–4.

Sullivan, J.W. *The Limitations of Science*. New York: Augustus M. Kelley Publishers, 1933.

Whitehead, A.N. *Science and the Modern World*. New York: Macmillan Co., 1926. Reprint. New York: Free Press, n.d.

PART II

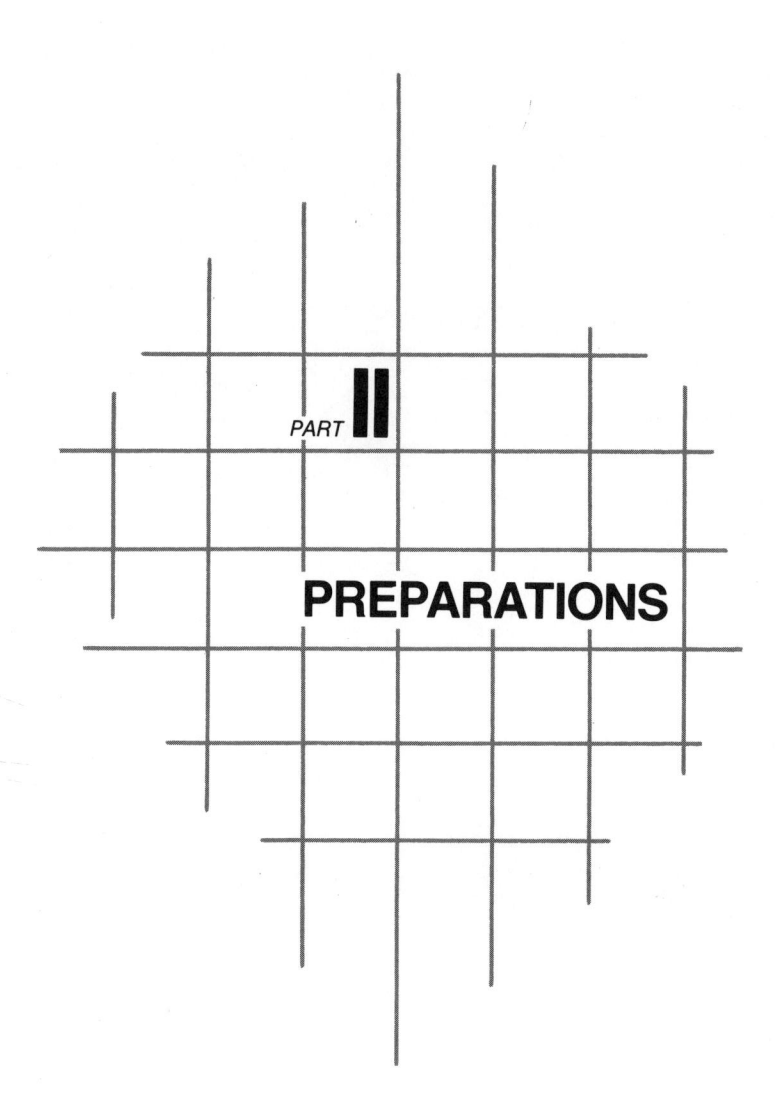

PREPARATIONS

CHAPTER 3
SELECTING AND DEFINING A RESEARCH PROBLEM

Marion R. Broer
University of Washington
Seattle, Washington

Dorothy R. Mohr
Sacramento State College
Sacramento, California

FREQUENTLY ONE OF THE GREATEST difficulties for a newcomer to research is the identification and complete definition of a problem. Being aware of the large number of research studies already available in his field, he may think that there are no more problems to be solved through research. On the other hand, he may jump enthusiastically into collecting a mass of data without formulating a clear purpose or hypothesis to test and with only a vague idea of the problem he wishes to solve. He does not realize that before the solution can be found, considerable thought must be given to a clear and specific definition of his purpose, the dimensions of the study, the possible hypotheses that might be examined, the assumptions upon which the study would depend, and whether it really has worth. This chapter attempts to guide the beginner through the steps involved in the selection and clear and complete definition of a research problem.

IDENTIFICATION OF THE PROBLEM

The first task of the research worker is identification of the problem. (As discussed in Chapter 2, pp. 25–26, the temptation to select a research problem for the wrong reasons must be recognized and handled objectively.) Research originates from a perceived problem in need of resolution. Any situation which cannot be handled by a satisfactory past habit pattern needs a new form of action, developed and validated through research. Thus any unsolved problem in an area of professional endeavor may become a potential research project. Any time there is insufficient knowledge for understanding a phenomenon or conflict of opinion, a possible research project is indicated. John L. Hayman, Jr., Director of Research for the Philadelphia Public School System, has said:

> Generally, there are three reasons why research in an area is needed: 1) there is no information at all on some particular and important aspect of the area; 2) there is incomplete information so that further investigation, suggested by the information at hand, is needed; and 3) there is information which appears to be complete and highly useful but which is not well substantiated. (4:15)

Many beginning researchers fail to realize that previous research, instead of solving the problem completely, may merely point the way to many more studies. Similarly, these earlier studies often need extension or duplication. For example, Carter V. Good explained that:

> Historical sources accumulate with each passing event, making necessary the extension of earlier historical narratives and sometimes a reinterpretation of older accounts. Descriptive-survey studies are soon out of date and must be repeated, as in the annual school census for a local system. Controlled experiments are repeated to test the validity of earlier investigations. (3:51)

To find a satisfactory research problem, the beginner may have to develop a sensitivity to problems. He will need to change his outlook if he has tended to accept without question 1) all that is printed in professional literature, 2) the procedures of his instructors, and 3) professional practices which he has observed. A critical attitude, linked with logical thinking, can lead the researcher to recognize problems which he never realized existed.

Thus, one source of problems for research lies within the researcher himself. He becomes alert to faulty reasoning of colleagues, instructors, and authors. He develops a keenness of perception, so that he becomes aware of procedures that may be questionable. He lessens his inclination to accept conclusions without sufficient evidence (those conclusions based on incomplete study or no research at all). He becomes especially critical of the assumptions upon which many professional procedures are based. He observes these procedures, continually asking himself, "why?" If a need for verification becomes evident, the thinking process has begun to direct attention toward a specific problem for research.

Van Dalen (5) has listed five ways of locating problems. The first was to explore the literature in a particular area of interest, list the theories developed by others, and examine studies designed to test these theories. While studying these theories, weaknesses, inconsistencies, or gaps in knowledge may point to problem possibilities. His second suggestion was to expose oneself to professional stimulation by engaging in intellectual discourse in graduate courses, seminars, professional meetings, lectures, visits to laboratories, and informal discussions with instructors and fellow students. Any conflict in ideas presents a potential problem that might be examined for its possibilities for research. Van Dalen's third source of problems lies in everyday experiences of the professional practitioner in the field. Here are encountered difficulties with students, equipment, tests, textbooks, guidance, discipline, parents, curriculum, staff, supervision, or administration. Fourth, he advocated keeping systematic notes prior to and throughout an investigation as a stimulant to critical thinking and the discovery of new ideas. Finally, he advocated the critical attitude discussed in the previous paragraph.

Whitney's clues for locating research problems reemphasize some of the same points and add a few more possibilities:

> In making a selection of a specific problem for study, such activities as the following should be engaged in: analyze everything known already, all previous research; look for gaps in explanations, find untested conclusions; follow clues; recognize conflicts in experience; survey concrete suggestions for needed research; become a scholar in one or more specialties; read, listen, and work continuously and reflectively; consider obstacles challenges for ingenuity; start a research and watch problems bud out of it; have a constant attitude of questioning every procedure in the field of interest; look for actual evidence on current procedures; and estimate the reliability of knowledge available about important issues. (6:95)

Ideas also abound in the recommendations for further research which often appear at the close of a completed study.

Considering the multitude of possibilities for locating problem areas, it should not be necessary for the beginner in search of a thesis problem to go to his professor begging for ideas. Instead, he should have so many possibilities that his need is for guidance in selecting, from many, the problem most suitable for him.

CRITERIA FOR ACCEPTABLE RESEARCH PROBLEMS

Since each institution granting graduate degrees in health, physical education, and/or recreation may set up its own specific criteria for thesis and dissertation problems, each student pursuing a degree must be responsible for ascertaining these criteria before seeking approval of his research problem. The criteria that are almost universally accepted are:

Professional Contribution

The problem should be worthy of the time and effort needed to solve it, in terms of making a distinct contribution to the professional field of interest. The scope must be broad enough to be of some significance to a segment of the profession, yet narrow enough to provide specific answers to the questions involved. Related factors are pertinence and timeliness. Although much can be said for basic or pure research, if the beginner is interested in applied research his problem should be relevant to practice in the field. Every facet of education is being challenged with respect to relevance; thus research should be pertinent to current and future procedures. Studies pertaining to traditional procedures of the past could be considered timely if they lead to recommendations for needed and relevant change.

Uniqueness

Most institutions place some stress on originality, but degree candidates are not expected to locate a problem that has never been researched before. Many experiments and descriptive studies need replication or extension to add to the research evidence available. Thus a proposed study may be considered original, even though it is replication or extension of earlier research.

Feasibility

Except for significance to the profession, this criterion may be the most important consideration. Research will require time and money, and often special tools or equipment. Many descriptive as well as experimental studies require certain types of subjects in order to secure the necessary data. Valid documents and/or artifacts must be available for significant historical research. If any of these requirements are lacking or beyond the resources of the researcher, the study may not be feasible for him to pursue, even though it might be for another worker at a different location. Although the scope of researchable problems is steadily enlarging, there still are some for which no techniques of solution have been discovered. Even with faculty guidance, the student may find a problem unfeasible in terms of techniques currently available for its solution.

Researcher's Qualifications

As indicated in Chapter 2, p. 42, some general qualifications are needed by all research workers. These include motivation and drive, intense interest in the problem, intellectual curiosity and honesty, the ability to locate and evaluate related research, the ability to reason logically and write coherently, and habits of accuracy, thoroughness, patience, and perseverance. In addition, a particular research problem may be entirely suitable for one student but relatively unsuitable for another because of personal qualifications and skills. For example, all experiments and many descriptive studies require extensive statistical competence for adequate analysis of the data. Surveys require the construction of survey instruments, such as questionnaires, and this involves a degree of skill in semantics not possessed by all research workers. Some descriptive, historical, and philosophical studies necessitate interviews; the interviewing skill possessed by the researcher may not be sufficient. Such specific personal qualifications must be considered before choosing a research problem.

DEFINITION OF THE PROBLEM

A complete definition of the research problem involves a great deal more than writing a title and stating a purpose. Besides stating a clear purpose, the investigator must indicate his hypothesis concerning the study, examine any assumptions underlying the research and any factors that could limit his conclusions, set definite limits for his study, establish its worth, and define any unique terms.

Statement of the Title

The title must indicate the complete scope of the study. Since it should fully and correctly describe the main subject of the investigation, it is helpful to first write it in broad, wordy terms, including complete and exact content and making no attempt for the best or shortest wording. Once on paper it can be examined for wording; unnecessary and redundant words can be omitted; it can be edited; and finally, it can be examined for interest and attractiveness. The final title should be as concise and brief as possible without sacrificing clarity. To avoid a wordy and involved title a subtitle may be necessary to convey the full meaning.

The words "A study of . . ." at the beginning of a title simply lengthen it unnecessarily. They add nothing to the reader's understanding of the scope or content of the study and should be deleted. If, however, it is important to convey the *type* of study, it may be helpful to start the title with words such as, "An electromyographic study of . . ." or "A survey of . . ." In such cases the extra words convey specific information.

It is important to remember that clarity should not be sacrificed for brevity, but any word not necessary for a clear statement of the study's scope should be deleted. If difficulty in writing the title is encountered, it may be helpful to write the purpose first and then the title.

Statement of Purpose

A study may require only a single general statement of purpose or it may need to cover subproblems as well. In either case, the purpose should be clearly stated and be as concise as is consistent with clarity. It is important that the statement clearly establish the direction of the investigation and, as in the title, clarity should not be sacrificed for the sake of brevity.

In all probability, if the researcher encounters considerable difficulty in stating his purpose he does not have a clear idea of the problem he wishes to study, and additional background reading, discussion, and thought are indicated. It may be helpful to jot down two or three ideas and then weave them into a general purpose which can be summarized in one good statement.

A stated purpose must never indicate a bias. Rather it should simply present a problem to be solved. For example, the purpose, "to show that when problems arise, high school students seek advice from physical education teachers more frequently than from other teachers," clearly shows a bias. It indicates that the researcher is *attempting to prove* that his opinion is correct. On the other hand, the purpose, "to discover *whether*, when problems arise, high school students seek advice from physical education teachers more frequently than from other teachers," indicates a desire to determine the situation as it is.

Subproblems

Every study does not have subproblems. However, in many investigations the main (general) purpose can only be achieved through the solution of smaller problems. They are not steps in the procedure, although they may dictate the order of procedure, since one must first solve these smaller problems. Subproblems, as the term implies, deal with questions that must be answered in order to solve the main problem of the study. Such steps as determining the appropriate tool, selecting the sample, and analyzing the data are steps in procedure rather than subproblems because they are not problems that are carried to a conclusion, but steps through which one must progress to reach the conclusion. If a tool for the collection of data must be *developed and tested* for reliability and validity before it can be employed in the study, this becomes a subproblem. The question of whether the tool is appropriate must be answered before the research can proceed.

In order to achieve the general purpose, "to assess the effectiveness of a general basic skills curriculum for freshman women of low motor ability," it may be necessary to solve a number of subproblems, such as:

1. to discover whether the general motor ability of students with low motor ability can be improved to a greater degree through a basic skills curriculum than through the regular activity program

2. to discover whether those who have had the basic skills instruction have greater success in selected activities than those of equal motor ability who have not had the basic instruction

3. to discover whether the attitude of such students toward physical education can be improved more through basic skills instruction than through the regular activity program. (1:2,3)

These are truly subproblems, since they must be solved before the effectiveness of the curriculum can be judged.

In a study "to compare the effectiveness of starting crawl stroke instruction with the human stroke and with the over-arm recovery when teaching beginning swimmers," the subproblems were:

1. to determine the difference in the rate with which the two methods facilitated beginning swimmers' adaptation to deep water

2. to determine the degree of skill in the crawl stroke developed when each method was used. (2:1)

Again, the solution of these two smaller problems was necessary before the main question could be answered.

It is possible to have one main purpose and one or two *secondary* purposes which are not *subproblems*, since their solution is not required for the solution of the main problem, but rather offers related information.

Hypothesis

As mentioned earlier in Chapter 2, pp. 33–34, it is perfectly legitimate for the investigator to indicate his belief concerning the solution of the problem to be studied. His hypothesis is his guess or supposition about the results he may find. Since it is his personal hunch, he may hypothesize any result he wishes so long as it is reasonable according to present information—it must be a conceivable result. It should be stated in the simplest possible terms. While the purpose should not indicate that the researcher is setting out to *prove* that his opinion is correct, he may have an opinion and if he does, he should state it as such. Using the example cited in the discussion dealing with the statement of purpose, the hypothesis might be stated: "The hypothesis to be tested is that students tend to seek physical education teachers more often than other high school teachers when they have a problem on which they desire advice." This simply tells the reader the researcher's belief without suggesting that he is going to attempt to prove himself correct.

If the investigator has no opinion or hunch concerning the results he will find, he has no hypothesis. Researchers are not in agreement on whether every problem must have a stated hypothesis. Some feel that if the investigator has no opinion, the hypothesis should be omitted, while others feel that in this situation the null hypothesis should be presented. In other words, if the investigator has no opinion, he should present the hypothesis indicating that no significant findings are anticipated. For some historical and philosophical studies, no specific hypothesis is possible or feasible, either because no hunch is conceivable or because the findings will constitute a myriad of details.

If a hypothesis is presented it must be shown to be supported or negated by the data obtained. There must be a conclusion which deals with each hypothesis or each point made in the hypothesis.

Assumptions

As defined in Chapter 2, pp. 31–32, assumptions are statements taken to be true without the presentation of data to support them. They must be consistent with present information and readily acceptable, i.e., statements that would not be disputed. They involve conditions which underlie the research—conditions upon which the research is built—in contrast to the hypothesis, which is tested by the study. If the assumptions are false, the whole research study will be inadequate. Just as there are assumptions upon which certain statistical procedures are based, there may be assumptions upon which the research study itself is based. If any of the formulae which assume a normal distribution are used with skewed data, the results may be incorrect; in the same way, a research study built upon a wrong assumption may lead to false conclusions.

Delimitations*

The delimitations set the frame for the research; they draw the borders, narrow down the problem, and define the scope of the study. They indicate exactly which factors the investigator will and will not study. All factors surrounding the study must either be specifically eliminated or studied. For example, in a study of the effects of selected types of activity on "physical fitness," the researcher must set the scope of physical fitness that is to be studied, the activities that are to be included, the level of skill involved in the selected activities, the sex, and perhaps the level of maturity of the students selected for investigation. All of these factors could influence the results; thus the investigator must indicate exactly

---

* Also called "scope."

which factors will be his concern. For example: "This study is limited to the physical fitness factors of abdominal strength as measured by the bent leg sit-up, arm and shoulder strength as measured by the bent arm hang, cardiorespiratory endurance as measured by the step test, and agility as measured by the shuttle run. It is further limited to the activities of swimming, tennis, track and field, and contemporary dance as engaged in by college women with advanced levels of skill in these activities." This clearly sets the limits beyond which the researcher is not attempting to carry his study. The researcher sets his own delimitations. Once these are set, all factors not eliminated must be considered in the study. The reason for indicating the method of measurement for the physical fitness variables is that various types of measurements give different results. For example, correlations between various so-called "agility" tests are low, thus the investigator needs to clearly indicate the type of "agility" he is going to consider.

Limitations

Limitations, on the other hand, are conditions about which the researcher can do nothing—conditions that cannot be controlled but are recognized as factors that could influence conclusions. Essentially, limitations are possible weaknesses in the study. When research is carried on in a school situation, there are always some factors that cannot be completely controlled. While these must be recognized and indicated by the investigator as limitations, they do not necessarily mean that the research is worthless. The number and importance of the limitations must be considered in judging whether it is worthwhile to pursue the study. Some common limitations are: the sample is made up of volunteers rather than selected at random; the sample is small; a questionnaire is mailed and the sample returns are not representative; there are geographical (or other) limitations which may affect results.

Obviously, every attempt should be made to keep limitations to a minimum. In some cases a factor that cannot be controlled can be studied. In considering the physical fitness study cited in the discussion of delimitations, several limitations are seen. The most obvious is the fact that it is impossible to control the subjects' activity except while they are participating in the particular activities being studied. While this is a limitation in the research, it is possible to study the amount of outside activity each subject engaged in each day during the investigation and to use this information in interpreting the data, that is, to discover whether those who improved more in certain selected fitness tests were more or less active in outside activities. While this does not eliminate the limitation completely, it will give insight into the degree to which this particular uncontrollable factor might be influencing the results of the study. For example, if a group of subjects who, for a period of six weeks, had worked on a certain exercise program (experimental group) improved significantly more in the step test than did a group who had not taken part in such a program (control group), one would need to know something about the outside activities of the two groups before drawing conclusions. If a study of the outside activities of the two groups showed that the experimental group had engaged in only the experimental exercise program and the control group had reported considerable time spent engaged in active sports and exercise, it would appear that the greater improvement of the experimental group was indeed caused by the experimental factor rather than some other physical activity. If, on the other hand, the experimental group reported more time spent in active sports and exercise beyond the experimental program than was reported by the control group, one could not conclude that the change was caused by the experimental factor.

Thus, all conditions that could influence the results and cannot be controlled must be acknowledged as limitations. In addition, whenever possible every effort should be made to study the effects of such factors.

Need for the Study

As indicated earlier, a problem should be worthy of the time and effort needed to solve it. The researcher must establish the worth of his study. The discussion of *need* should indicate the pertinence of the study, the way(s) in which it will be helpful, and the possible applications of its results. A study of previous literature will help the researcher in establishing this need.

Definition of Terms

Any term which is used by the investigator in a *unique* way must be defined. There is no need to define a term, even if it is a technical one, if it has a distinct meaning and is used only to indicate that meaning. However, if a term is being used in a *restricted* way, it must be defined. Also, if the term has many meanings and/or is interpreted differently by different authorities, its meaning—as used in the study—must be clearly indicated. Words such as "motor ability," "physical fitness," "personality," "secondary school," have been defined in many ways and thus the specific definition used in the particular study should be given.

THE RESEARCH PROPOSAL

Many departments granting graduate degrees provide guides for composing the thesis proposal. The proposal usually includes the statement of the problem and the related topics already discussed, as well as a detailed outline of the proposed procedures. The outline involves descriptions of tests and/or equipment to be used, preliminary drafts of questionnaires or other data-gathering devices, as well as the procedures planned for the collection and analysis of the data and the presentation of the findings. A tentative bibliography of related literature is often required at this point, because the student is expected to have read a great deal about the subject before putting his problem statement in final form.

Obtaining Research Funds

The research proposal to be submitted for obtaining funds from a foundation or government source will be similar to that just described, but much more extensive detail is usually required. Many foundations and research bureaus, as well as branches of the government, provide guides for the development of research proposals. Aid is available in locating local and national foundations and bureaus interested in funding scientific and educational research. Every two years the Russell Sage Foundation publishes *The Foundation Directory*, with information concerning purposes, interests, assets, and grants made by almost 7,000 foundations. Most college and university libraries have this directory. Another reference useful for information on obtaining grants is *How to Raise Funds from Foundations,* by Joseph Dermer, published by the Public Service Materials Center, 104 East 40th Street, New York, N.Y. 10016.

REFERENCES

1. Broer, Marion R. Evaluation of basic skills curriculum for women students of low motor ability at the University of Washington. *Research Quarterly* 26: 15–27, March 1955.
2. Broomell, Eileen. The effectiveness of two methods of teaching the American crawl stroke to beginning swimmers. Master's thesis, University of Washington—Seattle, 1967.
3. Good, Carter V. *Essentials of Educational Research: Methodology and Design.* New York: Appleton-Century-Crofts, 1966.
4. Hayman, John L., Jr. *Research in Education.* Columbus, Ohio: Charles E. Merrill Publishing Co., 1968. 122 pp.
5. Van Dalen, Deobold B. *Understanding Educational Research.* 2d ed. New York: McGraw-Hill Book Co., 1966. 525 pp.
6. Whitney, Frederick L. *The Elements of Research.* 3d ed. Englewood Cliffs, N.J.: Prentice-Hall, 1950. 539 pp.

CHAPTER 4
SEARCHING THE LITERATURE

Vern Seefeldt
Michigan State University
East Lansing, Michigan

THE LIBRARY IS A BASIC research tool for scholars. Its holdings represent the printed record of countless attempts to extend the frontiers of human knowledge. Libraries exist for the purpose of storing and preserving materials which have been committed to print and enhancing accessibility to them. Although it is neither possible nor feasible to store this vast amount of information in one location, librarians have evolved a system of classification and indexing which theoretically provides accessibility to any document regardless of its storage site. It is the purpose of this chapter to establish a methodology which will assist students in retrieving library information with a minimum expenditure of time and yet provide maximum relevance of the information obtained.

PLANNING THE SEARCH

The assignment of a research paper to be written presents a formidable challenge to many students. The task of gathering information from an array of diffuse and elusive sources appears overwhelming unless one is acquainted with library procedures for the storage and retrieval of information. Searching the volumes of available literature demands a procedure which is as orderly and sequential as the system by which the documents are classified and stored. *An essential step in the retrieval of library information is a plan for systematically conducting the search.*

Procedures for conducting library research vary with the investigator, the discipline, and the type of information desired. As one gains experience in library searches and becomes more familiar with his topic, it becomes apparent that some sources and authors yield a higher number of relevant articles than others. It is acknowledged that experience and personal shortcuts can expedite the search plan which follows, but the student without a plan will do well to follow its sequence of procedures.

Defining the Problem

The focus of every literature search should be determined by the statement of a problem (see Chapter 3, p. 49). It is important that it be stated in terminology which is conventionally used by writers who share similar or related interests. The key words or descriptors contained in the statement of the problem are the most direct path to catalogs and indices which contain the primary sources from which the bibliography is to be drawn. A vocabulary which neglects conventional language usage is one of the most serious impediments to communication among scholars.

The language in which a problem is stated also determines the scope of the library search. In the interest of an efficient search, it is imperative that the topic be defined as precisely as the investigator's vocabulary and knowledge of the subject allow. The care which is exercised in stating the problem at the outset is directly proportional to the relevance of the documents which are eventually retrieved for its solution. Although published materials generally report the problem in the form of a statement, many students prefer to phrase the problem as a question in the beginning stages of their investigation.

It should be noted that the statement of the problem at this stage is in temporary form. A search of the literature will provide the basis for modifications which must be made in order for the problem to serve as a useful guide to the investigation which is to follow.

Establishing the Scope of the Search

Initial attempts at information retrieval are likely to end in frustration unless the scope of the problem is established prior to the initiation of the search. Unless boundaries are clearly established, the search will probably end with the conclusion that either the literature is so voluminous that a selection of pertinent references is impossible, or very little, if anything, has been written about the object of the search. Although experienced investigators know that library research is more likely to be hampered by the searcher's inability to focus upon and locate the literature than by a lack of literature, this information is of little comfort to the student whose search has ended in failure.

A successful library search depends upon a thorough knowledge of the topic and its related areas. This presents something of a dilemma for the student because it is precisely the desire for additional information which prompts this venture initially. An orientation to the scope of the problem can be obtained by resorting to encyclopedias, textbooks, and reviews of literature. One of the most valuable sources of advice is the investigator who has conducted prior searches in this or related areas.

Orientation to the problem should also include the scrutiny of published works in closely related fields to examine research designs, methods, instruments, and results of such investigations. The perusal of related literature is also an ideal method of updating one's vocabulary. Specific information pertaining to instrumentation, research designs, statistics, and acronyms will be indexed according to the language of the discipline which most commonly deals in these terms.

A thorough orientation to the related literature should equip the searcher with the necessary information to establish the scope of the problem. It is advisable at this point to list the limitations to be imposed on the retrieval of literature. Maximum efficiency demands that the restrictions pertaining to subjects, equipment, age groups, ability levels, cultural groups, and geographical location be stated prior to the initiation of the library search.

DEVELOPING A BIBLIOGRAPHY

The bibliography may be constructed from a variety of sources, but it should be noted that no single volume, catalog, digest, or index is so comprehensive or up-to-date that it will suffice as the only vehicle from which to draw a list of references.

The *card catalog* is the logical place to begin the search for bibliographic sources. It contains every volume or document in the library's collection and therefore provides an excellent reference to that literature in which relevancy can be determined from the title. However, the card catalog has two limitations which should be called to the searcher's attention: 1) it usually contains only those documents which are owned by that particular library; and 2) it provides little or no information regarding the content of books or periodicals. For example, periodicals and serial publications are cumulated and bound at specific intervals. The catalog indicates the volumes of a periodical, but not the articles included in it. However, the card catalog does list reference publications in its possession, and these, in turn, provide information concerning specific titles in the periodicals.

Because the card catalog is of primary importance in information retrieval, a brief description of it is included. Material in the card catalog is arranged alphabetically and classified according to the *Dewey Decimal* or the *Library of Congress* systems. The Dewey Decimal System is usually found in small libraries or in larger ones in the process of converting to the Library of Congress system. The general classifications follow:

DEWEY DECIMAL SYSTEM

000–099—General Works
100–199—Philosophy
200–299—Religion
300–399—Social Sciences
    10—Statistics
    20—Political Science
    30—Economics
    40—Law
    50—Administration
    60—Associations and Institutions
    70—Education
400–499—Linguistics
500–599—Pure Sciences
600–699—Technology (Applied Science)
700–799—Fine Arts and Recreation
800–899—Literature
900–999—History, Geography, Travel, Bibliography

LIBRARY OF CONGRESS CLASSIFICATION OUTLINE

A	General works	LB	Theory and practice of education—Teaching
AE	Encyclopedias		
AI	Indices	LC	Special forms of education
AP	Periodicals	LH	University, college and school magazines
AY	Yearbooks		
B	Philosophy-Religion	LT	Textbooks
BF	Psychology	M	Music
CB	History-Auxillary sciences	N	Fine arts
CD	Archives	P	Language and literature
CT	Biography	Q	Science
D	General history	QM	Human anatomy
E & F	History of America and the United States	QP	Physiology
		R	Medicine
G	Geography-Anthropology	RJ	Pediatrics
GN	Anthropology	RM	Therapeutics
GR	Folklore	RT	Nursing
GV	Sports and amusements	S	Agriculture
H	Social sciences	SK	Hunting sports
HM	Sociology	T	Technology
HQ	Marriage family—Home	TJ	Mechanical engineering and machinery
HV	Social pathology		
J	Political science	TR	Photography
K	Law	U	Military science
L	Education	V	Naval science
LA	History of education	Z	Bibliography and library science

The information contained on the catalog cards is identical, regardless of the classification system employed. All card catalogs are arranged according to a cross-reference system which consists of *author, title*, and *subject cards*. The three cards pertaining to a specific source all bear identical information, but the order in which the information is presented varies according to the function of the card. For example, the *title card* lists the title of the document on the top line, whereas the *author card* gives the name of the senior author on the first line. Examples of the three types of cards are shown in Figures 1 and 2.

A cross-reference system of filing the catalog cards permits one to locate materials with a minimum of information. The searcher needs to know only the author, title, or subject.

In large libraries the author, title, and subject cards are usually filed in separate catalogs. It is also common practice to interfile the author and title cards, and to employ a separate catalog for the subject cards. Figure 2 shows an example of a small catalog in which all of the cards have been interfiled. To facilitate the search for references, all catalogs in a library are usually placed in close proximity to one another.

Abstracts, Indices, Digests, and Bibliographies

The most efficient method of locating pertinent sources within the periodical literature is through the categorized lists of titles contained in indices, digests, abstracts, and bibliographies.[1] Because the number of such publications is too great to give attention to the specific characteristics of each, their function is treated in a general way, followed by a selected list which acquaints readers with the breadth of selections available.

The searcher should extract key words, descriptors, synonyms, and acronyms from the statement of the problem and place them in alphabetical order. He should also refer to the "List of Topics Indexed," usually found at the beginning of a volume, for suggestions of descriptors under which titles could be classified. A chronological scrutiny of volumes, beginning with those published most recently, will guard against the omissions which are likely to occur in the absence of a systematic search procedure.

It should be noted that all reference lists are selective in their coverage. The beginning pages of each volume generally list the periodicals covered. Searchers should be aware of the selective bias involved in composing a bibliography entirely from lists prepared by publishers. It is essential that

---

[1] The direct search of periodical content is the most selective of all approaches and should be reserved for those who have a thorough knowledge of the literature in their field.

62 RESEARCH METHODS

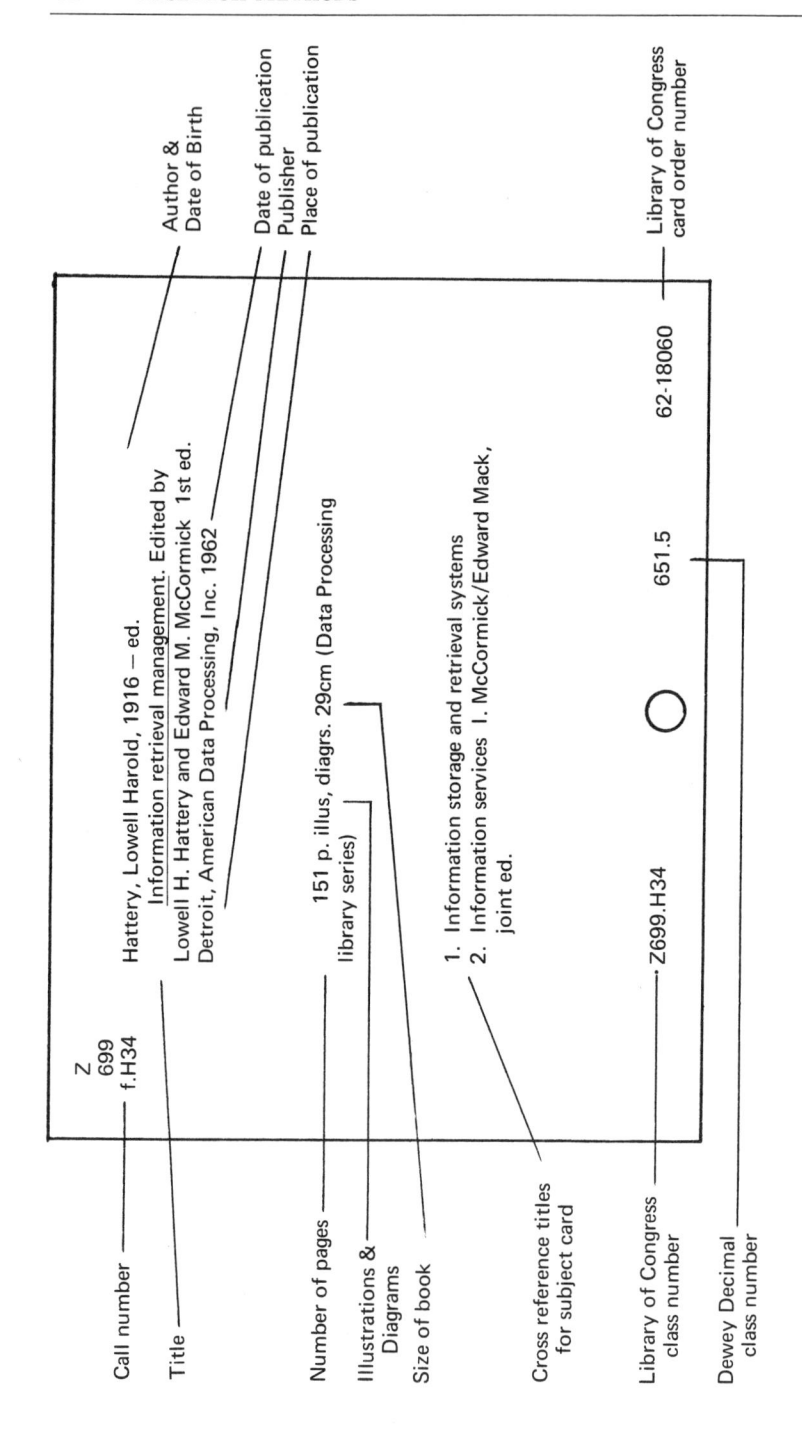

Figure 1. Author card, with an explanation of the information contained on it.

SEARCHING THE LITERATURE 63

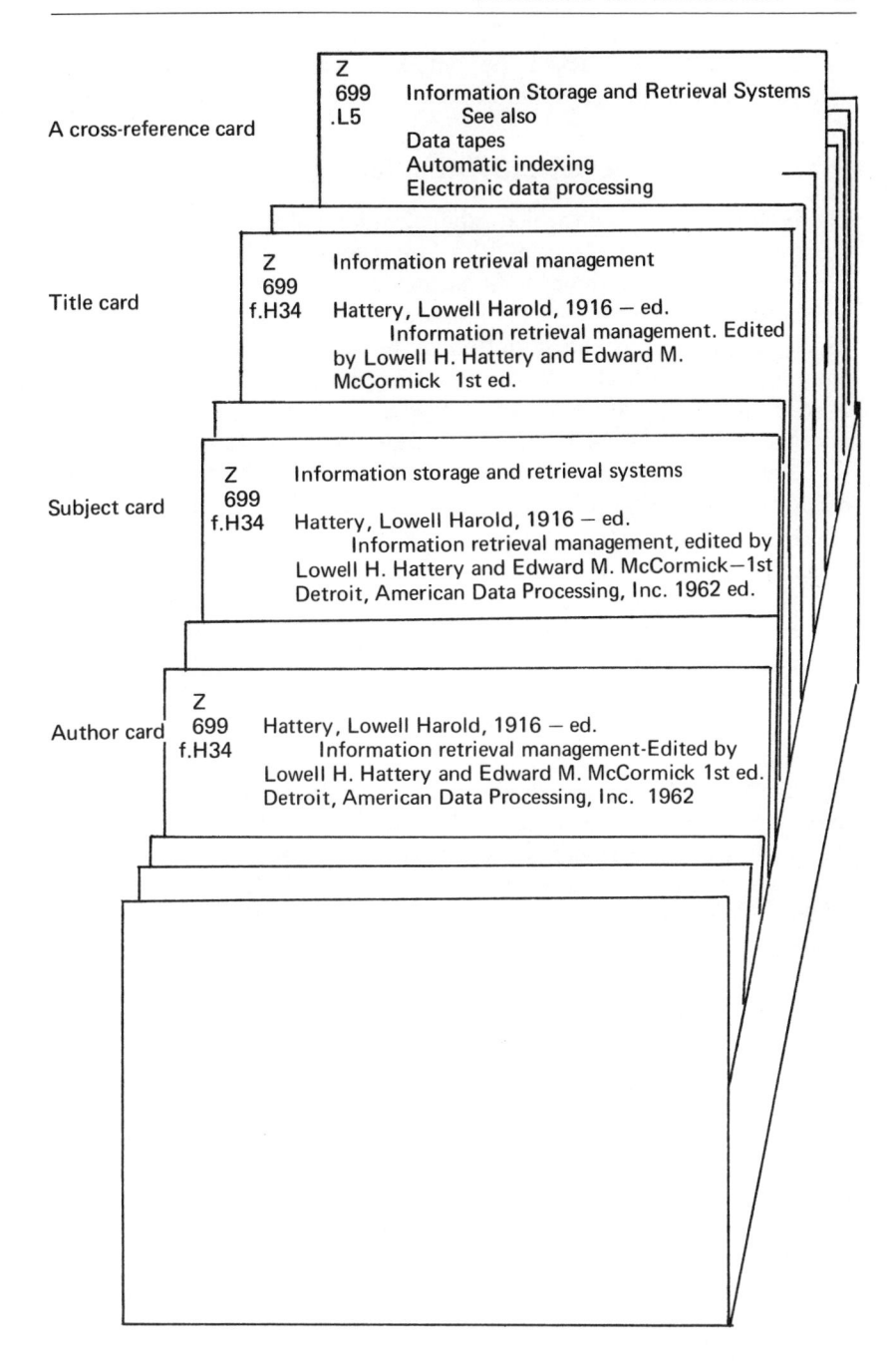

A cross-reference card
```
Z
699    Information Storage and Retrieval Systems
.L5          See also
       Data tapes
       Automatic indexing
       Electronic data processing
```

Title card
```
Z      Information retrieval management
699
f.H34  Hattery, Lowell Harold, 1916 – ed.
              Information retrieval management. Edited
       by Lowell H. Hattery and Edward M.
       McCormick  1st ed.
```

Subject card
```
Z      Information storage and retrieval systems
699
f.H34  Hattery, Lowell Harold, 1916 – ed.
              Information retrieval management, edited by
       Lowell H. Hattery and Edward M. McCormick—1st
       Detroit, American Data Processing, Inc. 1962 ed.
```

Author card
```
Z      Hattery, Lowell Harold, 1916 – ed.
699           Information retrieval management-Edited by
f.H34  Lowell H. Hattery and Edward M. McCormick 1st ed.
       Detroit, American Data Processing, Inc.  1962
```

Figure 2. An example of interfiling all cards within one catalog.

the "List of Journals Indexed" be compared to a list of potential primary sources to insure that pertinent references have not been omitted.

REVIEWING THE LITERATURE

The bibliographic search which exhausts all possible sources is likely to terminate with an abundance of titles. Even though care has been exercised in the selection of references, it is difficult to avoid those which are redundant or irrelevant. The elimination of extraneous titles is a process which commences at the initiation of bibliographic construction and continues until the final draft is written. The phase of library work devoted to scanning the literature places particular emphasis on determining the relevance of materials included in the original bibliographic list.

True efficiency in library searches requires the extraction of all pertinent information from a document at the time of its *initial* retrieval. However, the knowledge of subject matter which permits such efficiency is generally not within the student's grasp at this stage of the investigation. To avoid rejecting relevant sources and retaining those which are irrelevant, three approaches to acquiring information are presented, namely, the *brief abstract*, the *comprehensive abstract*, and *reproduction of the original article*.

The ability to distinguish between pertinent, extraneous, and superfluous material is generally enhanced as one becomes better acquainted with the topic. Those who prefer to postpone the decision of relevancy may elect the *brief abstract* method. Materials which clearly pertain to the topic are more efficiently acquired either through the form of a comprehensive abstract or via some process of reproduction. Regardless of the acquisition method, every retrieval should begin with the use of a bibliographic card.

The Bibliographic Card

Each potential reference should be recorded on a separate bibliographic card. The isolation of each reference on a single card is essential because of the numerous rearrangement and elimination procedures to which the bibliography will be subjected before the paper is completed. Before proceeding with the review of literature, the cards should be arranged alphabetically according to the name of the senior author. Cards should be numbered successively in the upper right corner, with each number preceded by the first letter of the author's last name. The numbering system should proceed in the following manner A1, A2, ... *An*; B1, B2, ... *Bn*.

After each card has been identified by author and number, the deck should be rearranged alphabetically according to the titles found in the

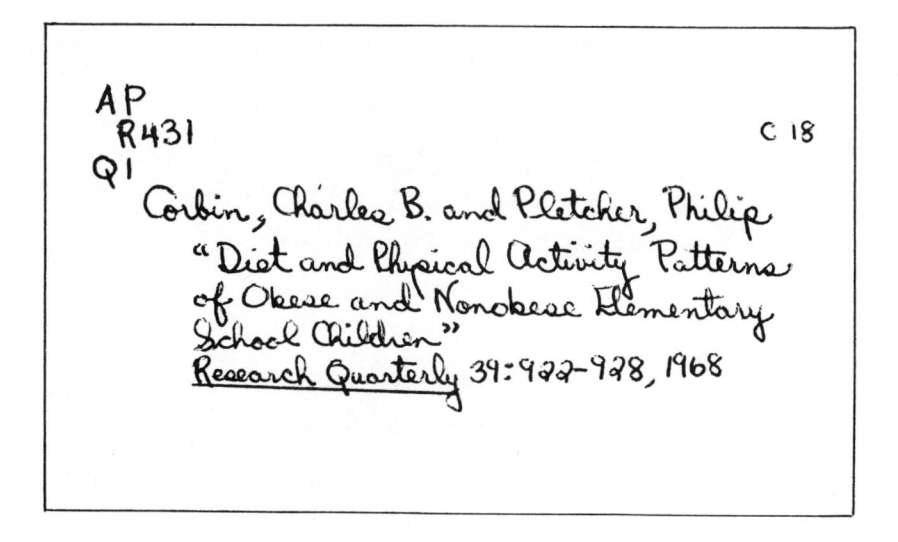

```
AP
  R431                                         C 18
Q 1
     Corbin, Charles B. and Pletcher, Philip
     "Diet and Physical Activity Patterns
     of Obese and Nonobese Elementary
     School Children"
     Research Quarterly 39:922-928, 1968
```

Figure 3. The bibliographic card.

abstracts, indices, digests and bibliographies. It is then a simple matter to proceed through the *title catalog* and record the call numbers.

The *bibliographic card* should include the following information: library call number; surnames, first names, and middle initials of all authors; complete title; volume number; inclusive pages; and year of publication. In addition, reference cards to books should list the publisher, the city in which the book was published, and the edition number. An example of a bibliographic card for a periodical is shown in Figure 3.

It is convenient to conduct the search for shelved information if the bibliographic deck is rearranged according to the location of the material in the library stacks. Every library provides a *directory* of shelved materials, but the location of the stacks is the prerogative of the local librarian. At the stack level it is obvious that the sources within one volume should be reviewed before one moves to another volume. An extension of this procedure suggests that all sources in a serial publication should be reviewed before progressing to the references listed under another title. Likewise, all references at one stack level should be reviewed before progressing to another stack.

It is recommended that the bibliographic cards within a serial publication be arranged chronologically so that the review commences with the most recently published article. This approach emphasizes current knowledge and controversy and permits the reader to develop a historical perspective regarding changes in methodology, instrumentation, and design. It also provides an excellent opportunity to compare one's bibliography with those of other writers.

66 RESEARCH METHODS

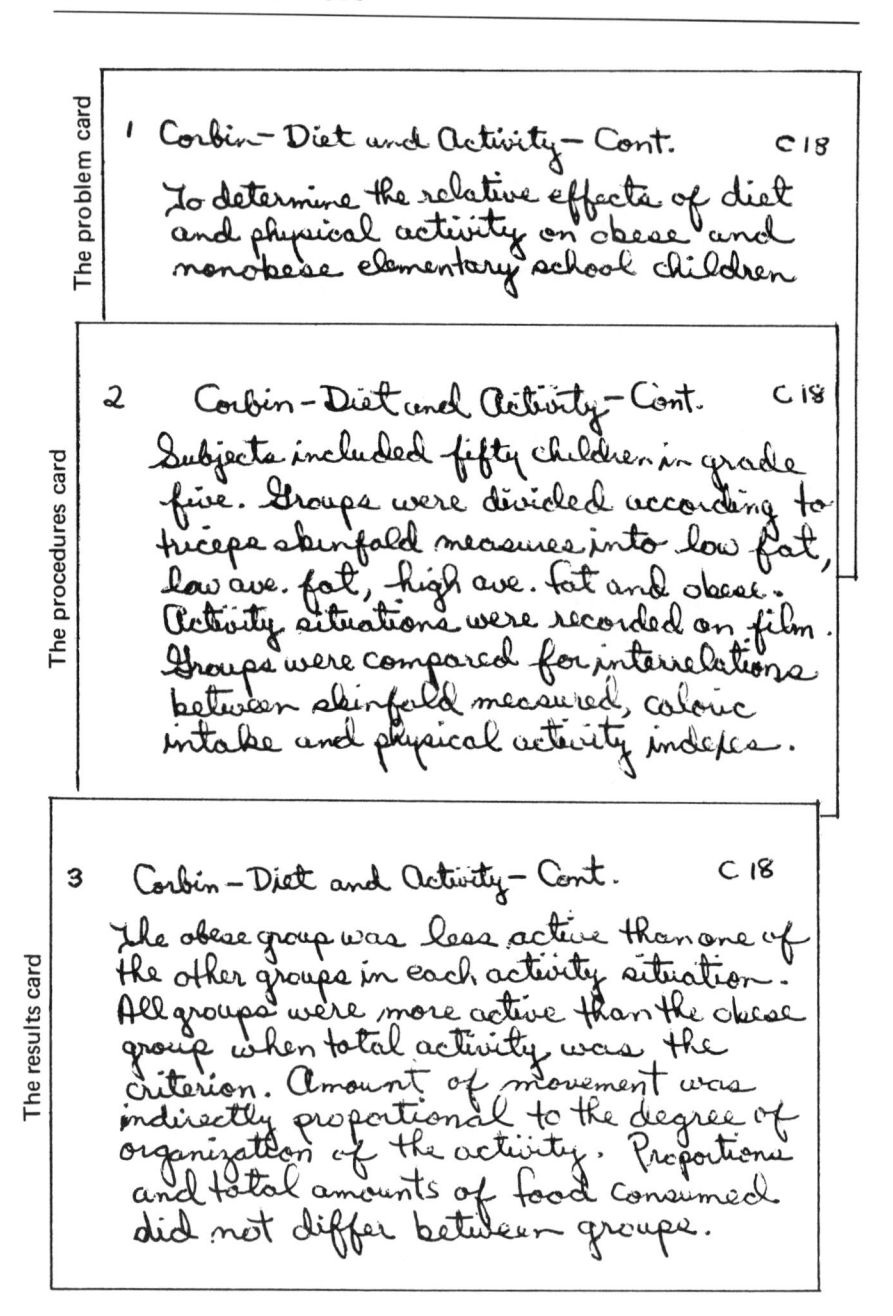

The problem card

1. Corbin — Diet and Activity — Cont. C 18

To determine the relative effects of diet and physical activity on obese and nonobese elementary school children

The procedures card

2. Corbin — Diet and Activity — Cont. C 18

Subjects included fifty children in grade five. Groups were divided according to triceps skinfold measures into low fat, low ave. fat, high ave. fat and obese. Activity situations were recorded on film. Groups were compared for interrelations between skinfold measured, caloric intake and physical activity indexes.

The results card

3. Corbin — Diet and Activity — Cont. C 18

The obese group was less active than one of the other groups in each activity situation. All groups were more active than the obese group when total activity was the criterion. Amount of movement was indirectly proportional to the degree of organization of the activity. Proportions and total amounts of food consumed did not differ between groups.

Figure 4. An example of the note cards used in the brief abstract method.

The Brief Abstract

The brief abstract method utilizes a series of note cards, each of which bears a specific kind of information. The cards are indexed according to the author number of the bibliographic card and filed alphabetically in separate decks by type of information. A common division of decks for note cards dealing with experimental studies is by *problem*, *procedures*, and *results*. Figure 4 illustrates the indexing system and samples of the information contained on each of the three note cards.

The *brief abstract* method facilitates the retrieval of specific information during the writing process. An arrangement of abstracts according to the type of information permits the writer to proceed directly within a deck instead of reviewing the entire collection of abstracts. Making the decision of relevancy with respect to specific portions of the article, rather than for the entire article, also insures a higher ratio of usable information. The brevity of the recorded information represents a minimum expenditure of time should the reference not be used in the paper.

As with most recommended procedures, there are disadvantages to the brief abstract method. The continuity of the article is lost when the information is divided by category. It can only be restored by retrieving the cards from their respective decks. Unless the information has been recorded with the writing process in mind it is likely that the total content from separate cards will not equal that of a comprehensive abstract.

The Comprehensive Abstract

Abstracting is the art of summarizing the content of printed material in in order to reduce the time required to read it and yet retain all of its essential information. The criterion for a comprehensive abstract is *thoroughness*. The *function* of the comprehensive abstract is to obviate the necessity of retrieving the document a second time.

The suggested format for a comprehensive abstract is shown in Figure 5. Preprinted 5 in × 8 in cards with similar formats are available in most bookstores. Recording the abstract on preprinted cards has several advantages. The format serves to remind the abstractor of the basic information which should accompany the abstract. The uniform procedure for structuring the abstract focuses attention on each section of the report. The heavy paper stock on which the cards are printed facilitates sorting and allows the user to attach index guides if the abstract is eventually filed in a deck. Space availability is comparable to a standard size sheet of paper (8½ in by 11 in) if information is recorded on both sides of the card.

68   RESEARCH METHODS

Call No.	Author(s)		Bibliographic
	Title		Card No.
	Vol.	pp.	Year
	Publisher		City
	ABSTRACT		
	(Problem, Methods and Procedures, Results, Interpretation)		

Figure 5. Format card (5" x 8") used in the comprehensive abstract method.

Writing the Comprehensive Abstract

The abstract should be written in brief, concise sentences. Phrases or incomplete sentences tend to become difficult to interpret at a later date and therefore should be avoided. A flowing literary style consumes too much space and the language lacks precision.

The quality of an abstract depends primarily upon the abstractor's ability to identify items of major importance and to refrain from including minor or incidental details. Abstracting an article involves condensing and paraphrasing the words of an author who has taken great care in choosing them. The abstractor should have a thorough knowledge of the literature with which he is working in order to preserve its true meaning.

The article should be read in its entirety before an attempt is made to abstract it. This procedure allows the writer to identify the items of significance and eventually to make a decision regarding the article's worth. It may be helpful to note items of importance in the initial reading to understand the author's perspective.

Quotes from the literature should be used sparingly. Care must be taken to record the author's wording accurately as well as the page, volume number, and title of the original source. Quotes taken out of context are apt to acquire meanings which do not correspond with those intended by the author. In all cases, material which may be selected for future quotes or paraphrases should be reproduced with sufficient comprehensiveness to avoid any possibility of misinterpreting the original meaning at a later date.

Abbreviations and acronyms contribute to the efficiency of abstracting, but their meanings must be clearly indicated. The original reference to an acronym should include its full wording, followed by its shortened form, for example, Education Resources Information Center (ERIC).

Reproduction of Original Documents

The practice of photocopying printed materials has gained impetus with the provision of reproduction equipment in most libraries. Photocopying allows the searcher to make maximum use of library time in the acquisition of materials. Possession of the photocopy also reduces the errors of interpretation which result from paraphrasing original material.

The writer who prefers to work from photocopied materials has documentation problems which are similar to those of other retrieval methods. It is advisable to check the accuracy of the bibliographic card with the citation of the original source while it is at hand. The complete citation and the bibliographic card number should then be recorded on the photocopy. Alphabetical filing by senior author provides ready access to the document as it is required in writing the review.

COLLATING THE SOURCES

There comes a time in every investigation when the search for library materials must cease. The focus now turns to writing that part of the report which must be completed before the experimental study commences, namely, a restatement of the problem, the review of related literature, and the methods and procedures under which the investigation is to be conducted. Essentially, the tasks which confront the writer at this point involve the organization and interpretation of the information procured in the library search.

The organization and interpretation of acquired materials present a major challenge to the inexperienced writer. A scholarly review should contain a chronological account of changes in important relationships, research designs, statistics, instrumentation, and knowledge related to the study. The initial step in writing the review of literature is to provide a sequential outline of the topics to be included. The topics represent the important areas identified in the scope of the problem, supplemented by the related information uncovered in the literature search. The compatible materials must then be condensed into a sequence which gives a "state-of-the-art" account of the topic. A chronological arrangement of the abstract cards provides a historical perspective and guards against the embarrassing situation in which an earlier author appears to contradict the work of one whose publication appeared at a later date.

Constructing the Bibliography

References within the textual material should be followed by the author's name and the number of the bibliography card, e.g., Corbin (C18). If the bibliography is to be constructed alphabetically it is advisable to proceed simultaneously through the text and the bibliographic deck, withdrawing the cards and arranging them alphabetically as you come to the reference in the text. They should then be numbered consecutively, according to their alphabetical sequence. The newly assigned number in parentheses is then substituted for the author's name in the text.

If the bibliography is to be arranged to reflect the order in which the references appear in the text, the cards should be maintained in a separate deck as the references are withdrawn and incorporated into the review. The process of numbering the cards and the textual references is identical to the one described previously, except that cards will be numbered consecutively as they appear in the text, rather than alphabetically.

The review of literature should culminate with 1) a summary and 2) a series of questions and testable hypotheses. The purpose of the summary requires no further elaboration. The questions or hypotheses also appear to be a logical outcome of the literature review, but to a student this position in the sequence of procedures may appear to be redundant. This misunderstanding occurs because students frequently fail to recognize the tentative nature of their original statement of the problem. The statement serves as a guide to the review of literature, but is subject to revision, depending on the results of the library search. Frequently the searcher discovers that his original concerns have been appropriately answered in the literature. However, during the course of his search he may uncover related problems of interest, thereby necessitating a revision of the original statement.

AUTOMATED INFORMATION RETRIEVAL METHODS

All scholars are concerned about the overwhelming volume of published literature. As publications become more numerous and established journals more comprehensive in their scope, it is obvious that the research worker cannot review all of the journals of interest to him. He must depend on intermediary sources, usually in the form of indices, reviews, abstracts, and bibliographies, for acquaintance with the newly published literature.

Although information retrieval is of national concern among scientists and educators, there is currently no operational system which has the responsibility for indexing and retrieving all of the published literature. Many disciplines and professions have accepted the challenge of managing their literature through the use of computer-based methods. These efforts are characterized by the variety of services available, the duplication and omission of citations from their selected lists, and a general inconsistency in the quality and quantity of services provided. This section provides a brief description of some information retrieval services which hold promise for more efficient management of printed materials.

Retrospective Searching Methods

Retrospective searching refers to the practice of retrieving information from computerized storage systems through the use of key words which describe the content of the material. Input to these systems consists of the complete citation and in some systems the citation accompanied by its abstract. One of the most widely used systems for retrospective searches of bibliographies is the *Medical Literature Analysis and Retrieval System* (MEDLARS).

MEDLARS is a computer-based system which became operational in 1964 for the purposes of indexing the international biomedical literature and preparing demand bibliographies for scientific publications. Citations contain the title, author(s), journal title, volume, issue, inclusive pagination, publication date, and language symbol for articles in foreign languages.

Questions are phrased according to the terminology of *Medical Subject Headings,* an alphabetical listing of subject headings with cross-references which is published annually as Part II of the January *Index Medicus*.

Each citation selected from biomedical science is assigned medical subject heading terms which describe the content of the article. The stored article is retrieved upon demand through the use of its assigned terms. Requests for bibliographies are initiated on MEDLARS Search Request Forms, obtainable at any medical library or directly from the National Library of Medicine, 8600 Rockville Pike, Bethesda, Md. 20014.

A computer-based system which deals primarily in unpublished educational literature is the *Educational Resources Information Center* (ERIC). ERIC is a nationwide information system sponsored by the United States Office of Education. Eighteen ERIC Clearinghouses, each focusing on a separate subject matter area, are functional within the United States. It is the responsibility of each clearinghouse to acquire, evaluate, abstract, index, and process documents for inclusion in the ERIC system.

Accessions to the ERIC system are published monthly in *Research In Education* in conjunction with bibliographic information, abstracts and the price of the duplicated document, either in hard copy or microfiche (a 4 in × 6 in film containing microimages of the pages of the document). Any documents in the ERIC system may be obtained from *ERIC Document Reproduction Service,* Bell and Howell Company, 1700 Shaw Avenue, Cleveland, Ohio 44107.

The subject matter areas of ERIC are: Adult Education, Counseling and Personnel Services, Disadvantaged, Early Childhood Education, Educational Administration, Educational Facilities, Educational Media and Technology, Exceptional Children, Higher Education, Junior Colleges, Library and Information Science, Linguistics, Reading, Rural Education-Small Schools, Science Education, Teacher Education, Teaching of English, Teaching of Foreign Language, and Vocational and Technical Education.

Information Retrieval via Microfilm

The microfilm method of information storage has advantages over other computer-based methods of information retrieval in that it handles the original rather than abstracted material. The user has direct access to the copy and may browse through it electronically or read the entire article. The equipment involves a special microfilm camera and microfilm reader. At the microfilming stage the material is coded by page into machine-readable binary codes. The film is loaded in magazines and can be electronically searched by code numbers at a rate of 10 ft/sec. Upon location of the appropriate information, the page is projected on a 10 in × 12 in viewing screen. The film will advance and stop according to a signal code which is controlled by the user.

The electronic search of microfilmed material permits the viewer to select, for reproduction, any portion of the document which is contained on the film. Material may be photocopied upon a signal from the viewer as the image appears on the viewing screen.

The user at the reader-retrieval station can alter his search command according to the kind and amount of information desired. If the search is producing irrelevant data, the user is immediately aware of it and can adjust his search procedure accordingly.

Special Indices

A number of publications use the traditional method of cataloging the literature according to author or subject headings. However, many alphabetized lists have currently become too long for rapid scanning and the subject index frequently includes a variety of dissimilar articles under common titles. The problems encountered in searching the conventional indices led scholars to explore more efficient ways of organizing the literature. Two methods which have gained wide acceptance are the *Key-Word-In-Context* and the *Key-Word-Out-Of-Context* indices.

The Key-Word-In-Context (KWIC) index is a computer-based program designed to print bibliographic titles according to a preselected series of key words or descriptors. The key words in the title of an article are sorted out and printed in alphabetical order, with a substantial portion of the title "wrapped around" it. The key word may have most of the title printed before or after it, depending on its position in the title. This is called a "permuted" index because the article will appear as many times as there are key words in the title. The printing is limited to one line of 60 spaces. Therefore a long title will not be printed in its entirety. The right-hand portion of the card usually contains the first six letters of the senior author's name and his initials, the year of publication, and a reference code.

KWIC indexing is a double-entry system. After the user has located a title of interest he must use the reference code to enter the author-alphabetized bibliography for complete information on journal title, volume, month and year of publication, and pagination.

The KWIC index has two disadvantages: 1) the title of an article must be descriptive of its content if the key words are to have meaning to the user. A way to insure that the article is identifiable is to add appropriate descriptors to the title. 2) The double-entry system is time consuming because it requires the user to search a second bibliography in order to obtain the complete citation.

The Key-Word-Out-Of-Context (KWOC) system differs from the KWIC index in that the complete citation (including author, title, and source) is printed in a single-entry listing. The key words are printed in alphabetical order to the left of the citation, and the key word within the title is underlined. The KWOC index is uneconomical in its use of space, but its single-entry search and the complete citation make it a favorite of many users.

Selective Dissemination of Information

This is an intermediate step in the provision of retrospective searches in response to questions. The selective dissemination system automatically notifies subscribers of new titles or abstracts which are of interest to them. The subscriber's interest is determined by a "user profile," consisting of key words reflecting his literary interests. As new materials are acquired the key words are compared to the subscriber's profile. If a sufficient number of key words appear, the article title or abstract is retrieved. A weighting system allows the subscriber to attach a value to each key word, thereby insuring a certain relevancy in the citations retrieved in his name.

The science of managing library materials through computer-based methods is in its infancy. Although electronically controlled systems offer greater efficiency because they are capable of surveying, indexing, and retrieving vast quantities of printed material, students should refrain from relying entirely on such prepackaged information. Bibliographies and abstracts prepared by others serve as valuable current-awareness devices, but the true scholar prepares his bibliography after seeking all possible references, and interprets his literature only after he has personally evaluated the original documents.

SELECTED READINGS

Bookwalter, Carolyn and Bookwalter, Karl. Library techniques. In *Research Methods in Health, Physical Education, Research,* 2d ed., edited by M. Gladys Scott. Washington, D.C.: American Association for Health, Physical Education, and Recreation, 1959.

Boyd, Jessie et al. *Books, Libraries and You.* 3d ed. New York: Charles Scribner's Sons, 1965.

Guide to Medlars Services, A. Bethesda, Md.: U.S. Department of Health, Education and Welfare, National Library of Medicine, 1966. (Out of print)

Janda, Kenneth. *Information Retrieval.* Indianapolis: Bobbs-Merrill Co., 1968. 230 pp.

Kent, Allen. *Textbook on Mechanized Information Retrieval.* 2d ed. New York: Interscience Publishers, 1966. 268 pp.

Meetham, Roger. *Information Retrieval.* Garden City, N.Y.: Doubleday & Co., 1970.

Research in Education. Washington, D.C.: U.S. Government Printing Office, 1969.

Rubinoff, Morris, ed. *Toward A National Information System.* Washington, D.C.: Spartan Books, 1965. 242 pp.

Williams, William F. *Principles of Automated Information Retrieval.* Elmhurst, Ill.: Business Press, 1965. 439 pp.

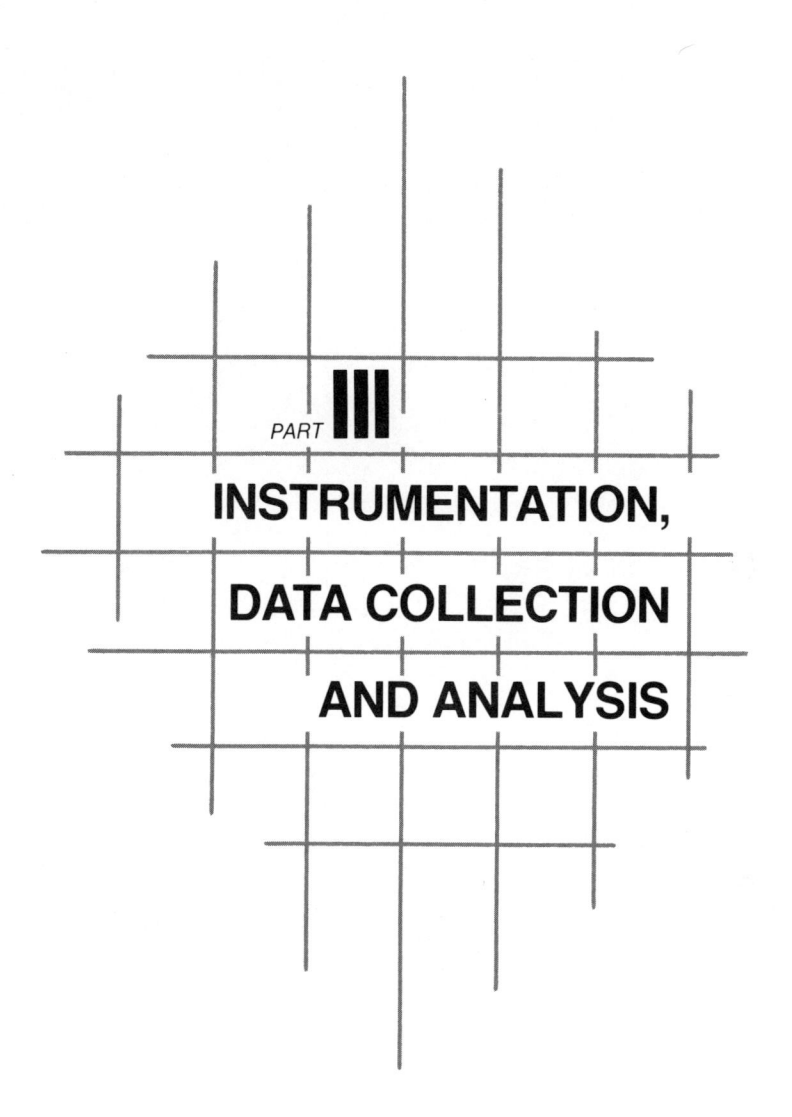

PART III
INSTRUMENTATION, DATA COLLECTION AND ANALYSIS

CHAPTER 5
INTRODUCTION TO INSTRUMENTATION

Marlene J. Adrian
Washington State University
Pullman, Washington

THE EMERGENCE OF THE PRESENT "computer age" has created a vast improvement in the sophistication and applicability of instruments utilized in research. Transistorized automatic digital programming, myoelectric controls systems, automatic colorimetric analysis, computer feedback circuits, and data processing equipment are but a few of the types of instrumentation which have evolved. The trend is toward automation, electronic operation, and continuous recording.

Coincident with these improved instruments has arisen new terminology. Instrumentation has been divided into hardware and software components. With respect to the computer, the hardware is the computer itself, that is, the mechanical and electrical machinery. The software consists of all machine stored instructions, such as computer programs. This terminology has become useful in education, managerial analysis, engineering, and other fields as well. In physical education, health, and recreation research, the hardware includes such instruments as oscillographs, force plates, electrodes, movie cameras, chronoscopes, electron microscopes, electrogoniometers, culture baths, Douglas bags, and treadmills. The software consists of written and verbal response tests. In addition, sport skills tests constitute a third type of instrumentation which may not fit precisely into this new language but will be considered as software in the next chapter. Although these terms may be helpful in categorizing some types of instrumentation, they are inadequate for defining instrumentation and its role in research. The next chapter will describe the latter process.

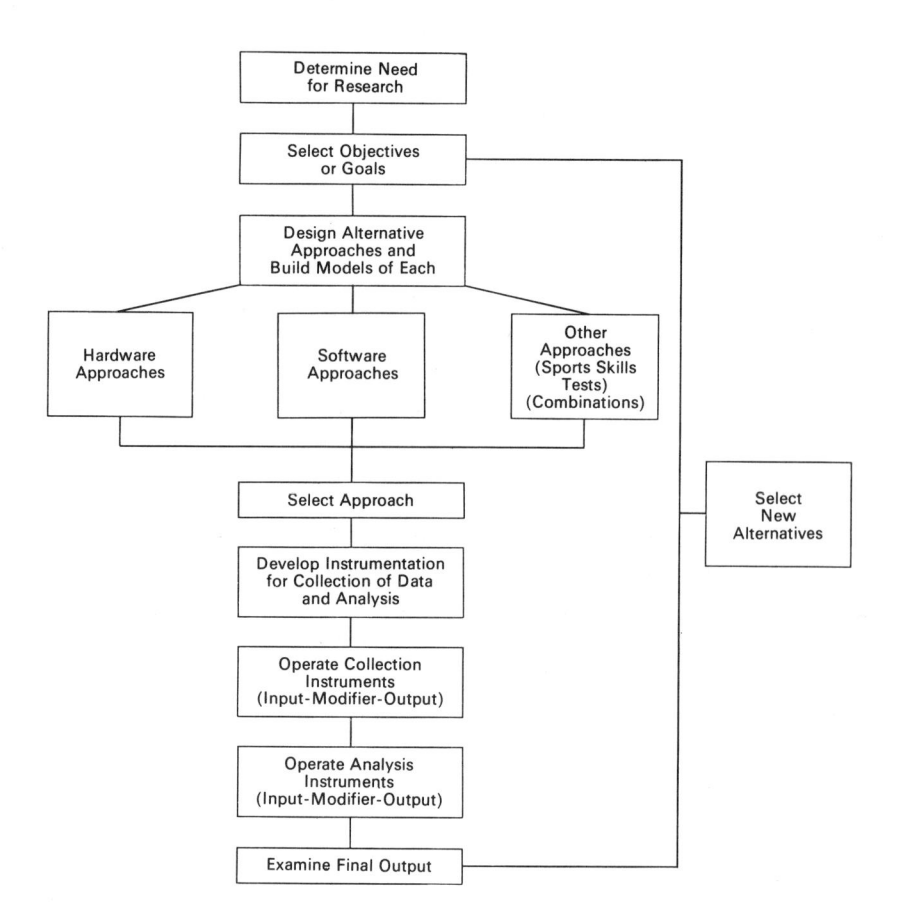

Figure 1. Research model showing instrumentation substations.

THE SYSTEMS APPROACH TO INSTRUMENTATION

Instrumentation serves two purposes in research: 1) to obtain information pertaining to the nature of an investigated object or process or 2) to control the object or process. This implies that a testing or measuring situation exists in which data are being collected under specified, reproducible conditions. Instrumentation, therefore, is an integral part of the research process, and as such should be viewed as part of the whole. This is done most effectively through the systems approach which forces the investigator to consider instrumentation from a functional rather than structural point of view. Instrumentation becomes one of the subsystems or operations of the total system of research.

The system consists of a complex of interrelated components, physical and/or abstract, as diagrammed on Figure 1. This simple research model (Figure 1) depicts two instrument subsystems: one for the collection of initial data and one for analysis of data. Each subsystem usually consists of three processes: an input (that upon which the process is to operate); the modifier which controls, amplifies, or otherwise modifies the previous process; and the output or desired data. In some instances, there is no modifier process.

More complex research models consist of three or more instrument subsystems. For example, a subsystem to regulate temperature and humidity may be used in conjunction with an electrocardiogram subsystem, psychological testing subsystem, and metabolic assessment subsystem. In addition, one or more analysis subsystems may be incorporated. The outputs of the collection instruments constitute the inputs of the analysis subsystems. Statistical techniques become the modifier process and the results constitute the final output. Only the modifier processes of collection subsystems will be considered in this chapter, since statistical techniques are discussed in Chapter 9.

The system model will be used to discuss general principles for instrumentation selection and its operation.

PRINCIPLES FOR SELECTION OF INSTRUMENTS

Understanding Research Objective

The first principle for selection of instrumentation is that the investigator understand completely his research objective in order to select the instrument which will allow him to attain it. In case the reader thinks this is an obvious statement, three examples are given depicting instances where investigators failed to identify their research objectives and systems models.

1. A series of psychological projective tests were given to determine differences in personality characteristics in four groups of subjects with various levels of athletic ability. After securing the data, the investigator attempted to tabulate his data but found that he was unable to quantify the responses from these projective tests. He decided to see if the computer could solve his problem. Since the research design had failed to consider the use of this instrument, the programming and key punching of cards was long and tedious. Furthermore, his data printout yielded a stack of pages four feet high. The output, then, was virtually worthless. This could have been prevented by prior specification of the objective in more definitive terms and consideration of the interrelationship between collection and analysis instruments.

2. The effects of heat and high humidity on work output were investigated by measuring these environmental factors with the necessary thermometers and recording the duration of treadmill running of college students during three months of the summer. Unfortunately, after collection of data was completed, it was found that no scores were obtained from several ranges and combinations of heat and humidity. Failure to select the instrument capable of controlling the environment produced this inadequate output. Three choices were available to the investigator—change the objective, temper the conclusions, or keep testing until all the missing data were completed.

3. Elementary school subjects were given sports skills tests in which scores were recorded as average, above average, and below average; pass or fail; or as ranked scores. The investigator wanted to compare these data with other groups and subgroupings of sex and grade using the analysis of variance technique. He discovered that he could not use this technique since his measurement scale was of the ordinal type (ranked numbers) and also that no comparisons could be made between the ranked scores. Thus the last step and the feedback loop of the research model needed to be altered because the testing instruments were not viewed as subsystems of the research system.

The research objective largely determines the instruments which need to be used. Table 1 illustrates five subsystems which provide varying degrees of information output concerning the patellar reflex in man. It readily can be seen how the objectives of research would differ with respect to the information output derived from the various collection instruments.

Listing Approaches and Instruments to Fulfill Objectives

The second principle for instrument selection is to compile a list of the possible approaches and types of instruments for fulfillment of the objective. Too often the availability of an instrument determines the objective, rather than the objective determining the instrumentation. All too frequently, the available instrument is that one which is in common vogue. But it may not suit a particular investigator's purposes. Furthermore, the adage that the most sophisticated machinery is the best is not necessarily true. These assumptions prevent a researcher from making a scientific choice and narrow his list of alternative approaches. Therefore, the following guidelines are presented to aid the beginning researcher:

1. determine what other investigators are using
2. list instruments available commercially
3. build models for design and construction of new instruments
4. categorize each instrument according to needed input and desired output.

Evaluating Instruments

The list enables the investigator to evaluate the instruments. Initially, one should look for simplicity of design, a simple mechanical instrument or skills test rather than a complex electrical one. In many research problems, the simpler and more direct the means involved, the better the instrumentation. However, since many advantages accrue with introduction of electrical instruments, the simple and direct methods should not be selected unless they perform according to acceptable standards. The four criteria for evaluating the performance of instruments regardless of whether they test, measure, or control, are: 1) accuracy, 2) precision, 3) sensitivity, and 4) rangeability.

Accuracy

Accuracy of the instrumentation system essentially refers to its validity. Does the instrument actually measure what it purports to measure? Does the input consist of only the variable to be measured, the measurand? Rigid control of the testing situation makes it possible to eliminate all or most extraneous or interfering inputs. Failure to establish these controls, however, results in inaccurate outputs. Written tests of self-evaluation that have unwanted social desirability response inputs and sports skills tests which include inputs based upon lack of comprehension or motivation will not produce true output performances. This latter situation has been noted particularly when testing children who are mentally deficient. Motor performance scores of some of these children indicate inability to perform the skill at the time of testing. Yet in another situation, they perform the skill without difficulty.

TABLE 1. Five Collection Instrument Subsystems Showing Input, Modifier, and Output Processes Concerned with Patellar Reflex Testing

Instrument Subsystem	Input	Modifier	Output
hammer and investigator	hammer tap	a. none b. different forces c. different locations	leg extension a. reflex exists or does not exist b. reflex is strong or weak
hammer and investigator chronoscope and break circuit	hammer tap current	a. none b. different conditions, e.g. after exercise under heat stress	reflex time a. quantification
hammer and investigator electrogoniometric recording system	hammer tap resistance changes	a. amplifier or attenuator	goniogram a. range of movement b. reflex time c. movement time d. movement velocity
hammer and investigator photography	hammer tap subject	a. film speed	film a. action of body parts b. reflex time
hammer and investigator electromyographic recording system	hammer tap electric current	a. amplifier	electromyogram a. muscle response

Unless an instrument system can be calibrated, its accuracy cannot be ascertained. Calibration consists of comparing the instrument output with a known standard or criterion. For example, stroboscopes usually are calibrated with the 60-cycle power line. Sports skills and written tests usually are calibrated with existing tests. If no standard for calibration exists, validity by definition must be sought.

In no case will the calibration standard be 100% accurate. True values are impossible to attain since all measurements are approximations and some random errors always must be assumed. These errors, however, are dealt with by systems of statistical methods and do not affect significantly the accuracy of the final output of collection instruments. Systematic errors (those inherent in the system), however, adversely affect the output and are related to the precision of the instrument.

Precision

Precision refers to reliability, that is, the property of showing agreement of outputs with repetition of inputs. All instruments are reliable if assurance of identical inputs can be made, and assurance that the modifier process has the same effect upon the input without regard to time, temperature, or other factors. Inconsistent operation of the instruments and drift of electrical components decrease their reliability. Systematic errors produce precise outputs, but the instrument may be measuring something other than the identified measurand. A steel tape used in below freezing temperatures or a cloth tape stretched beyond its original length will give precision output, but values which deviate from true scores. Thus, a precise instrument may not be an accurate one. An acceptable instrumentation system must possess both accuracy and precision.

Sensitivity

Knowledge of the sensitivity of the instrument aids in ascertaining the validity of its use in a particular experiment. A control system not sensitive to minute changes in the variable may render the experiment worthless. A written test utilizing a seven-point scale has greater sensitivity than a five-point scale. Likewise, sports skills tests which do not differentiate among finite levels of performance are not sensitive instruments and may have limitations for linkage with analysis instruments.

Investigation of finite changes in the variable requires instrumentation which is able to detect these changes. For example, measurement of reflex or reaction time with a stopwatch with a precision of tenths of a second would not give valid results. Strain gauges unable to detect changes of less than 2 pounds cannot be used to measure strength differences among weak muscle groups.

Sensitivity may be increased by attenuation or amplification as in the case of recordings from electrical instruments (for sensitivity, see p. 122). Pen deflections or other readout components are amplified in order to provide records which can be analyzed with greater precision. However, care must be taken not to overload the amplifier and introduce noise into the system. Noise refers to any interfering signal or undesired input which affects the output. It is a constant source of worry to those using hardware approaches. However, it also exists in other types of instrumentation systems. For example, a ball rolling across the path of a person being tested on the 50-yard dash or any type of distracting element interfering with the concentration of a person being tested for reaction time would constitute noise.

Rangeability

Rangeability is the ratio of maximum to minimum scale or score output for which stated acceptable precision is available. Therefore, as the range decreases the percentage of error and the limitations as a precision instrument increase. This implies that calibration should be checked over the complete range of use—a micrometer at different openings, an electrogoniometer throughout the range of movement, and a stopwatch or a spring-wound movie camera at different durations. Details are described on p. 124.

Some instruments are linear throughout a part of their operation but become nonlinear at other phases. Potentiometers used in electrogoniometry and oscillators used in telemetry circuits may have these properties. The proper operation of these elements in a system is necessary for assurance of valid results.

DESIGN AND CONSTRUCTION OF NEW INSTRUMENTS

If, after following the previous guidelines the investigator decides to design and construct a new instrument, he is confronted with a decision which may be outside his realm of knowledge (3). Hardware instruments may require knowledge of mechanical, optical, pneumatic, hydraulic, or electrical components and systems. Unless the investigator is familiar with these types of instruments, he should contract with an engineer to design and construct the new instrument. Even with knowledge sufficient to build it himself, the investigator should consult an engineer. Software instruments and sports skills tests probably can be designed by the majority of investigators.

Several guidelines are given to aid the investigator in his design and construction.

1. Designers should use the systems approach.

2. They need to gain an understanding of materials' specifications, e.g., tension, flexibility, size, signal transmission distance, density, viscosity, resistance to shock or chemical action, frictional and magnetic properties. For example, different specifications are required to emit a signal 40 ft as compared with only 10 ft. If a force is being measured with a spring scale dynamometer, distortion of the spring may cause erroneous results if the spring is not of the correct tensile strength. Temperature increases may cause viscosity, frictional and magnetic properties, size, and pressure to vary to such an extent that materials become unacceptable

as components for the system being constructed. Knowledge of minimum performance levels for each component of the system is indispensable.

Although "homemade" devices may be acceptable as research instruments, often they are built of inferior materials to save money. Instead, time and money are wasted. An example of this is an investigator who attempted to build a strength testing instrument. Force exerted against a lever produced deflection in a load cell. However, slippage in the pulley belt connecting the two components had to be corrected. A second pulley belt was added and then a floor platform was constructed and some angle iron supports erected to prevent the force from being absorbed by the frame of the machine. After all compensations were made, including compensations for compensations, the machine still failed to function with accuracy and had to be discarded.

3. All preliminary models need to be built according to desired limits of precision, accuracy, sensitivity, and rangeability.

4. Each instrument model should be tested before the final model is built.

5. As altered by testing results, selection and construction of the new instrument is made. The model which best meets the criteria is selected. In addition to the criteria, safety features and cost of the instrument may affect the decision.

SIMULATION OF INSTRUMENT SYSTEMS

The computer and the systems approach in research have led to the use of simulation as a common research tool. Simulation involves two systems—the real and the model. The model, mathematical or physical, is manipulated, tested, or otherwise operated upon in order to gain information about the real system. Biomechanical and biomedical research has used this tool extensively since treatments which would be prohibitive on the real system can be used on the models. For example, the biomechanics of head injuries is studied by imparting various types and amounts of forces to a model of the human head. Causes and prevention of concussions and deaths may be ascertained from this approach. Manufacturers of new sporting equipment and safety devices, park and playground design and facilities may well save costs and lives by using this approach.

Reed and Garrett (1) have used a computer graphics system to produce motion simulation of a jumping pattern. Simulation systems with the computer show great promise in the area of software and sports skills testing. Models could be built to test validity of the new instrument and to predict responses to a new test.

In general, models allow one to gain a better understanding of the real system. However, the investigator must determine the amount of error between his model and the real system. The worth of the final output hinges upon the designer's ability to simulate as nearly as possible the real system (2). As with all measurement, some error exists with all simulation systems. Fortunately, the principles and evaluation of instruments used in simulation systems remain the same as those used in real systems.

PRINCIPLES FOR OPERATION OF INSTRUMENTS

The investigator must understand completely the characteristics of the measurand. Furthermore, he needs a basic understanding of the operation of the instrumentation system and how the system affects the output when properly or improperly operated. The operator introduces errors in the form of mistakes, independently of and in conjunction with inherent errors of the system. The reliability of the operator, then, becomes one of the major problems to be considered.

Proper manipulation of equipment avoids errors. Improper physical handling of instruments usually lowers the reliability of the testing instrument. Skin calipers and other anthropometric measuring devices without pressure gauges rely upon the ability of the investigator to "feel" equal and correct pressure. His ability to be consistent from subject to subject as well as day to day depends upon precise manipulation.

Positioning of display scales—chronoscopes, dials and other read-out panels—should be made with the purpose of preventing parallax errors. The reader should be able to stand or sit at the same location, view the display data at eye level directly in front of him, and read the true value of the output.

Operation should be standardized. A set of directions usually is provided for operating all instruments, including commercial hardware, software, and sports skills tests. If no set exists, as with newly constructed instruments, a set of precise steps to follow should be identified. Steps for software and sports skills testing instruments need to specify how the instrument is used, what the operator does, and what the subject does.

Instruments need to be checked periodically: the time interval depends upon the stability of the instruments. Hardware needs to be cleaned, lubricated, magnetized, and repaired. Necessary consideration should be given to storage of instruments under suitable climatic conditions. Some tools need to be calibrated before each use, others after short periods of operation, and others at infrequent intervals.

While frequent use of instrumentation may accelerate deterioration, it is likely that deterioration will be considerably less than that which would accrue from disuse. In addition, more consistent and reliable functioning results from frequent use. Not only will the system function better, but so will the operator of the system. This has been noted, for example, with those who analyze gas samples via chemical techniques or administer sports skills tests. They are less precise after lack of practice.

REFERENCES

1. Reed, Walter S. and Garrett, Richard E. A three-dimensional human form and motion simulation. In *Kinesiology Review 1971,* pp. 60–65. Washington, D.C.: American Association for Health, Physical Education, and Recreation, 1971.
2. Shigley, Joseph Edward. *Simulation of Mechanical Systems: An Introduction.* New York: McGraw-Hill Book Co., 1967.
3. Wilson, Edgar B. *An Introduction To Scientific Research.* New York: McGraw-Hill Book Co., 1952.

CHAPTER 6 INSTRUMENTATION: SOFTWARE

M. Gladys Scott
University of Iowa
Iowa City, Iowa

SOFTWARE IS DESIGNED TO OBTAIN RESPONSES from subjects, responses which may be more or less precisely translated into quantitative values. Each item in software is unique in its approach to subjects and in the data yielded. The selection of an instrument is determined by the objective of the investigation and the design of the study. For purposes of this discussion, four groups of instruments are presented. Classifications of these graphs by the method of measurement and nature of the response expected, are as follows:

1. direct approach to subject for information
2. evaluation of subject or his actions
3. direct measurement of subject with respect to ability or knowledge
4. indirect approach to measurement of subjects' beliefs, attitudes, or behavior.

DIRECT APPROACH TO SUBJECTS

If one wishes to obtain information from a subject, he may question the subject under circumstances which call for either a spoken or written response. In general, one can assume that if the subjects can be met face-to-face verbal response should be solicited, and remote subjects should write out their answers. However, it is not quite that simple.

One may contact subjects as a group, but desire individual responses. Subjects may be asked questions to which they prefer to make anonymous replies. At other times, one may ask questions on which the respondent is expected to spend some time seeking information from files or thinking through a problem before answering. In each of these cases a questionnaire is indicated.

On the other hand, one may wish elaborate answers which the subject may dictate but would not take the time to write. Or one may wish immediate reactions to ideas and not the deliberative, cautious response from mulling over the "sounds of one's answer." The interview may be the ideal tool in these cases.

Questionnaires

The questionnaire is a carefully prepared series of questions with more or less guided form to the answers. The initial step in preparation of the questionnaire is the determination of topics and details to be queried. Only information which cannot be obtained from any other source and is valuable should be requested in a questionnaire.

Questions should meet the following requirements for information which can be summarized.

1. The questions should be brief and concise, with no ambiguities.

2. The questions should be clear to the least informed or least intelligent of the subjects.

3. Terms should be defined if there is any doubt. The question should mean the same thing to all subjects, i.e., no interpretation should be needed.

4. The spaces for answers should be in a column on either the right or left side of the page, if possible. This makes for easier tallying.

5. The nature of the response should be apparent, i.e., a choice from options presented, an approximation or generalization, or a free response statement. Examples:

Choice. How would you describe your swimming classes?

    _____ small, permitting individual attention

    _____ small, but too many for the size of pool

    _____ large, sufficient instructors for class

    _____ large, insufficient space and individual attention

Approximation. How many are in your swimming classes on the average?

    _____ 5–10

    _____ 11–15

    _____ 16–25

    _____ 26–40

Free response. How many are in your swimming classes on the average?

The format of the questionnaire is extremely important in securing responses. Poor wording of questions or poor arrangement on the page is apt to send the questionnaire to the wastebasket rather than into the return mail.

A questionnaire which is too long is discouraging to the recipient. Printed copy reduces pages and provides better arrangement than typed copy, as well as less actual weight for mailing. Likewise, a double column on the page can frequently be used to give the impression "this is easy."

The questionnaire should in no way reveal the opinions of the investigator or carry any other clues as to responses that might be expected. Likewise, the respondent should be assured of anonymity of responses if information is of a personal nature or might carry repercussions if answered frankly. Identification can be avoided by some categorization of the respondent; for example, the important detail may be the type of school and its location. Therefore, questions covering these two points may be much more pertinent than having a name.

The time at which a questionnaire is sent can greatly affect the returns. For example, questionnaires should never be sent at the time of a holiday or immediately preceding it. School personnel cannot be expected to answer a questionnaire at the beginning or end of a school term. The absence of a self-addressed, stamped envelope can destroy rapport with the subject; on the other hand, use of such an envelope will greatly enhance the chance of obtaining a response.

Questionnaires have been so overused that potential subjects often refuse to answer or do so hastily. Careful construction may avoid some of this rejection.

Emphasis on careful work seems necessary at each of the following stages of research employing this instrument:

1. in deciding the suitability of the questionnaire as a research tool for a particular study

2. in preliminary preparation and construction

3. in defining the population to be queried and selection of the sample to be questioned

4. in transferring responses to tally sheets or computer cards, summarizing them, and drawing meaning.

Interviews

The interview may be regarded as an oral questionnaire. Therefore, most of the rules covering questionnaires should be applied to interviews. However, interview questions tend to be more general and to invite the individual's free response more frequently. The interview permits a topic to be persued in greater depth than is usually achieved by a questionnaire. The interviewer usually deals with fewer subjects and with less attempt at compiling descriptive summaries and generalization on the data. However, exceptions can be found to both points. For example, the public opinion polls deal with many subjects but also report each option in its proportion to the total.

The questions on the interview are planned in a coordinated pattern. A general question may draw all the information needed from one subject, some of the related questions may be needed to get full coverage with a second subject, and still other subquestions are needed with a third subject.

The interview is a planned and guided conversation in which the interviewer draws out the respondent, but never divulges his own views by direct (or indirect) statement or challenge. Above all there should be no debate or arguments.

The interviewer must be trained in the interview technique. The willing talker or conversationalist may not make a good interviewer. He may need experience with the age group or subpopulation being interviewed. For example, the interviewer without vocabulary and rapport with the dissident student of today would probably not get the information he was seeking. Similarly, the interviewer unacquainted with old people might not have patience to hear the subject out and to understand the meaning of some of the reminiscences.

The interviewer must have a thorough background in the problem; otherwise the more knowledgeable respondents soon sense the futility of trying to put some of their explanations across and either terminate the interview or give the briefest possible answers.

Note taking is essential but must not be distracting to the subject or absorb the attention of the interviewer. In many studies it may be desirable to use a tape recorder for the interview. If this is done, the approval of the subject is essential. In this case, as well as with written notes, the responses must be kept confidential unless the subject is willing to be quoted. Care must be taken to minimize indirect or subtle influence that may result from interviewer bias.

Diary

The research diary calls for the recording on certain items, at specified intervals and in certain form, on a prescribed record sheet. It is not a free response channel for the subject. For example, a child's play activities before school, during breaks in the school day, and after school may be recorded twice daily, and an adult's recreational activities may be recorded daily. The adult's activity may be reported in blocks of an hour or more, whereas the child's will probably be in 5, 10, or 15-min units.

The diary produces a much more exact record of a subject's activities than does the questionnaire, which deals frequently with recall and memory. The diary is especially suited to problems dealing with diet or other health practices, with recreational pursuits, or with details of work tasks for job analysis.

Summary of Direct Approach

Whichever software method is used, the subjects' cooperation is crucial. They should be given some information concerning the study so that the project may be sold to them on its merits, not on a personal appeal.

In studies using any of the techniques explained above, there is an advantage in obtaining prior consent from each subject. A respondent who has promised to answer a questionnaire is less apt to discard it when it arrives than if faced with it unexpectedly. The interviewee is more apt to have time to devote to the interview when an appointment has been made.

The questionnaire and diary tend to be expensive because of printing and mailing costs. Interview costs come mostly from travel expenses. In either case, adequate underwriting should be assured before undertaking the study. The researcher using any of these instruments is encouraged to study resource materials further elaborating on construction and use (4, 21).

EVALUATION OF SUBJECT OR HIS BEHAVIOR

Sometimes there is merit in studying subjects in activities they perform regularly or in which they would engage even if research was not being done. Instruments used in each situation vary with the data sought. Some studies call for highly specific information. Others seek decisions or judgments on the part of the investigator or his collaborators. A brief presentation of methods follows, and the reader is referred for further discussion to sources such as Selltiz and co-authors (21).

Observations

The observation is a planned procedure designed to note and record specific occurrences. The choice of tools and techniques determines what kind of data will be obtained. *Checklists* and *scorecards* aim simply to tally specific kinds of happenings, the *anecdote* provides a narrative of the sequence of happenings, and the *rating* puts a qualitative value on the happening. Use of the observation technique is almost unlimited.

The observation does not necessarily require cooperation of the subject. In fact, he may even be unaware that he is being observed. The one-way window permits the observer to obtain full view of the action of the subject without the knowledge of the subject. It is a technique for studying "normal" or customary conditions, rather than those staged at a particular time with specified conditions or equipment. It is used in both one-time descriptive studies and in longitudinal studies on growth or learning. It has been used more on case studies of children and of the atypical than of individuals in group learning in school. Nevertheless, it would appear to have value in the class situation.

Whether the observation is made by one person or by a team of observers, certain qualifications must be met. Each observer must be knowledgeable in the action being studied. He must be open-minded about outcomes and the individual differences observed. Training for the particular kind of observation to be used, definitions of certain items or events to be seen, and explanations of methods of recording should be provided for all observers. They should observe concurrently.

Observations should be long enough and repeated enough to produce a reliable record of what has been taking place. Judgment and experience enable the investigator to estimate in advance how much time will be needed. But as long as new information is being secured and the overall relationship between items is fluctuating, more observation is desirable. Variation in time of day may be essential. On the other hand, certain times of the day may be expected to yield no information because the subjects are otherwise engaged.

The direct personal observation may be augmented by such devices as the videotape or motion pictures. These enable the observer to see the subjects repeatedly in a given action, thus yielding clearer information. Also, tape or motion pictures may be used as a training experience for the observer. If the data are to be used in a case study and a follow-up with cases is made, this technique would be useful. Also, if comparative observations are planned at stated intervals, then the permanent record is desirable. The still picture frequently used in posture analysis, somatotyping, and body symmetry also constitute a permanent record for more accurate observation and analysis.

In order to use results of an observation in a research study, the results must be recorded in some form. Following are some types of records.

Ratings

A rating represents a judgment made by the observer. The rating actually compares the subject with other subjects in terms of the particular ability or factor being observed. Individual cases may be placed in very broad descriptive categories, i.e., when very few levels are recognized. Or they may be placed in one of many categories, if judgments can be made accurately enough. It is easier to rate in a few broad categories than in finer gradations.

A rater must have a background on the trait or activity he is rating. He should be experienced in making ratings and be familiar with the particular rating scale used. Reliability of the rating improves with frequency and length of the observation and with freedom from distractions while making the rating.

It is preferable to have several raters work simultaneously and to use the sum of their ratings. They should work independently. They will not agree perfectly and could do so only by collaboration. Their differences reflect differences in background and orientation to the task as well as the different points from which they make the observations. Slight differences are desirable. One should not be unduly concerned if one rater is always higher, or always lower, than the others. This simply reflects his difference in level of expectation and as long as he places subjects in the same relative rank, and rates all subjects, the exact level is unimportant.

There are several forms of the rating scale. When judges are to observe motor activity and rate individual performers, the most commonly used scale is one of five points. Each of the five categories has a key descriptive term and a very brief statement of what characterizes the individual in this category. Such a scale might read as follows on basketball:

5 *Superior* player. Passes effectively, covers court well, moves to receive passes advantageously, is consistently accurate when shooting.

4 *Good* player. Most passing and receiving are good, may be a little slow, does not always anticipate or initiate appropriate play, has a reasonably good shooting record.

3 *Average* player. Is satisfactory in floor coverage, passing, receiving and shooting; is not a real asset to the team.

2 *Fair* player. Is slow, not very dependable, is unable to advance the ball, has a poor scoring record.

1 *Poor* player. Is ineffective as a team player, is avoided by teammates when possible, no shooting ability.

The same five categories may be used in another way when asking respondents whether they agree with some statement made. The options would then be as follows:

5 strongly agree
4 agree
3 neutral
2 disagree
1 strongly disagree

Some scales may have only three categories, others seven or nine. The last two are difficult because they require fine discrimination. It should be noted, however, that all of these have an uneven number of categories. This provides for a middle category where differences are harder to distinguish than they are when further from the median.

The ratings are valuable only if the raters 1) have adequate evidence on which to base their judgments, 2) are competent for the assignment, and 3) work conscientiously. In planning a research study one does his best to insure the first two conditions and assumes the third is met.

Checklists

The checklist is prepared for a specific type of situation in which the observation is used to obtain data. It contains a list of actions which may be seen occurring, and on which the observer tallies each occurrence. One example might be used on beginning bowlers in a learning study.

Foul line violations _____
Hits in 1–3 pocket _____
Gutter balls _____
Split leaves _____

Another example might be used in a class designed to develop fitness.

Number of exercises or activities used _____
Number of rest periods _____
Number of stations S performed at _____
Evidence of fatigue _____

Anecdote

The anecdotal report is most likely to be used in case studies. The anecdote is a narrative account of an incident in which the subject was a participant or had opportunity to be one. The account must briefly state the situation, what the subject said and/or did, and how he reacted to his own role in the incident. An example follows:

> The squad leader was assigning squad members positions for the game. There was one extra player. The leader asked Mary to be a substitute, to help the scorer for four minutes and then

come in as rear guard. Mary protested, "I want to play," pouted, and refused to help the scorer. She was angry when she entered the game four minutes later and played poorly.

A single report on a subject has little meaning, but a series of reports begins to show a pattern when reported by various observers over a period of time.

Motion Picture Films and Videotape

The permanent record of a motor performance provides an ideal way to observe the performer. Cost of equipment and operation is largely responsible for the fact that such records are not used more extensively in physical education research. The use of slow motion film, that is, film with very small intervals between frames, provides an added value when motor analysis is desired.

A film which is to be used for mechanical analysis requires more than clear photography. Landmarks may need to be placed beforehand; at any rate, contours and landmarks must be observable, clearly outlined, devoid of shadow. Movement usually covers space and therefore may result in distortion on the film. Wide angle and telephoto lenses can help to solve that problem. Measurements must be possible, precise, and undistorted.

When movement is essentially in one plane with the camera angle perpendicular to it, it is possible to study range of motion and relative body positions. Movement in another plane creates problems for the analyst which must be solved before filming. The solution is frequently a second camera, operating at right angles to the first, or directly above the performer. The two camera views should include synchronized timers so that cross-analysis can be made from the two films. All movements of the human body are rotatory. Therefore, trigonometric computation of position can also be made on the two-dimensional projection.

Since movement occurs over a time span, it is also necessary to have an accurate record of the passing of time. First thought would seem to indicate that the frame would be adequate as a time unit. However, it is subject to enough variation to make this unsatisfactory. The optimum is a timer within the photographic range. This may be a large clock face with a hand which makes one circuit per second, and distinguishable one-hundredths of a second calibration. Or a digital timer may be read from the photograph if it is large enough and placed in clear view.

The analysis of the film may take one of several forms.

1. A tracing of the outline of body parts can be used to show similarity of position and sequence with one or more performers in the same act.

Deductions of the mechanics used by the performer can be made and differences between good and poor performers identified.

2. Stick figure drawings may be made instead of outlining the body part. The segment is then represented by a line from one articulation to the next. This, too, is a fairly simple form to use and can also be used to indicate range and velocity and to compare the various parts in these aspects.

3. Body positions and angles of motion may be measured. This measurement requires a clearer projection than the methods already mentioned. A film reader with a glass window is particularly good for this work. Such measures are usually used to compute a measure of central tendency and variability for a group of subjects. If a sample of good performers is so presented, single subjects may be compared with the average on each phase of the movement.

DIRECT TESTING OF LEARNING AND KNOWLEDGE

The research worker in physical education seldom finds the exact test of knowledge and understanding that he needs for his project, even in tests of motor performance. Since measurement is used in so many forms of research, it is apparent that the young researcher would do well to learn the techniques of test construction. Neither written test nor skill test construction is beyond the abilities of the competent graduate student.

The research worker may use various printed sources and may find one or more tests which seem to be appropriate in coverage or face validity for his specific needs. He must know the requirements of good tests if he is to evaluate the statistical evidence on the test items adequately, or to pass judgment on the quality of the test.

The teacher also usually finds either that no test is available to meet his needs or that he must choose a test as the research worker does on the basis of whether the test meets basic criteria. It seems probable that of all the research procedures, those pertaining to test construction are used more than any other by the average teacher of physical education and health education.

Written Tests

The term "written test" is used here with reservation. This term, like "paper and pencil," simply indicates the equipment or process by which the subject responds. If one followed this analogy through to tests calling for motor performance, one would have to be more versatile in terminology and refer to the "ball and bat" test, or the "running test," or the "in-water" test. We tend to be more accurate in identifying the ability represented in the performance test than in those tests where the student exercises recall, or passes judgment, or otherwise makes a mental reaction.

An appropriate term which is coming into more general use is "test of knowledge and understanding." While knowledge and understanding are not the same, most tests include some of each. Perhaps the best way to understand the difference is in the terminology presented in *Taxonomy of Educational Objectives, Cognitive Domain*, edited by Bloom (5). The first level in that taxonomy represents simple recall or memory of factual material. The upper five levels range from comprehension of meaning through various forms of analysis, application, and use. The student is exhibiting knowledge when he indicates that the tennis server is foot faulting when he steps over the baseline. He is showing understanding when he indicates whether it is best to cross the baseline or move behind it to play a specific return into his court. In terms of examination form, he is showing knowledge when answering the following:

What form of test is usually used for boys in measuring arm strength?

1. bent arm hang
2. straight arm hang
3. free hanging pull-up
4. modified pull-up

But he is showing understanding when he answers the following correctly:

Which exercise will best prepare boys to pass the pull-up test?

1. press with weights
2. push-ups
3. practicing on push-pull dynamometer
4. rope climbing

There may be instances when the examination should be weighted heavily with items of knowledge. For example, candidates for the job of sports official must know thoroughly the rules, the penalties, and which official calls the infringements, administers the penalties, and keeps the game moving. Application of the rules and understanding of where to be in the flow of game activity is better demonstrated by being in the right spot than by writing responses to either descriptions of the game's progress, diagrams of the game, or motion pictures of a game.

The steps in constructing a test are as follows:

1. deciding on purpose and scope
2. writing items and preparing preliminary forms

3. checking effectiveness of the items
4. selecting items and preparing final form of the test
5. determining standards on the test for a given population.

The purpose of an achievement test is to measure the level of understanding, or increment in understanding, over a certain scope of content by a specific group of subjects. This is true of an examination given at the end of a learning period. On the other hand, the purpose may be to diagnose strengths and weaknesses in several aspects of the content area. This requires more questions than the achievement form.

The content must first be defined. If an examination is to be used at the end of a learning unit, then the purposes of the unit and the outline of content provide the framework. The exam may be inclusive and detailed or it may sample a smaller part of the total material. If the examination is broad and not restricted to one course, the scope of the exam must be defined also. If one is trying to establish a standardized test, then textbook content and a survey of typical course content must be used to help define the scope and make the final form of the examination useful.

When the scope of the examination has been defined, then the relative importance of each item in the list must be decided. This may be done by one person developing the exam, a committee of teachers, or a jury of experts in the content for which the test is being prepared. The completed framework of content and the relative proportion each part contributes to the exam is the *table of specifications* for that examination. The outline of content may be appropriate but the distribution of emphasis poor, and a poor exam results. Both are important.

The builder of the examination is now ready to start writing items. Extreme care at this point is essential, just as it is in building the table of specifications. While the items will be revised several times before the trial run, and many items will be dropped later, it will ultimately save time to strive for optimum form in the first draft.

Unless the purpose of the test is to measure memory of facts and rote learning, it is best not to use true-false or recall questions. The multiple choice question is best adapted to evaluation of students' understanding and ability to make decisions in which knowledge is basic. Most health and physical education content adapts to this form readily.

There are several forms of the multiple choice question. The following illustrate some of these, but the reader is referred to textbooks (7, 13, 20) for help in writing and to Bloom (5) for help in building items calling for some form of reasoning. The most common multiple choice form is this:

1. Why does one "give" in catching a ball?
    a) sounds better

b) makes possible a quicker return

c) provides contact long enough to close fingers on ball

d) forces the arm into flexion.

The following is the same basic form of question but uses pictorial foils.

2. Which figure is most characteristic of a flight imparted by a #5 iron?

a) ⌢

b) ⌒

c) ∩

d) ⌒⌒⌒

The above items simply ask a question and provide a choice of answers, one of which is best.

These questions are probably answered on the basis of a memorized fact by most subjects. The following might be an example of a question requiring some thought and analysis:

3. Which parts of the stroke add most to the accuracy of the placement of a forehand drive when carefully controlled?

a) transfer of weight, angle of racket face

b) waiting position, playing ball immediately off the bounce

c) firmness of grip, position on court

d) speed of the ball, facing of player while stroking.

Still another form might be arranged as follows on an anatomy examination.

4. Choose the best of the following possible answers for each question below.

a) does not cross the articulation or does not work at all

b) is a weak but primary mover

c) is the chief of the agonistic group

d) is a weak synergist

e) is a supporting muscle

f) is an antagonist

   (1) What role does the triceps play in elbow extension?

   (2) What is the role of the abdominals in back lying, leg raising?

   (3) What is the role of the pronator quadratus at the elbow joint?

When preparing a preliminary form of the exam, there should be many more items prepared than will be used eventually. The inexperienced test writer may find it necessary to have half again to twice as many questions as the number believed to be desirable for the final form.

For research purposes the preliminary form is administered to a sample from the same population as that for which the exam has been designed. This sample should be no less than 50 to 60 persons, and preferably at least 100 to 120. The examination is then scored and the questions submitted to an *item analysis*.

There is some option in the way an item analysis is computed; however the purpose is the same irrespective of method. First, the item must differentiate between those who did best on the total examination and those who did worst. In testing parlance this is validity, but the derived figure is called an index of discrimination. An item with a high index contributes to the total purpose of the exam.

Second, one needs to know how difficult each item is. Any item which is either passed or failed by almost all students does not contribute to differentiation. But it is independent of discrimination, i.e., an item may be mid-level in difficulty but have no discriminating power. The *difficulty rating* is simply the percent of the total group who answered correctly.

The third bit of information derived from an item analysis concerns *nonfunctioning foils*. These are foils that are chosen by none or too few persons; when this happens the foil is not an adequate distractor. If there are three or more functioning foils remaining after the analysis, the item may be considered further. If less than three, it should be dropped immediately.

The reader is referred to textbooks (7, 13, 20) and exemplary studies (10, 16) in deciding on the exact technique to use. Probably some variation of the Flanagan technique (which yields a product-moment coefficient of correlation indicating how well a test item differentiates good and poor performance) is most widely used. (7, 14) Most of these techniques are designed to compare each item with total performance on the test.

In other cases the purpose of the study may be to establish a test with predictive value. That which is to be predicted then becomes the criterion. For example, if one wishes to predict the success of college freshmen starting a physical education major, the test would have to be given on entrance. The criterion would be available when the year was finished. It might take more than one year to obtain enough freshmen for purposes of correlation. The test content would be defined by the kinds of abilities the student must have to perform successfully freshman work in that institution. This would have to be determined with the same care and in similar fashion as the table of specifications for an achievement exam.

Most of the item analysis procedures use the upper and lower 27% of the distribution. This gives two groups which are at different levels of whatever is represented by the test. The actual percentage may be violated a little as long as all members of each group are distinctly different by test score from the other group. A total sample of 100 or a little over enables one to use two extreme groups of 25 each thereby establish a reasonably stable picture of the performance. Also it simplifies most of the computations. Aschenbrenner (2) also demonstrated that where very large numbers of examinees are given the test, only 10% at each extreme is needed. This 10% might very well be as many as 100 or more.

The use of the two extremes enables one to make calculations without exact use of the specific score. This is a partial safeguard if there are several poor questions in the examination.

On the basis of the item analysis the final form of the examination can be prepared. Items may be used if they:

1. have three or more functioning foils
2. satisfy some point in the table of specifications
3. are appropriate in difficulty
4. are appropriate in the answering process in terms of taxonomy
5. are of adequate discriminating power as determined statistically.

Usually the items are arranged in the final form according to their difficulty—progressing from easy items in the first part to increasingly difficult ones through the exam. Other details of format, printing, answer sheets, and administrative time are determined. Such an exam can be given to the subjects of a research study, or to a class, with confidence that scores derived are valid and dependable.

If the completed examination is long enough, one can assume reasonably stable scores if it is administered on more than one occasion in a project. However, this is, at best, a difficult assumption because students do not approach a given exam a second time in the same mind-set or with the same effort.

A reliability estimate is not always made. The most commonly used computation is that proposed by Kuder-Richardson (7) or Angoff (1).

Guilford (9) points out that the following factors affect the reliability of a test:

1. Item difficulty. Items of moderate difficulty, where 50% pass and 50% fail, are the most reliable.

2. Item intercorrelations. Reliability is highest when the items correlate highly with the total score and lowly with each other.

3. Range of difficulty. The more nearly equal the test items are in difficulty, the higher is the test reliability.

4. Length of test. Reliability increases with an increase in length of the test.

5. Item discrimination. Item discrimination, which is the correlation of an item with the total test score, is a good index of item intercorrelations (see No. 2, above). An effective way to increase the item intercorrelations is to improve the discriminative quality of the test items.

Ebel (7) points out further that reliability values also are influenced by the types of subjects used in developing the test. He states that it is easier to get high reliability when the students range widely in level of achievement than when they are more nearly equal.

If one needs norms on an exam, the exam must be given to large numbers from the population on which it has been validated and to which it will be applied. With a sample ranging from several hundred to perhaps a thousand or more, the derived scale becomes smoothed and usually more symmetrical. The percentile is used most commonly and because of its general use in education is most easily interpreted to students or laymen.

It is highly improbable that a satisfactorily written examination can be found in the literature or purchased from a testing agency which is specific to a research study dealing with knowledge and understanding in some aspect of physical education. Therefore, the investigator will need to carry on a preliminary study of test construction as outlined above.

Motor Performance Tests

Motor performance tests may be used in research studies to measure status, to measure changes in performance from time to time, to compare ability of groups or individuals, or possibly to motivate subjects to demonstrate abilities under certain conditions.

Motor performance tests are of several types to measure various abilities. Examples are tests: to measure 1) certain abilities, such as balance, flexibility, or agility; 2) certain aspects of fitness, such as cardiorespiratory endurance, muscular endurance, or strength; 3) a somewhat general motor ability or the specifics of skills used in particular sports; 4) posture and body mechanics or responses of kinesthetic control; or 5) developmental movement patterns accompanying maturation. The researcher involved with use of motor performance tests should start with study of one or more of the books in measurement and evaluation in physical education (3, 13, 14, 17, 18, 20).

All types of performance tests must undergo both subjective and statistical evaluation. The subjective is the first step and is largely one of *face* validity. In some instances, this may be sufficient. For example, if a subject is asked to exert a maximum effort in pulling on a dynamometer this appears to involve little except strength and willingness of the subject to put forth effort. Likewise, if subjects are asked to run for a long period of time, the various times demonstrated are directly related to endurance and willingness to persist. Or, a subject asked to move an extremity in a given plane through as great a distance as possible exhibits flexibility of at least a certain type in that particular area. Such tests are not open to debate on the function being tested, but the way in which they are administered and the way in which the subject is motivated to cooperate are always open to question.

Therefore, the investigator must be thoroughly conversant with the various ways of eliciting subject performance and scoring the performance, and he must train himself for consistency. The characteristics of the subjects which make them exert much or little effort may be partly understood as differences of interests and of personality. These will be discussed later. Subject cooperation is a requirement of all research.

Most performance tests do not lend themselves to such quick assessment of quality. Whatever type of test one considers, all go through essentially the same process of construction. These steps are as follows:

1. selecting a criterion
2. developing experimental test items
3. computing objectivity and reliability
4. computing validity
5. computing a basis for combining into a battery if a single test is inadequate
6. establishing norms if necessary.

Criterion

A criterion is a yardstick of that which the investigator wishes to measure. There is some option as to the type of criterion which may be employed.

In many situations there is no alternative except to have a group of judges rate ability as they see the subjects in action. The usual procedure for establishing and using rating scales is employed. The sum of ratings is used to indicate the subject's ability.

In a few cases there may be a known, or previously established, measure of the ability being studied. While a project's objective may be to shorten the known measure or develop one which is administratively more feasible, the longer test may serve as a satisfactory yardstick.

In the case of individual sports it is sometimes possible to run a ladder tournament. If seeding can be done in advance, this will probably speed up the determination of proper place on the ladder. Such a tournament yields essentially a rank order and provides a suitable criterion for testing the experimental items.

Experimental Items

Ideas for test items should be centered around an enumeration of the main skills in a sport. Working with such a selected list, the tasks established should be performed in a situation as much like a game as possible with only one performer involved. All details should be worked out on such things as equipment needed, lines, targets, etc., distances and time regulations, instructions to performer and assistants on scoring method, and number of trials.

Every item should be prepared with the greatest care. At the same time, one must recognize that a number of items will be lost in the successive stages of statistical evaluation. Therefore, it is advisable to start with at least twice the number of items that one expects to use ultimately.

Objectivity and Reliability

Objectivity can be predicted on the basis of the method used to score the test and on the amount of training the test administrators have had. Objectivity may be expressed in terms of correlation. For computation, more than one scorer is used and the scoring of one judge is correlated with each of the others.

Reliability (see pp. 83 and 37-38) is the consistency with which a test measures at a given level of performance. The optimum procedure is to administer the test twice, preferably on successive days. The scores of the two administrations are then correlated. Another option is to use a test that may have several trials. In that case, the alternate halves would yield a correlation a little lower than two administrations of the test since the number of trials being correlated is only half the total.

Any test which is not high on objectivity and reliability should be dropped from further consideration, or additional trials given to subjects immediately, to be used as part of the total test score. Increasing the number of trials usually improves reliability.

Validity

The procedures for determining validity (see p. 81) are relatively simple. Since the criterion has been determined and data collected on the subjects, the correlation of each test with the criterion yields a coefficient of relationship (variability). The more careful one's estimate of face validity and building for pertinent characteristics, the more apt is the test to yield a high validity correlation. If one believes in the criterion which was used, one can accept the r as an indication of validity. The r should be as high as possible.

If any item fails to reach a satisfactory validity level it should be dropped from further use. It would not be used in the next calculations. Neither would it be used in the future with the possible exception of use for practice purposes.

Battery Construction

The first step in constructing a battery of tests is to select only those with a satisfactory level reliability and validity. Intercorrelations are computed among all remaining tests. For example, if 6 tests survive to this stage, each of the 6 will be correlated with each of the other 5, for a total of 15 correlations.

The objective in battery construction for research is to select a combination of items which will yield the best possible prediction of that ability represented by the criterion. If the battery is being built for regular class use, then a further consideration is administrative ease and economy.

The combinations of items are selected on the basis of high validity and low intercorrelation. Such observationally selected combinations are then checked for validity by computing a multiple correlation. Several combinations may be tried and the ultimate choice is then made on the basis of battery validity and feasibility of administration.

Norms

If norms are constructed, they are usually percentiles or other forms of standardized score. Norms are always specific to the group on which they are established and their wider applicability is dependent on the representativeness of the sample.

INDIRECT MEASUREMENT

The term indirect measurement seems almost contradictory. This is not really true. Measurement may be quite precise, but the interpretation is derived by inference. The development of such measuring tools requires the same type of processes as already outlined for direct measurement, but frequently lacks the identification of a criterion in the way outlined for skill tests.

Attitude Scales and Inventories

Attitudes are usually considered to reflect the tendency of a subject to react in a certain way under given conditions. But on a written test of that tendency (attitude) he does not always respond as he might behave. This may be because in a written answer he may think over alternatives rather than answer spontaneously as he might overtly react. Or, he may be defensive and try to protect himself or appear in some light other than as he is.

Attitudes toward a specific subject can be obtained only if the scale is built on components of the same entity. For example, if one wishes to know the attitude of subjects to physical education, one must deal with the range of experiences which to the subjects constitute physical education. These would include activities, playing with others, being in a gymnasium, getting hot and tired, acquiring skills, being tested, or demonstrating skill. Dealing with such specifics gives a better evaluation of the attitude toward physical education than simply asking the subject to give a structured response to the question "how do you like physical education?" (very much, some, neutral, little, resent).

It is essential that all statements in the scale be related or be a part of the same attitude. This is a matter of face validity and internal consistency.

Thurstone's technique for factor analysis is one of the older methods. He employed statements reflecting degrees of attitude favorability or unfavorability. This technique requires a jury of judges and considerable subjectivity in development. The more commonly used technique at present is that developed later by Likert. This scale allows the subjects to give differential responses (such as "strongly agree," "agree," "disagree," and "strongly disagree") to a number of statements.

Inventories attempt through a long list of items to obtain a description of the subject's attitudes or opinions. Usually the subject's answer is in the form of a *yes* or *no*. For example, Doudlah (6) developed three inventories which she called Body Image, Self-Concept, and Movement Concept. Tufts (23) used this technique with members of a weight control class and found that the inventories reflected changing concepts with weight loss and increased activity.

Projective Methods

The projective technique attempts to draw out a more honest answer from the subject than he might give if he knew the purpose of the questions. The best known of these are the Rorschach test and the TAT (Thematic Apperception Test) (19). The TAT uses silhouettes or pictures rather than the completely abstract stimulus of the Rorschach test. The TAT has been used in several studies of physical education, for example,

Jaeger (12), Williams (24), Sheffield (22), Glasscock (8). Jaeger found in her study that experienced physical education teachers could evaluate the reports on attitudes toward physical education as adequately as could the trained psychologist. This seemed to contradict the statement of the psychologists that a jury of clinical psychologists must be employed on such tests, and thereby opened the door to further development of the technique in physical education research. Williams, Sheffield, and Glasscock all demonstrated the use of multiple choice foils rather than the free response of the earlier forms. Pilot studies are essential to establish suitable foils, but the actual scoring later is less laborious.

From the field of sociology came another form of the projective instrument. Kuhn (15) developed the TST (Twenty Statements Test) commonly called the "Who Am I Test." It consists of asking the subject to write 20 answers after asking himself that question. The attitudes revealed are analyzed through three techniques: 1) social anchorage, 2) nonconsensus answers, and 3) saliency of answers, or manifestation of trait. Isenberger's (11) study applied this technique in a study of women physical education majors.

Most of the projective instruments permit the subject to construct his own response. This has the advantage of permitting individual expression, but the disadvantage of not lending itself to the single scores which permit the comparisons between individuals possible with other types of measurement.

Sociometrics

Sociometry is a series of techniques for studying the patterns of interpersonal relations within a given group. It is essential that members of the group have enough acquaintanceship to have built some group structure.

A sociometric test attempts to determine within the group the nature of that structure, i.e., is it a unified, cohesive group, or is it made up of subgroups which are more or less mutually exclusive? The test attempts to identify leaders and to quantify the degree of leadership. It also identifies those within the group who are accepted and those who are rejected by the group and the scope of acceptance or rejection.

A sociogram is frequently used to depict the group structure. It shows graphically the nature of an individual's relationship with others in the group.

As in all forms of testing, it is essential in a sociometric test to have full cooperation of all subjects. The nature of the questions asked is governed by the need to obtain an honest answer and one which reflects true feelings.

The most frequently used form is the Functional Choice Test (21). This is a technique for finding with whom group members wish to play a game or serve on a committee and with whom they would be unhappy. The situation to which the question refers is specific to the group.

The Personal Distance Test (21) is similar in end result, but asks directly about the other members of the group without creating a situation on which to base choice. Similarly, the Acquaintance Volume Test asks subjects to name specific members of the group. This has the advantage of being usable on a group with limited exposure since it deals only with knowledge of names. It provides the possibility of measuring changes over a period of time.

The sociometric test provides certain information, but not a diagnosis of contributing factors or the dynamics of cause. It must be viewed as an instrument for finding facts about the status of group integration at any given moment.

REFERENCES

1. Angoff, W. H. Test reliability and effective test length. *Psychometrica* 18: 1, 1953.
2. Aschenbrenner, Harry R. A study of reliability of one type of discrimination index for test items. Master's thesis, University of Iowa, 1949.
3. Barrow, Harold M. and McGee, Rosemary. *A Practical Approach To Measurement in Physical Education.* Philadelphia: Lea & Febiger, 1964 (2d ed., 1971).
4. Bingham, W. V. and Moore, B. V. *How To Interview.* 4th ed. New York: Harper & Row, 1959.
5. Bloom, Benjamin S. and Krathwohl, D. R. *Taxonomy of Educational Objectives, the Classification of Educational Goals Handbook, I, Cognitive Domain.* New York: David McKay Co., 1956.
6. Doudlah, Anna. The relationship between the self-concept, the body-image and the movement-concept of college freshmen with high and low motor ability. University of North Carolina at Greensboro, 1964 (Microcard BF295).
7. Ebel, Robert L. *Measuring Educational Achievement.* Englewood Cliffs, N.J.: Prentice-Hall, 1965. 481 pp.
8. Glasscock, Martha. Attitudes of an upward bound youth group toward recreation. Ph.D. dissertation, University of Iowa, 1968.
9. Guilford, Joy P. *Fundamental Statistics in Psychology and Education.* New York: McGraw-Hill Book Co., 1959 (4th ed., 1965).
10. Hennis, Gail M. Construction of knowledge tests in selected physical education activities for college women. *Research Quarterly* 27: 301–309, Oct. 1956 (Microcard PE 220).
11. Isenberger, Wilma. Self attitudes of women physical education majors as related to measure of interest and success. Ph.D. dissertation, University of Iowa, 1957 (Microcard PSY 62).
12. Jaeger, Eloise. An investigation of a projective test in determining attitudes of prospective teachers of physical education. Ph.D. dissertation, University of Iowa, 1952 (Microcard PE 121).

13. Johnson, Barry L. and Nelson, Jack N. *Practical Measurement for Evaluation in Physical Education.* Minneapolis: Burgess Publishing Co., 1969.
14. Knapp, Thomas R. *Statistics for Educational Measurement.* New York: Intext Educational Publishers, 1971.
15. Kuhn, Manford and McPartland, Thomas S. An empirical investigation of self attitudes. *American Sociological Review* 19: 68, 1959.
16. Ley, Katherine L. Construction objective test items to measure high levels of achievement is selected physical education activities. Ph.D. dissertation, University of Iowa, 1960 (Microcard PE 471).
17. Mathews, Donald K. *Measurement in Physical Education.* 3d ed. Philadelphia: W. B. Saunders Co., 1968.
18. Montoye, Henry J. An introduction to measurement in physical education. *The Physical Educator* 1: 5, 1970.
19. Ricciuti, H. Development and application of projective tests of personality. *Review of Educational Research* 32: 64, Feb. 1962.
20. Scott, M. Gladys and French, Esther. *Measurement and Evaluation in Physical Education.* Dubuque, Iowa: William C. Brown Co., 1959.
21. Selltiz, Claire et al. *Research Methods in Social Relations.* Rev. ed. New York: Holt, Rinehart & Winston, 1959.
22. Sheffield, Dorothy. Construction of a projective test for analyzing individual swimming fears. Master's thesis, University of Iowa, 1955.
23. Tufts, Sharon A. The effects of diet and physical activity on selected measures of college women. Ph.D. dissertation, University of Iowa, 1969.
24. Williams, JoAnn Kay. The high school girls' image of physical education as a profession. Master's thesis, University of Iowa, 1964.

SELECTED READINGS

Fleishman, Edwin. *The Structure and Measurement of Physical Fitness.* Englewood Cliffs, N.J.: Prentice-Hall, 1964.

Gronlund, Norman E. *Constructing Achievement Tests.* Englewood Cliffs, N.J.: Prentice-Hall, 1968.

Latchaw, Marjorie and Brown, Camille. *The Evaluation Process in Health Education, Physical Education and Recreation.* Englewood Cliffs, N.J.: Prentice-Hall, 1962. 267 pp.

McCollum, Robert H. and McCorkle, Richard B. *Measurement and Evaluation: A Laboratory Manual.* Boston: Allyn & Bacon, 1971.

Multiple Choice Questions—A Close Look. Princeton, N.J.: Educational Testing Service, 1963.

Thorndike Robert L., ed. *Educational Measurement.* 2d ed. Washington, D.C.: American Council on Education, 1970.

Vincent, Marilyn F. Attitudes of college women toward physical education and their relationship to success in physical education. *Research Quarterly* 38: 126–132, March 1967.

Wood, Dorothy A. *Test Construction: Development and Interpretation of Achievement Tests.* Columbus, Ohio: Charles E. Merrill Publishing Co., 1960. 144 pp.

CHAPTER 7
INSTRUMENTATION: HARDWARE

W. D. Van Huss

Michigan State University
East Lansing, Michigan

THE BROAD DIVERSITY OF RESEARCH LABORATORIES under the umbrella of physical education is to be expected and is a healthy sign of professional growth. However, this breadth of scientific effort precludes comprehensive coverage of specific instruments in this chapter. Therefore the basic principles and procedures which apply to the broad spectrum of hardware utilized across the varied research efforts in the profession are presented first herein. Since electrical hardware seems to be the most forbidding to neophyte researchers, the next section emphasizes electrical theory and deals with the more traditional laboratory hardware, in which the phenomena are usually measured directly. Selected references and readings are presented at the end of the chapter and there is a bibliography in the Appendix for the reader who wishes further information concerning these areas of instrumentation, i.e., flow, pressure, volume, temperature, specific gravity, time, mass and weight, and linear measures.

BASIC PRINCIPLES AND PROCEDURES

Instrument hardware consists of the physical pieces of equipment utilized in research. Hardware is used to obtain direct or indirect measures, to provide better control and precision of measurement, to amplify or reduce data, to alter the time base to permit sequential study of fast or slow

---

The assistance of Robert Wells, engineer, in the preparation of this section is gratefully acknowledged.

occurring phenomena, to make temporary or permanent records, and to modify or perform computations of the basic measures.

Hardware users in physical education tend to fall into three categories:

1. Those who know nothing about an instrument and who learn only enough about it to be able to list its name in their thesis. In most instances these individuals, fortunately (for the instrument) have someone else collect their data for them.

2. Those who learn how to operate, calibrate, and make minor adjustments. These individuals learn the basic scientific principles upon which the instrument operates but are incapable of repairing it. Graduate students should attain this level, at least.

3. The highly competent technician who is capable of both operation and repair.

Most new graduate students exposed to research where sophisticated hardware is being used are understandably apprehensive. Since too few have been permitted to use hardware in undergraduate training, it looms as an unknown, forbidding quantity. The initial reaction is to withdraw, saying to one's self, "I could never operate *that.*" Everyone experiences this reaction but one should not let it linger. *Become involved as soon as possible to break down the resistance.* The longer one waits the harder it seems to be. Here are some guidelines:

1. Read the instrument manual, particularly the portion describing the scientific principles upon which the instrument is based. *Remember that the single components of all hardware are basically simple.* Most instruments consist of many simple components working together. The unit appears more complex than it is.

2. Read the directions for operation to learn *all* precautions and to obtain a working knowledge of all the various switches, connections, gauges, and dials.

3. Observe an experienced operator.

4. Request someone to teach you to operate the instrument. *Don't be embarrassed in making this request. It is an unwritten law in research laboratories that people help each other.*

5. Perform calibrations, and if possible check your technique on standard samples. When standard samples check within the specified limits of error, the ability necessary to conduct research using that piece of hardware has been achieved. Generally, learning to operate other instruments becomes progressively easier. However in every laboratory there is at least one "beast" around which seems to defy satisfactory operation.

Calibration

Testing the accuracy of measurements by an instrument in normal operation in comparison with measurements made on known standards is known as calibration (pp. 38, 82–83). The *accuracy* of a measurement is defined as the closeness with which the instrument reading approaches the true value or standard (pp. 81–83). Since no instrument is accurate in the absolute sense, giving only an approximation of the value of the variable being measured, it is necessary to know the degree of accuracy inherent in the instrument under normal operating conditions. The accuracy of a measurement thus is reflected by the degree of error in the final result. For example, a thermometer may be described as having an error not in excess of $\pm 0.1°$ C between 0 and 100° C. In the calibration process, however, usually a table or graph is constructed (Figure 1) by which units of the standard can be determined. In some instances ad-

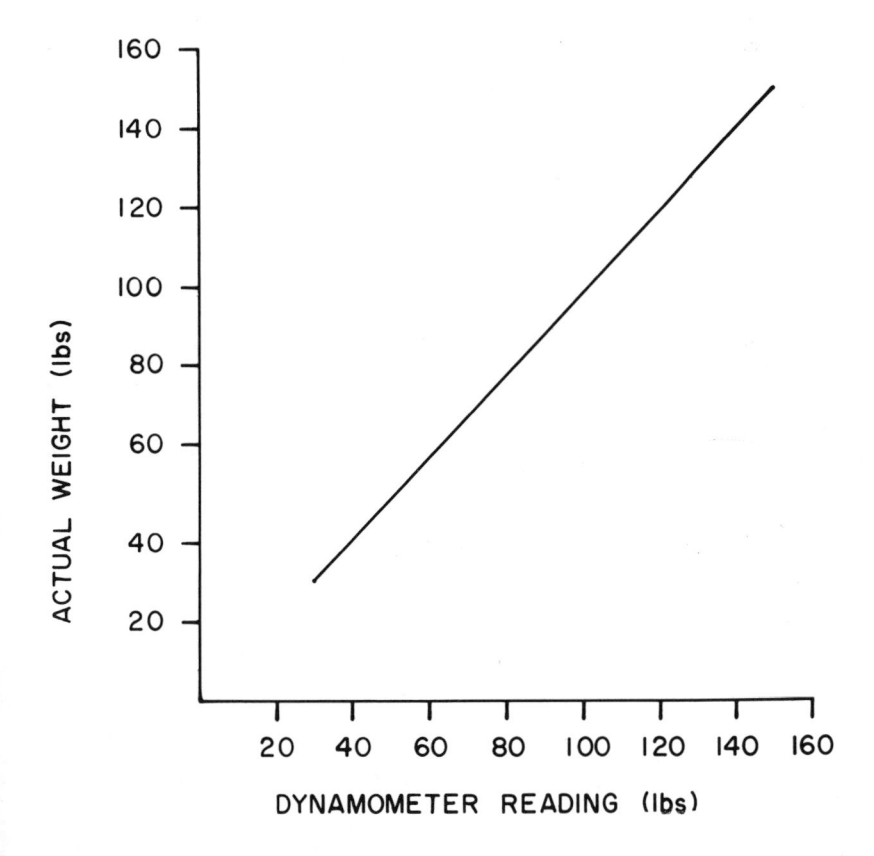

Figure 1. Calibration curve — hand dynamometer.

justments are made on the instrument to make it conform to a known standard. *No measurement should proceed without calibration. It is also a sound rule for the investigator to calibrate his own instruments so that he has confidence in his own data.*

The accuracy of an instrument may be expressed in a number of ways. The manufacturers usually give the intrinsic accuracy of the hardware. This is the accuracy of the instrument when calibrated at the plant under controlled conditions. This is not necessarily the same as the accuracy obtained under practical laboratory usage. In some cases it is necessary to sacrifice the intrinsic accuracy of a delicate instrument to obtain one which is more rugged and therefore likely to maintain a higher degree of accuracy under difficult laboratory conditions.

Accuracy as Percent of Scale Range

The accuracy of an instrument with a uniform scale is often expressed in terms of the scale range. Accuracy expressed this way can be confusing. For example, a balance with a range of 0 to 100 g (grams) could be quoted as being accurate to within $\pm 0.5\%$ of the scale range. This means that all readings will be accurate to $\pm 0.5\%$ of 100 g or ± 0.5 g. At the top of the scale range, this error may be negligible. Near the bottom of the scale range, however, an error of ± 0.5 g may be significant. For example, if a reading of 10 g is accurate to ± 0.5 g, this is an error of 5%.

Accuracy in Relation to the True Value

Accuracy is sometimes presented in terms of the percent of the true value. If a thermometer with a range $0°$ to $100°$ C was quoted as being accurate to within $\pm 0.5\%$ of the true value, at $10°$ C the thermometer would be accurate to $\pm 0.05°$ C, but at $50°$ C it would be accurate to only $0.25°$ C. A statement of accuracy of this type means that as the reading gets less so does the size of the error and vice versa.

Point Accuracy

Accuracy presented at only one point in the scale range is called point accuracy. It does not give information on the general accuracy of the instrument. Point accuracy may be expressed in actual values or as a percentage. For example, with a thermometer at $50°$ C, if the error was $\pm 1°$ C it may be written $50°$ C $\pm 1°$ C, $50°$ C $\pm 1\%$, or $50°$ C $\pm 2\%$. It would be written $50°$ C $\pm 1\%$ if given in terms of a scale range of $100°$. If the point accuracy is given in relation to the true value, it is written $50°$ C $\pm 2\%$ ($\frac{1.0° C}{50} \times 100 = 2\%$). *The investigator should be wary as to how accuracy values are presented, in particular where percentages are used.* Point accuracy is rarely used for a single point but it is commonly used to present the accuracy information for a number of points in the scale range.

The Hysteresis Loop

If more complete information is desired, a graph should be drawn showing the error at numerous points on the scale. The points should be plotted against the true value as the measured value is increased in steps and the process repeated as the measured value is decreased by the same steps. Inaccuracies arising from such causes as friction, bearing or gear clearance, spring changes, backlash in the mechanical movement, or the aging of materials is reflected by such a plot. It is not unusual for an instrument to deviate when the measured variable is applied and when it is released. The hysteresis loop shown in Figure 2 gives the error at each point for

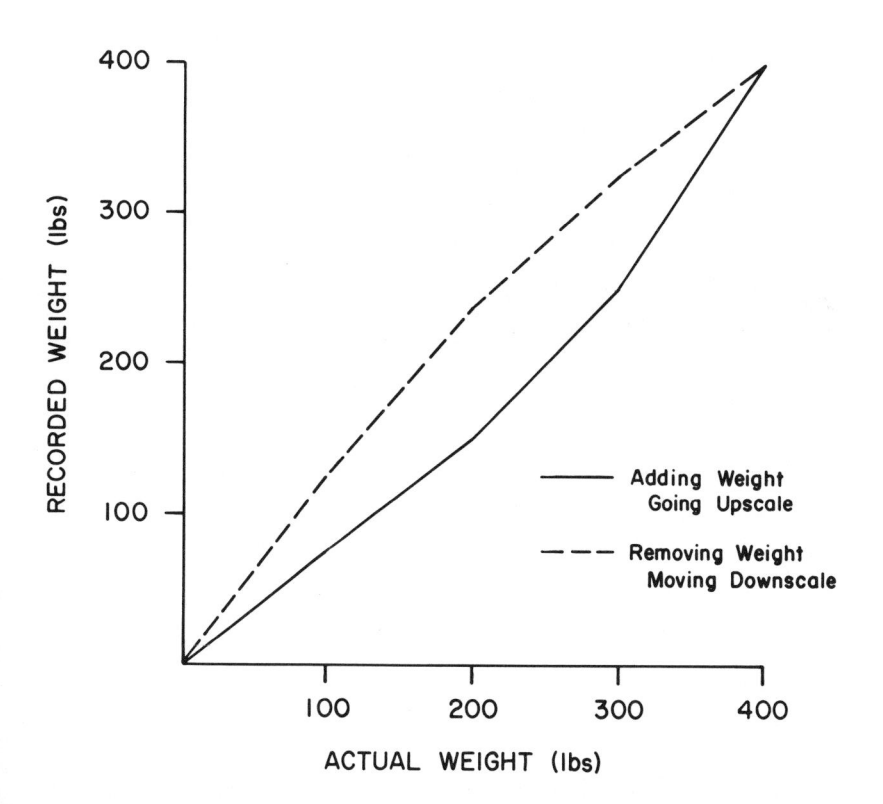

Figure 2. Hysteresis loop. Tension-compression strain gauge.

movement up or down scale and is thus a fairly complete picture of the accuracy of the instrument.

Multiple Instruments or Components

If four components with individual freedom for error (or four instruments) are interconnected for the measurement of some phenomenon, each unit would have its own limits of error. If we identify these errors by $\pm a$, $\pm b$, $\pm c$, and $\pm d$, it becomes apparent that the maximum error possible is $\pm(a + b + c + d)$. This may be the error limit for the instrument linkage. Usually, it is unlikely that all units will have the maximum error possible at the same time, so the accuracy is often expressed in terms of the root square error $\pm\sqrt{a^2 + b^2 + c^2 + d^2}$. Although accuracy is sometimes expressed in this manner, the reader is urged to calibrate such linkages against the true values and to plot a single multipoint accuracy graph or hysteresis loop, whichever is appropriate.

Standards

The National Bureau of Standards, Washington, D.C., maintains absolute standards and provides the methods and instruments required to utilize those standards. *Absolute standards* are devices constructed to legal international specifications of the fundamental units of measure. The standard kilogram and standard meter are examples. Primary-standards laboratories outside of Washington directly relate their measurements to the Bureau of Standards. *Secondary reference standards*, such as those commonly used in Bureaus of Weights and Standards in the states, are designed and constructed from the absolute standards. *Working* standards are calibrated in terms of secondary standards. These are usually used for the routine laboratory calibrations. In the Michigan State University laboratory, for example, working standards for weights needed for scale, dynamometer, cable tensiometer, and tension-compression strain gauge calibrations were obtained by having a representative of the State Bureau of Weights and Standards bring their secondary weight standards to the laboratory. The most sensitive scale was calibrated utilizing the secondary weight standards. Regular weight lifting disks were then weighed and the "true" weight value painted on each disk. These disks have continued to serve as working standards. Weight lifting disks cannot be used as working standards without comparison to the secondary standards. A 25 lb disk may be off as much as 2 lb and this error is not usually in both directions. In the disks used in developing the working standard, all were short-weighted.

Obtaining working standards often can be a problem which taxes one's ingenuity or for which engineering help must be sought. For example, it is routine for many laboratories to utilize standard gas samples for the calibration of electronic gas analyzers. Even though suppliers will provide analyses for a fee, this is often accurate within only $\pm 0.1\%$, whereas the recognized limits for carbon dioxide analysis are $\pm .03\%$. Thus it is essential that all standard gas samples be checked by repeated analyses using the accurate but slower Scholander or Haldane chemical analyzers to obtain the working standards needed.

An example of such a calibration problem involving a working standard follows. Several years ago it was desired to collect some energy expenditure data under various work conditions. The Franz-Muller calorimeter was designed for this purpose and there were six available on campus. This calorimeter, which is supported on the back by shoulder straps, meters expired respiratory gases and draws off a small gas sample which is collected in a small rubber bag for subsequent analysis. From the gas analysis and volume data, the energy expenditure can be calculated. The calorimeters needed to be calibrated for the accuracy of their measurement of gas volume before use, to be sure they would do the job adequately. This raised a series of interesting questions which will give the reader some idea of the process of developing a working standard and the calibration process.

How could such a calibration be done? First a working standard was needed. In the laboratory there was a small, supposedly accurate, wet-test meter for measuring gas volumes. If accurate, the wet-test meter could serve as the working standard, but it had to be calibrated first. Thus the first step was to figure out how to calibrate the wet-test meter.

It was finally decided to calibrate the wet-test meter by air displacement. Water at room temperature was poured into the jug, which displaced air, forcing it through the wet-test meter (Figure 3). Repeated pourings of known quantities of water showed the wet-test meter to be accurate within $\pm .02\%$. The next step was to evacuate and fill Douglas bags at the same rate of flow. The Douglas bag volumes were then pumped through the wet-test meter at varying rates to determine the flow rates at which the wet-test meter performed accurately. The meter recorded inaccurately above 4 liter/min (Figure 4). Now, knowing the capacity and accuracy of the wet-test meter, a working standard had been developed and the calorimeters could be worked on.

To calibrate the calorimeter, gas was pumped through the wet-test meter at a constant flow rate of $2\frac{1}{2}$ liter/min. The bags of known volume were then pumped through the Franz-Muller calorimeter and timed until evacuation was completed to determine the flow rates.

The results were surprising, in that not one of the six calorimeters met the manufacturer's calibration at a low rate of 25 liter/min. The closest one was .8% off the manufacturer's calibration. The best calorimeter

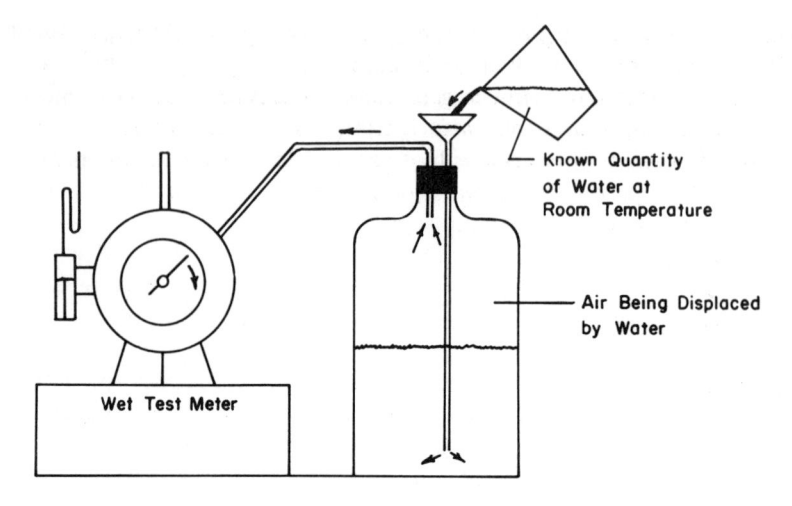

Figure 3. Calibration procedure: wet-test meter, accuracy.

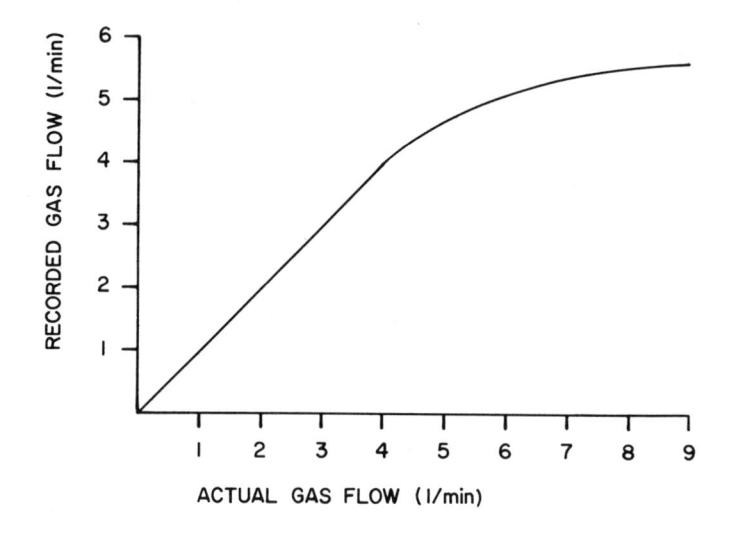

Figure 4. Calibration curve: wet-test meter, rate of flow.

(Figure 5) was accurate up to 80 liter/min utilizing *our* correction factor, whereas the capacity of the others was closer to 50 liter/min (2). Since peak flow rates of over 300 liter/min are obtained in exhaustive work and over 100 liter/min in manual labor (6), it was painfully clear that the available calorimeters could not be used.[1]

Subsequently the rubber gas sample collection bags were checked for CO_2 diffusion and were also found to be unsatisfactory. The point in this discussion, obviously, is that one should carefully calibrate instruments before proceeding in *any* experiment.

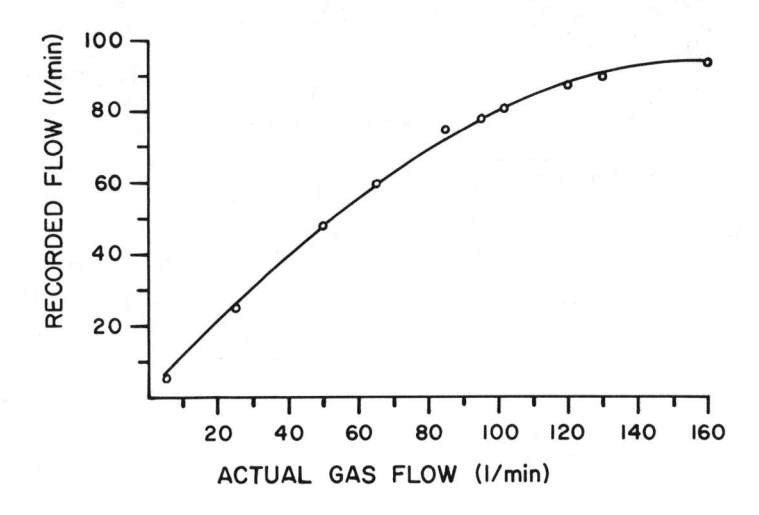

Figure 5. Calibration curve — best calorimeter.

Precision

The *precision* of instrument readings is the agreement of the readings among themselves (p. 83). If the same value of the measured variable is measured many times and the results agree very closely, the instrument has a high degree of precision or reproducibility.

Accuracy and precision have two distinct meanings. Two hand dynamometers, for example, may have identical precision but give quite different readings to identical compressive forces. In such a situation the accuracy of one or both of the dynamometers would be in error. To resolve this problem the dynamometers must be calibrated against a known standard. *It is the responsibility of the investigator to take the necessary precautions to insure that the hardware is functioning properly so that no controllable outside phenomena are influencing the accuracy of the measurements taken.*

---

[1] This work is over 10 years old and is used only as an example of the need for calibration. It is not intended to imply that the current Franz-Muller Calorimeters are inaccurate.

Sensitivity

The sensitivity of an instrument is the size of the deflection for a given change in the measured variable. (See p. 83.) Frequently the term is used to denote the smallest change in the measured quantity to which the instrument responds, but this is responsiveness. Sensitivity is an important property of instruments and is determined by design. The numeral value is influenced by the requirements of application.

Significant Figures

The number used in recording the reading of an instrument is determined by the sensitivity and error of the instrument. In writing a measured value, certain of the digits have an element of doubt associated with them. The significant figures are the figures which should be retained as valid. They are dependent upon the probable error associated with the reading. For example, in measuring knee extension strength with a strain gauge (which in this instance is an electronic means of measuring tension), a reading of 129.82 lb is recorded. If the probable error of this reading is $\pm .5$ lb, the reading should be taken as 129 lb, as these are the significant figures.

Responsiveness

Responsiveness and sensitivity are frequently confused. Responsiveness is the smallest alteration in the quantity being measured that will produce a perceptible change in the instrument reading. It may refer to time lag, as in the Beckman E-2 paramagnetic oxygen analyzer, where 90% deflection is obtained in 1 minute. Because of low flow values through the measurement cell (200 cc/min) and the relatively large volume of the measurement cell, 1 minute is required to obtain a representative gas mixture in the cell. Differences in responsiveness are also attributable to inertia, friction, gear lag, or wear in the instrument indicating mechanism. It is quite possible the responsiveness value may be different at various points within the range of the instrument. Since responsiveness is so important, yet can be so easily overlooked, several additional examples follow.

Recently, a serious error of this nature was observed. It was desired to test the grip strength of early elementary school children utilizing an adjustable grip dynamometer. The dynamometer was calibrated (Figure 1) but its responsiveness was not tested before including the measure in a battery given to 600 children. What was not known was that the dynamometer required more than 30 lb compressive force before it recorded. Many kindergartners could not be measured at all and the remaining data were questionable. Thus a great deal of time and effort were wasted.

Two principles of measurement were violated in this effort. The responsiveness should have been determined *throughout the range* and the measurement should have been pilot tested on some children in the same age range as the sample.

Care must be taken not to violate the responsiveness capacity of an instrument, because it is so easy to do innocently. For example, several years ago a study of the protective capacities of football helmets to various blows to the head was initiated (3). The instrumentation first involved the construction of a wooden head upon which a helmet could be fitted and within which an accelerometer could be mounted to provide an output in *g*'s (gravitational units). Initially, an arm writing recorder was used to attempt to record the accelerometer output. However, this was a gross error. The blow to the head takes place in less than .005 sec. This time is so short that it exceeds the responsive capacity of an arm writing recorder so that *what was recorded was not the record of the blow at all but the rebound of the writing arm*! In such instances one must use an oscilloscope, in which the trace can be held on the scope and read, or in which the fast-moving trace can be photographed. By use of an oscilloscope, the response time for recording is measured in millionths of a second.

Another less extreme example portrays an area of common violation of instrument responsiveness. Arm writing instruments are commonly used in human electrocardiography. Thus, it is often reasoned that this same instrumentation is also adequate for small animal electrocardiography. The phenomenon is the same and the order of amplification is similar. However, in animals which are smaller than man, the various waves of the electrocardiogram (*P* wave, *R* wave, *T* wave, etc.) have durations which are very short compared with the same waves in man. These waves may be recorded inaccurately by an arm writing recorder because the writing arm cannot move rapidly enough. Thus, these instruments are often useless for anything other than determination of heart rate. Figure 6 shows comparative ECG waves of the rat as recorded by an arm writing recorder and as photographed from an oscilloscope. Note that the greatest deflections are affected the most, with a consistent pattern of reducing these deflections (*R* and *S* waves, in particular).

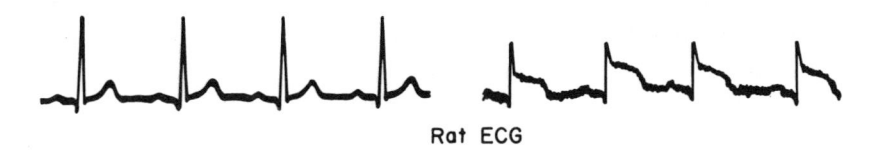

Rat ECG

Figure 6. Oscilloscope — arm writer.

Rangeability

The span between the lowest and highest units which can be measured with acceptable accuracy is the range of an instrument (p. 84). The usable range is fixed by both design and condition of the instrument. The range may not be the same for different experiments, as it is dependent upon the amount of error that can be tolerated. Obviously, range may be greater in instances where greater error can be tolerated.

The upper limit of the range reflects the capacity of the instrument. For example, in Figure 5 the Franz-Muller calorimeter accurately records volumes from 8–80 liter/min, which is that instrument's effective range. To exceed this effective range, under any conditions, would yield erroneous results.

ELECTRICAL HARDWARE

This section covers measurement of bio-electrical potentials produced by living organisms, circuits utilized to measure extrinsic phenomena, recording procedures, and computer applications. Examples of some of the more common indirect measurements of phenomena are presented. In this section no pretense of sophisticated coverage is intended. It is presented for the naive reader's understanding and orientation to this type of instrumentation.

Bio-electrical Potentials

Electromyography

Nerve and muscle fibers, the primary excitable cells of the body, are capable of transmitting electrochemical impulses along their membranes. In the resting fiber an excess of positive ions is present on one side of the cell membrane while an excess of negative ions is present on the other side, resulting in a membrane potential. When the fiber is stimulated the membrane potential undergoes a sequence of changes called the action potential, which causes electrical currents to flow momentarily along the inner and outer surfaces of the fiber membrane. The magnitude of the change is roughly from a resting potential of $+80$mV (1 millivolt $= 1/1000$ volt) to -50mV at the fiber site. It is possible to record such changes, but often it is impossible or inconvenient to reach the site. With electrodes some distance away, attenuation of the signal occurs, so that at the recording site it may amount to only 20 μV (1 microvolt $= 1/1,000,000$ volt) or less.

It is obvious that amplification of such a small electric potential is required. This magnitude of potential is observed in electromyographic

(EMG) determinations, often studied in physical education, as well as in electroencephalographic (EEG) measures. Discussion here will be limited to EMG. For careful study it is essential that the amplification and recording equipment magnify the small voltages without distortion and place a negligible load on the biological system. The amplification can be accomplished simply (usually by triode or pentode tubes) but at such a high order of amplification all kinds of noise or interference is picked up. The most common source of noise is AC interference from electrostatic induction from the laboratory electrical supply. This may be eliminated by placing a grounded copper screen around the subject. In most instances, however, the newer amplifier-recorders are constructed to eliminate this common source of interference. Since AC interference in this country is a consistent 60 cycle/sec, electronically this is not a difficult problem. Only in difficult environmental situations should screening be necessary.

The magnitude of the deflection can be determined by recording a known input. In most instances amplifier-recorders have internal calibrating devices. Although these tend to hold constant, they should be checked periodically for accuracy.

The recording schema may be bipolar or monopolar. In monopolar, a single electrode is used with a distant indifferent electrode. The active electrode might be on the forearm with the indifferent electrode on the forehead. The current density is progressively reduced as one gets further from the active electrode. The monopolar arrangement has been used with success in the evaluation of relaxation training programs. For this purpose active electrodes have been placed on both legs and both arms and the indifferent on the forehead. The output from the four active electrodes is then integrated (averaged in this case) to give an overall rating for the individual (90 μV, for example).

The bipolar arrangement samples a local field between and immediately around the electrodes. Bipolar techniques are useful for recording gross responses such as the activity of a single muscle, or with microelectrodes where the desired activity site is particularly small (Figure 7).

Various electrodes are used in electromyographic study. Surface electrodes (silver platinum coated or stainless steel) are used almost exclusively with monopolar applications and with some bipolar applications where gross activity is under study. The stainless steel subdermal electrodes are used primarily in bipolar applications where gross muscle activity is under study. If placed over a superficial muscle, the amplified output will show when that muscle is active. Hubbard (1) used such electrodes in his classic work on motion by recording the amplified output from antagonistic muscles during movement of the arm. Studying various rates of movement, he was able to determine exactly when the muscles under study were working. The subdermal electrodes cannot move around (therefore less electrode noise is present), but they have the disadvantage in that the skin must be penetrated. Thus the electrode must be both sharp and sterile, and sterile procedures must be followed to prevent infection.

Bipolar   **Monopolar**

Active Electrode

Distant Indifferent Electrode

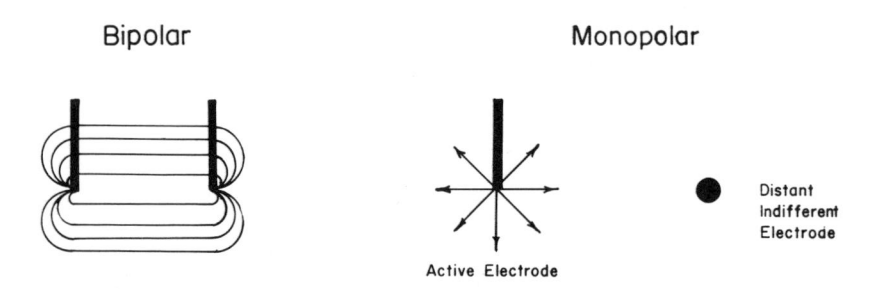

Figure 7.

The concentric needle electrode designed by Adrian and Bronk was used by Seyffarth (4) in his research on motor unit activity. Since each motor unit has an identifiable firing pattern, Seyffarth was able to work out patterns of motor unit activity for different types of movements. The disadvantage of the deep concentric needle electrode is that there is some tissue destruction and pain with its use. The electrode consists of an 0.8 mm stainless steel hypodermic needle with a central stainless steel wire which has been varnished for insulation and cemented into the lumen with the tip exposed. Thus the needle and the tip of the wire in the lumen provide the two poles of the electrodes (Figure 8).

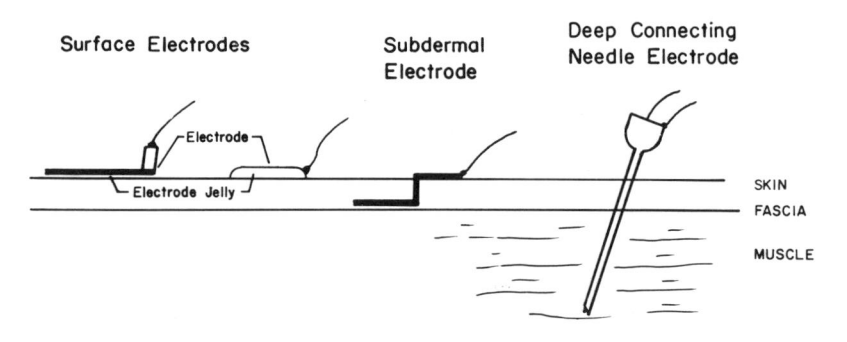

Figure 8. Various types of electrodes for EMG.

Electrocardiography

The heart muscle is not innervated in the same way voluntary muscle is. It consists of two syncytiums, the atrial and ventricular, with a bundle of Purkinje fibers, called the A-V bundle (bundle of His), which pass through the atrial and ventricular muscle to provide a single conducting pathway between the two syncytial masses. Prior to each contraction of the heart, an electrical impulse initiated in the sino-atrial (S-A) node travels through atria and via the A-V node through the ventricular muscle. As the impulses pass through the heart, electrical currents spread throughout the body. Electrodes placed upon the body permit recording of these electrical potentials generated by the heart. The potentials are of the magnitude of 1-2 mV or larger even in the extremities; thus the amplification required is much less than with the the EMG.

Multiple combinations of lead placements can be used for recording the electrocardiograms (ECG). Currently, 12 leads are most commonly used for diagnosing heart damage. The general idea is that the damage disrupts the potential, resulting in altered configurations of the recording which are identifiable. The electrocardiogram taken for diagnostic purposes is most often taken at rest but may be taken under exercise conditions. This area of research is too highly specialized to be approached here. However, the exercise electrocardiogram provides a simple and inexpensive means of obtaining exercise pulse rates, frequently utilized in physical education research.

If electrodes are placed on the body on opposite sides of the heart the electric potential generated by the heart can be recorded. The closer to the heart the electrodes are placed, the greater the signal will be. Since the electrodes are led off from the body surface, potentials from skeletal muscles will be picked up also. In general, for pulse rate measurement this is not disturbing, as the magnitude of the heart signal is much greater. If it is desired to record the ECG free from interference by muscle potentials, this can be accomplished by the use of a filter which will separate out the muscle potentials on the basis of frequency. (EMG is 50 cycles/sec and up, whereas the ECG frequency is below 20 cycles/sec). Since most commercial ECGs are now filter equipped, obtaining an ECG for pulse rate purposes is a relatively simple procedure.

The electrodes shown in Figure 9 are all effective for picking up the signal. The electrode placement shown in Figure 10 with a ground electrode placed on the back approximately 4 cm to the left of the spinal column and about 10 cm above an imaginary line across the crests of ilium works quite well; other placements are also effective. It is especially important that the electrodes are firmly attached to the skin so that no movement occurs and that the lead wires are in good condition. Electrode movement or small breaks in the lead wires will result in interference which may completely mask the signal. It is important before attempting any recording to have the subject move around, possibly jumping up and down several times, as loose electrodes, frayed lead wires, or other loose connections may not be evident at rest. Figure 11 shows the ECG heart rate recording.

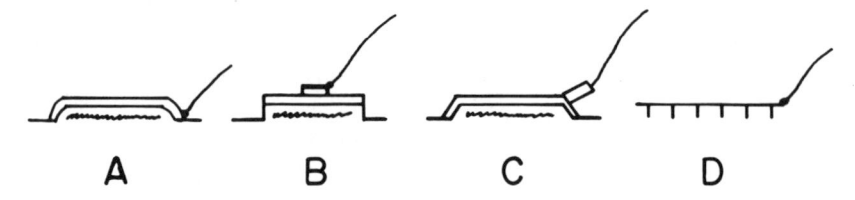

Figure 9. Various electrodes for ECG.

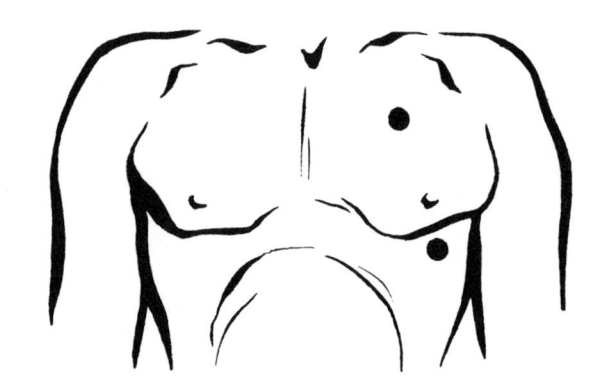

Figure 10. Electrode placement for exercise ECG.

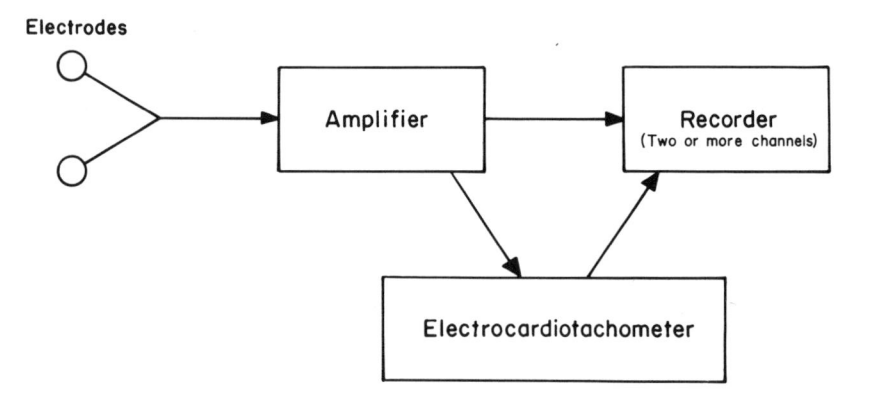

Figure 11. Heart rate recording of the ECG.

In addition to recording the actual electrocardiogram from which the pulse rate is counted, electrocardiotachometers (ECT) are available which count the pulse rate, giving either a numerical value visually or an output which can be recorded. Some of the instruments sum several preceding seconds, whereas others give the beat-to-beat rate. By and large the latter are more dependable. The instruments are adjusted to count the single largest deflection (usually the R or S wave). If the electrocardiotachometer is to be used for research purposes it is recommended that the usual electrocardiogram be recorded and the ECT output be recorded on another recorder channel, preferably one in which large deflections are possible (15–20 cm) to permit accurate reading of the rate. If both are collected, unexplained deviations in the ECT tracing can be reviewed in the ECG. Since the possibility of interference is ever-present, having the ECG tracing usually permits unexplained deviations in the ECT record to be resolved.

Measuring Circuits

A brief review of electrical theory and practice is in order before presenting the more common measuring circuits and their application. The discussion is restricted to direct current (dc) circuits which are most commonly found in laboratory hardware. Some standard symbols are presented in Figure 12 for review.

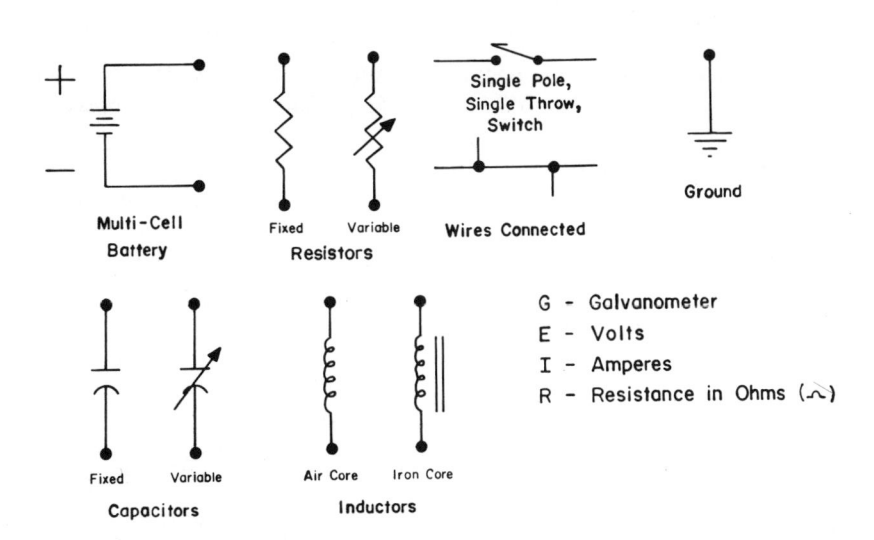

Figure 12. Standard graphic symbols.

Current (I, amperes) in terms of electromotive force E (volts) and resistance R (ohms) can be expressed, $I = \frac{E}{R}$, $R = \frac{E}{I}$, or $E = I \times R$. This is Ohm's Law, which is basic to all circuitry. When the switch of a simple circuit such as that shown in Figure 13 is closed, the current assumes a steady-state value. If the emf, E, is doubled and trebled the current, I, is doubled and trebled.

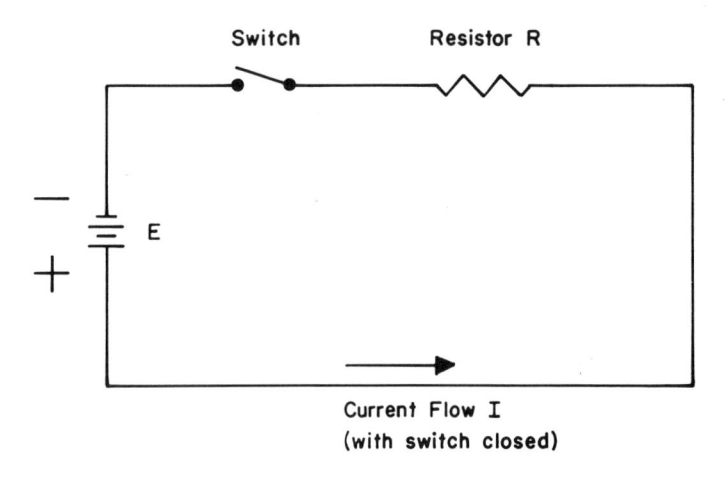

Figure 13. Simple electric circuit.

An electric circuit seems to be best understood using analogies from simple hydraulic systems. For example, it is well known that water pressure in a standpipe is determined by multiplying the weight of water per cubic foot times the height of the standpipe. This difference in pressure between the top and bottom of the standpipe is analogous to the electric pressure, or electromotive force, measured in volts present in a battery. The flow through the water pipes which can be measured in gal/sec is analogous to current, I, which represents the flow of electrons. One ampere is defined as 1 coulomb/sec, which is a flow of 6.24×10^{18} electrons/sec. The narrowing of the inside diameter of a water pipe would resist the flow. This narrowing is analogous to the resistance R in an electric circuit, which is measured in ohms. Thus, $R(\text{ohms}) = \frac{E(\text{volts})}{I(\text{amps})}$. This value is constant and is a specific property of the circuit. Materials vary widely in specific resistance and are often selected for use in circuits because of their resistance characteristics. Copper has a low specific resistance, thus is used for wire. Nichrome has a very high specific resistance, thus is used in heating elements.

Inductance and capacitance are confusing terms. Current flow in one loop of a coil induces a reverse current (and back *emf*) in the adjacent loops. These reverse currents resist the original current flow and also changes in current flow. Inductances are normally used in electronic circuitry to smooth current (and voltage) variations by resisting current variations. But proximity of circuit components may produce unwonted inductance. Capacitance refers to components, not actually condensers, behaving like condensers. An electrostatic potential on one plate of a condenser induces a reverse potential on an adjacent, but not connected, plate. No current flows between the plates unless excessive voltage produces an arc. Condenser coupling in amplifiers permits transferring voltage changes in one stage to the next. This is useful condenser behavior. Unwonted inductance and capacitance can (or must) be eliminated by isolation or electrostatic shielding.

A galvanometer is an instrument for indicating or measuring a small electric current. It is capable of measuring current flows in either direction and in most instances is quite sensitive. The galvanometer is discussed in more detail in the section on recorders.

Wheatstone Bridge

The Wheatstone bridge is a type of resistance network commonly used in instrument practice for determining resistance changes in one arm of the bridge which can be recorded. The arm of the bridge of interest is connected to a transducer, an electromechanical device which converts a physical quantity being measured, such as tension, pressure, or temperature, to a proportional electrical output. In the Wheatstone bridge the transducer is essentially a variable resistor in which the resistance is altered in direct relationship to the change in the physical quantity. Many versions of the Wheatstone bridge are used. A typical one is shown in Figure 14.

The battery supplies a current to two paths, each having two resistors in series. A galvanometer is connected between C and D to indicate current flow. With R_2 and R_4 fixed resistors and R_1, the transducer (variable resistor) in use, the bridge would be balanced so that the galvanometer would read zero deflection by adjustment of variable resistor R_3. This would be the null position. In practice, as the conductivity of R_1 (the transducer) is altered by the physical quantity, the current flow pattern would be altered, which would produce a galvanometer deflection. The galvanometer deflection could be observed visually or if connected to a writing arm could be recorded. If an appropriate calibration has been made between galvanometer deflections and the physical quantity, the measured deflection could be converted to the physical quantity.

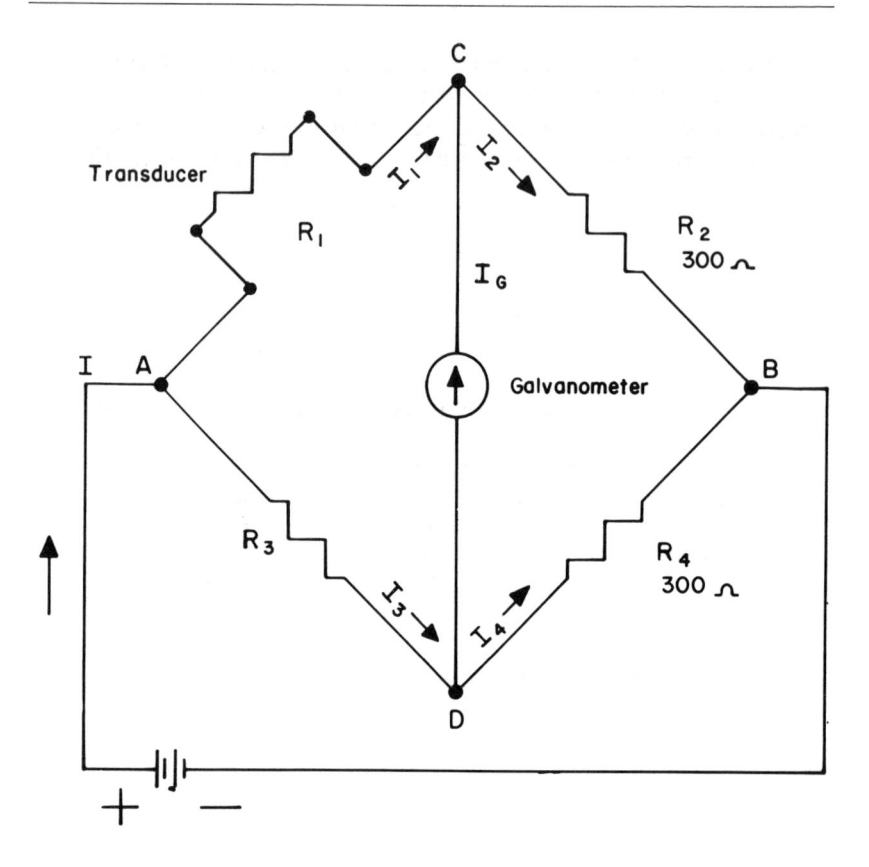

Figure 14. Typical Wheatstone bridge circuit.

The Potentiometer Circuit

The potentiometer is one of the basic laboratory instruments which serves primarily to compare *emf*s (volts) between a known output and one which is being determined. By appropriate calibration of the difference in *emf* with standard values for physical quantity being measured, differences in *emf* may be converted to the physical values.

The principle is shown in Figure 15. AB is a long, uniform, calibrated resistance wire with a slide at C. The voltage produced by the thermocouple is balanced against the voltage produced by the battery. The slide wire is moved until the galvanometer reads zero, i.e., the circuit is in the null balance position. The position of the slide is a measure of the *emf* produced by the thermocouple, thus a measure of temperature utilizing the calibrated temperature scale.

INSTRUMENTATION: HARDWARE

More sophisticated null-balance, automatic, and recording potentiometers are utilized but all function on the same basic principle. The potentiometer is the appropriate instrument to use where the sensor or transducer produces an *emf* in response to some physical change. Thermo-

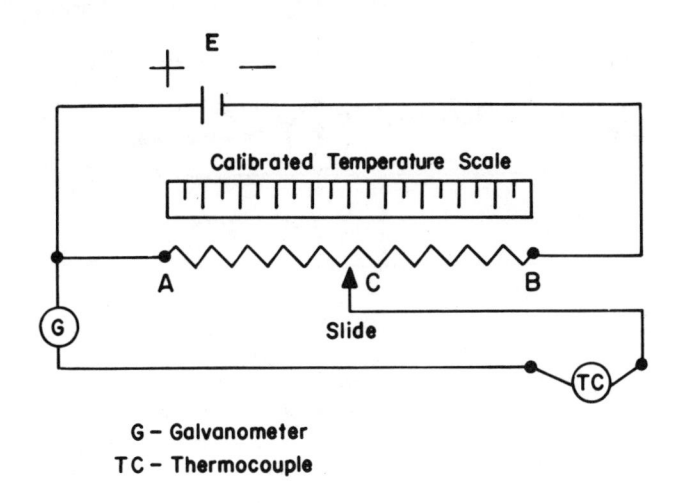

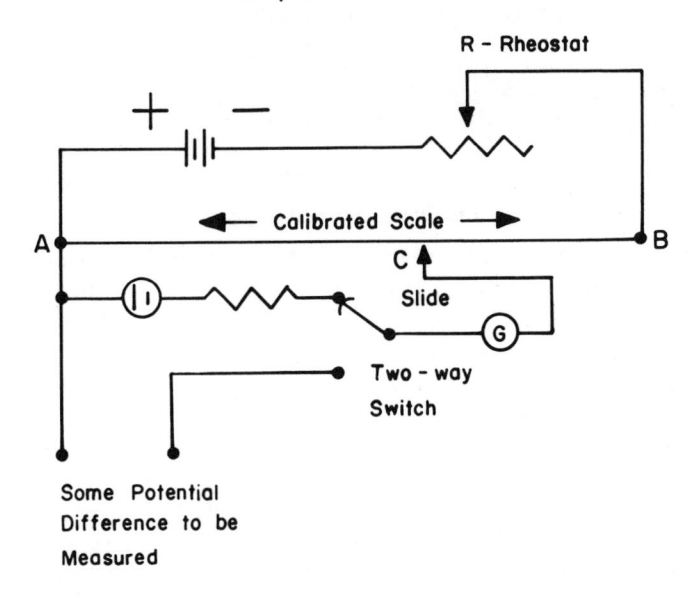

Figure 15. Basic potentiometer circuit.

couples[2] used in temperature measurement and piezo-electric[3] components used in some pressure and accelerometer units are examples.

Transducers

Transducers convert physical quantities into related electrical values. The function of a transducer in a measurement system is shown in Figure 16.

```
┌─────────────────────────────────────┐
│  Physical Quantity to be Measured   │
└─────────────────────────────────────┘
                  │  Input signal
                  ▼
┌─────────────────────────────────────┐
│            Transducer               │
└─────────────────────────────────────┘
                  │  Electrical output signal
                  │  as a function of input signal
                  ▼
┌─────────────────────────────────────┐
│       Modification of Signal        │
│  (Bridge, Potentiometer, Amplifier) │
└─────────────────────────────────────┘
                  │
                  ▼
┌─────────────────────────────────────┐
│       Measurement of Signal         │
│  (Visual, Auditory, Recording, etc.)│
└─────────────────────────────────────┘
```

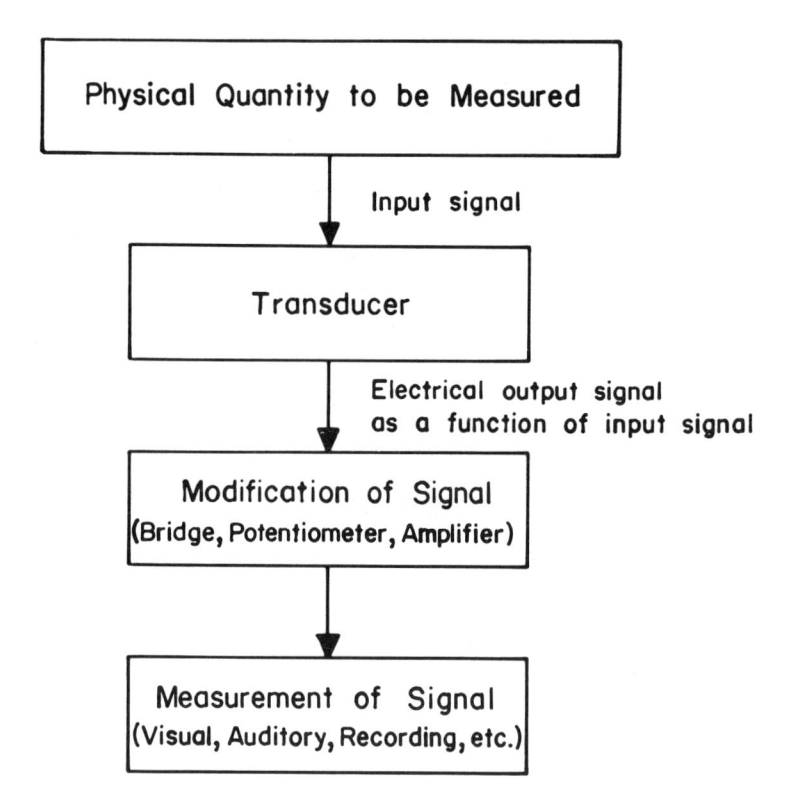

Figure 16. Function of transducer in measurement system.

---

[2] The thermocouple is based on the Siebeck effect, i.e., if a closed circuit is formed by two metals and the two junctions of the metals are at different temperatures, an electric current will flow around the circuit. Thus when used on man the junction is the sensor and the cold junction is placed in ice water at 0°C.

[3] The piezo-electric component usually consists of specially cut quartz crystal placed between two metal plates. With pressure on the plates an *emf* is set up and with a potentiometer the *emf* which reflects pressure may be measured. This property of the crystal is called the piezo-electric effect.

Basically any device which converts one form of energy into another is a transducer. Examples include thermistors which reflect temperature by altered resistance; thermocouples, which transform heat energy into an equivalent electrical potential; photocells, which convert light energy into electric current; strain gauges, which convert tension or stress into electrical energy; piezo-electric components, which convert force or pressure into electrical current; thermal conductivity cells in which the resistance is altered in relation to the surrounding gas medium; accelerometers in which rate of acceleration alters resistance or generates a current; and a multitude of others.

Laboratory hardware is required to measure many different physical characteristics and phenomena. Without transducer development, which is ongoing, the giant strides made in hardware would have been impossible. Transducers have become convenient, relatively economical, and highly efficient. Although it is impractical to attempt to cover the theoretical basis of the multitude of transducers available, the young investigator should be forewarned to study carefully the theoretical base, applications, limitations, and calibration of the transducer which is to be used in data collection. One cannot be too careful in this regard.

Recording Techniques

Electrical inputs for ECG, EMG, or transducer recording are amplified appropriately and fed to galvanometers. The galvanometer (Figure 17) consists of a narrow coil wrapped parallel to the axis of a cylindrical soft-iron core on a shaft between the poles of a permanent magnet. Having the faces of the magnet concentric with the core surface keeps the effect of the permanent magnetic field constant as the coil-core turns so the angular displacement is linear. A variable current in the coil produces a proportional magnetic field in the core. Attraction of opposite poles in the variable core and permanent magnetic fields produce a variable torque against spring resistance. The spring restores the coil-core to a neutral or zero position when current flow ceases. A mirror on the shaft reflecting light from a fixed source permits observing amplified movement of the coil-core on a graduated scale or photographic recording. A pointer on the shaft also permits observing coil-core rotation. Substituting a capillary tube filled with ink from a reservoir permits writing on moving paper. A hot wire pointer writes on heat-sensitive paper. A current-carrying pointer writes on electrosensitive paper. The mass of the coil-core pointer introduces inertial lag and overshoot that distort quick changes in the input. High quality galvanometers record sine waves accurately up to about 100–120 Hz. They are adequate if the exact wave form is not a critical factor. High speed transients require more complex and expensive oscillographic recording. The electron beam of a cathode-ray oscillograph has zero mass and is free of inertial distortion.

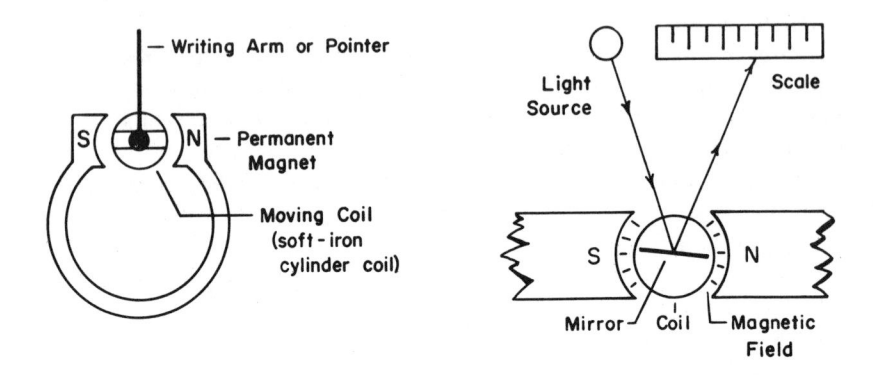

Figure 17. Galvanometers used in recorders.

In most commercial recorders the speed with which the recording paper passes under the pen arm is adjustable. *Care must be taken to be certain the paper speed is accurate and consistent.* If the paper speed is critical (as in all rate measures) it is a good idea to make all records with the recorder's timing unit "on," so that a mark is placed on the record every 1 or 2 sec to permit a periodic check of paper speed.

All arm writing recorders have frequency limitations beyond which the configuration of the response curve is altered. The limitation is primarily due to inertia of the writing arm; thus it is related to both the mass and length of that arm. Within the acceptable frequency range of a recorder, inertia is compensated for by damping. Without damping, for example, an upward deflection would "overshoot." By careful design the damping force is proportional to the angular velocity of the moving system, resulting in a true wave configuration.

If the frequency limitations of a recorder are knowingly being exceeded, the amplifier output should be introduced into an oscilloscope. The oscilloscope face can then be photographed and measured. Polaroid camera attachments are especially handy for this purpose as the picture is available almost immediately. If a question exists as to either the damping qualities of the recorder in use or the possibility of exceeding the frequency limitations, simultaneous recording, using both an oscilloscope and the recorder, will permit comparative wave measurements of the same signal.

Recording may also be accomplished using magnetic tape. Magnetic tape recorders are inertia free, tapes may be easily stored, and they have the added advantage that they are readily used as input for an analog computer programmed to perform calculations on the data. Disadvantages of the tape recorders are that currently the expense is prohibitive and there is usually no visual readout of the data.

Practically all of the amplifier-recorders purchased today from reputable suppliers are equipped with a range of amplification which enables the investigator to enlarge small signals and reduce large ones. In most instances, within this range the response is linear, i.e., if at an $X - 1$ setting a deflection of 5 mm was observed, at an $X - 5$ setting the deflection should be 25 mm. In working with a recorder it is a good idea to check this, as there may be some hysteresis. In some instances it is necessary to calibrate at one range setting and to record at another. However, error is usually less by calibrating at the range setting being used, if this is possible.

Telemetry

The procedures discussed up to this point have utilized direct connections from the electrodes to the recorder. There are numerous instances where information is desired and direct connections are impossible. The heart rate during an athletic contest is such an example. Through the use of telemetry it is possible to collect such data (Figure 18). Utilizing miniaturized, lightweight, battery-operated amplifiers and radio transmitters, the bio-electric potential is picked up by the usual electrodes (or other sensing equipment), amplified, and transmitted. Utilizing a receiver and compatible recorder, the potentials may be continuously recorded. Telemetry development received much of its impetus from the space program. The development of transistors (with low current needs) made miniaturization of circuits possible.

A. Direct Connections

(S) ———— Amplifier ———— Recorder

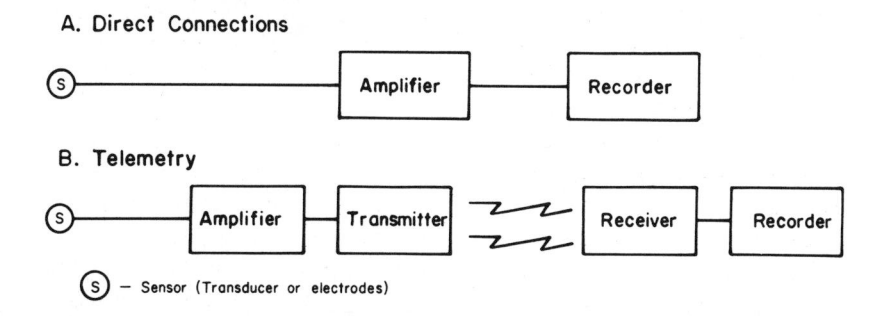

B. Telemetry

(S) ———— Amplifier ———— Transmitter ∿∿ Receiver ———— Recorder

(S) – Sensor (Transducer or electrodes)

Figure 18. Schema of recording procedure.

Telemetry of the pulse rate is common, with numerous commercial units available for purchase. Texts presenting appropriate telemetry circuits and applications are available.

Telemetry, as a research tool, appears to have almost unlimited applications where direct connection data collections are either impossible or unwise. Multichannel transmitting and recording is possible. Transmitters which can be implanted in animals for monitoring multiple physiological phenomena currently exist. There is little question but that this technique will receive a great deal of attention in physical education research when more investigators become sophisticated in its use. Telemetry, except for the use of commercial units, is not for the naive investigator, but it does involve unique skills that could serve in good stead a young investigator who wishes to make research a career.

Computers

Modern computers fall into two categories: analog and digital. The analog computer processes analog signals. These are continuous electrical signals which may vary in size. The computer is interested in how large or small the signal is. The digital signal, by contrast, has a discrete, discontinuous numerical value. The digital computer is interested only in the presence or absence of a signal, not its value.

Analog and digital computers have advantages in different applications. The analog computers are used where there is the continuous-variable electrical signal to solve problems which involve large numbers of repetitive calculations. It is best used for problems which can be reduced to a mathematical equation and which require fast solutions of limited accuracy. A digital computer is used when high accuracy, memory, decision making, and control capabilities are required. Most computers that students come in contact with are digital.

In some instances analog and digital computers are combined to utilize the advantages of both. An analog computer, for example, might receive a variable electrical signal from a recorder, make standard calculations of the data, and provide the output in an electrical signal. This signal might be converted to digital form, further calculating completed by the digital computer, and the output provided in digital form. Computers of this type are hybrid, in that they utilize both the analog and digital procedures. Today there are mutiple applications of hybrid computers.

Digital computers can store vast quantities of data and retrieve portions on demand. Information retrieval in which article titles and/or abstracts of articles are stored for retrieval on demand is an example of this function. Such procedures are coming into vogue because of the vast quantity of research literature and the fact that it is becoming increasingly difficult for man to locate what he needs. The computer is a useful tool for such purposes. Digital computers also can solve intricate scientific equations and long series of mathematical calculations at extremely high speed. The complex operations are accomplished by breaking them down into a few simple operations which are repeated many times. Most digital computers use a binary system.

The most common use of the digital computer that students become acquainted with is in performing statistical calculations. The elements of the computer complex are shown in Figure 19. Two warnings on the use of the digital computer for statistical calculations are in order:

1. Remember the statistical results are no better than the basic data. There is nothing magic about the computer which enables it to make sense from nonsense.

2. Be extremely careful about statistical assumptions. For example, it *is* easy to obtain a correlation matrix but are you sure your data are linear? Further complex statistical analyses of a correlation matrix based on nonlinear data would yield confusing results. Certainly the digital computer has been misused in this regard. It is not a "black box" which can correct all of our errors.

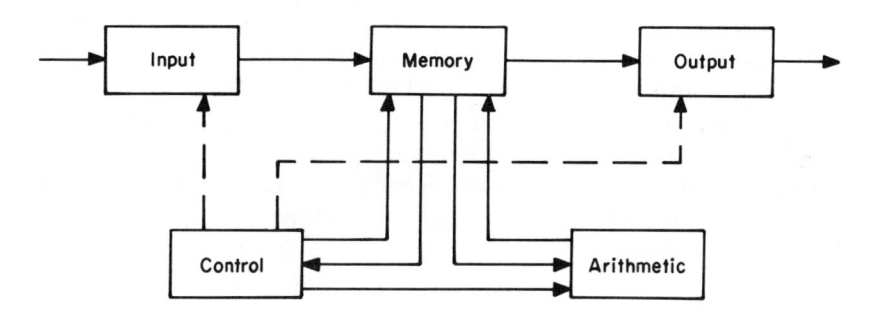

Figure 19. Elements of digital computer.

The analog computers have not, as yet, been used much in physical education research. They are so versatile, however, that it is just a matter of time before they will be widely used. They can be used to perform intricate, routine calculations "on line" from a recording system, which saves hours of valuable technician time. They can also be used to simulate biological systems, which enables the investigator to obtain some idea of the type of response he might obtain *before* proceeding on some highly sophisticated, expensive biological experiment. The analog computer family consists of all those devices in which measurable physical quantities (which may be converted to a variable electrical signal) are made to obey mathematical relationships comparable with those existing in a particular problem. The computer is simply an electronic model of the physical system. It consists of the basic building blocks which can be interconnected so that they are governed by the same set of equations as those describing the system. How the components are set up is dependent upon the particular problem of interest. Components are capable of summation, integration, multiplication, and numerous servo operations. The solutions to problems solved on an analog computer appear as voltage variations in the output of various operational amplifiers throughout the computer. The output devices used to record are essentially recording voltmeters. The most common recorder used is the direct writing magnetic recorder.

An example of analog computer application is the calculation of energy expenditure during work. To calculate the oxygen consumption, the oxygen and carbon dioxide concentrations of the expired gas, the volume of expired gas, the gas temperature, and the barometric pressure must be known.[4] All of these can be measured directly "on line" as the individual is working. With the output of these analyzers fed into a properly programmed analog computer, an output reflecting breath-by-breath oxygen consumption is possible.

For simulation of biological systems usually that which is known and can be reduced to mathematical formulae is utilized to determine how alterations of these known parameters might affect another parameter for which more information is desired. For example, a model of the electrical conductivity of the heart might be constructed on the computer which would yield a normal electrocardiographic configuration. By varying the parameters until the S-T segment depression thought to be associated with cardiac ischemia is altered, ideas and further insight into cardiac dynamics might be obtained.

The new graduate student may feel that computer use is above him. However computers are realities which are going to be used increasingly. In our complex culture they have become necessities for man to keep pace.

SUMMARY

It should be clear that a measurement whose accuracy is unknown has no use whatever. The science of measurement is concerned with errors and their effects on the end results as much as with the measurements themselves. Instrument and applicational errors represent important sources

---

[4] Since barometric pressure is not highly variable in a short period of time, it would not need to be continuously monitored.

of error, but design, subject, experimenter, and environmental biases discussed elsewhere in this text are equally important to the conduct of careful research.

The investigator assumes the responsibility to study systematically the capabilities of the instruments before undertaking any research investigation utilizing hardware. Calibration for accuracy and precision and a clear understanding of the sensitivity, responsiveness, and effective range ultimately saves time. Such care prior to undertaking an experiment is more satisfying, in that the investigator has greater insight and confidence in his data.

REFERENCES

1. Hubbard, A. W. The upper limits of slow movements and the lower limits of ballistic movements. Ph.D. dissertation, University of Illinois, 1950.
2. Montoye, Henry J. et al. An investigation of the Muller-Franz calorimeter. *Arbeitsphysiologie* 17: 28–33, 1958.
3. Nelson, R.: Montoye, Henry J.; and Van Huss, W. D. An investigation of various measures used in impact testing of protective headgear. *Journal of Sports Medicine* 4: 94, 1964.
4. Seyffarth, Henrik. *The Behaviour of Motor-Units in Voluntary Contraction.* Oslo: Skrifter, Norske Videnskaps Akademie, Matematisk-Naturvidenskapelig Klasse, Nr 4, 1940. 63 pp.

SELECTED READINGS

Hubbard, A. W. Muscular force in reciprocal movements. *Journal of General Psychology* 20: 315–325, 1939.

Mackay, R. Stuart. *Bio-Medical Telemetry.* 2d ed. New York: John Wiley & Sons, 1970.

Respiratory Protective Devices Manual. Ann Arbor, Mich.: Braun & Brumfield, 1963.

CHAPTER 8

COLLECTING DATA

Henry J. Montoye
University of Tennessee
Knoxville, Tennessee

IT IS EVIDENT THAT before an investigator can effectively plan the collection of data, he must have a clear understanding of the problem to be studied and the research design to be employed. This applies to the established investigator undertaking an extensive study as well as to the neophyte considering a possible project to serve as a master's thesis or a doctoral dissertation. The hypothesis to be tested must be clearly defined before details of data collection receive the investigator's attention. The selection and design of the investigation are discussed in other sections of this text (Chapters 3 and 4), therefore they will not be treated in detail here.

Problem Population and Data Population

Sampling methods are described later in this chapter, but the importance of delineating the population to which research results are to be generalized will be introduced at this time. The concept of a problem population and data population has been set forth using a variety of labels. Very briefly, the *problem population* refers to the population (i.e., the collection of human beings, animals, or inanimate objects) to which the results are ultimately to apply. When a research problem is stated in a formal way, the problem population, or the population for which the answer is sought, is generally specified or implied. For example, if one sets out to assess the physical fitness of schoolchildren in the United States (a status study, see pp. 272–273), the problem population becomes all children in regular and special schools, both public and private. It includes children of both sexes and all grade levels. If the research objective is to determine the physical fitness of boys in the seventh grade attending public schools in Michigan, the problem population is, of course, more limited. The applicability of results will be correspondingly limited. The *data population,* on the other hand, is the population of subjects providing the data for analysis and study.

Ideally, the data population should be the same as, or a representative sample of, the problem population. Although this aphoristic statement would hardly precipitate an argument, the concept is often violated in obvious or subtle ways—sometimes when it is crucial that the data population be representative of the problem population. It should be recognized at the onset, however, that violations of this concept are not equally serious in all research methods and designs. For example, if one wished to determine the muscular strength of male college freshmen in the United States, the investigator would hardly be justified in studying male freshmen at one university, since it is highly likely that muscular strength in male freshmen at one university is different, on the average, from that of the male freshmen at another university. On the other hand, if one wished to investigate the relationship between body weight and muscular strength in male college freshmen, testing male freshmen in only one school is likely to reflect the relationship between these two variables as it exists in other male college freshmen. Even in this instance, it would be better for the data population to be the same as, or a representative sample of, all male college freshmen. If the determination of status (surveys of various kinds) is the primary focus, discrepancies between the problem and data populations are most serious. When relationships are of primary concern, discrepancies are less important. In experimental studies (effect of diet, effect of conditioning, etc.), the consequences of disparity between the data and problem populations are least serious. As an example, the effects of many regimens, first demonstrated in lower animals, were later shown to hold for human beings.

Therefore, before data are collected, the concept of a problem population and of a data population should be clearly understood. Furthermore, the consequences of discrepancies in these populations should be evaluated at the onset.

Plans for Statistical Analysis

It is typical of human nature when enthusiasm is running high and a problem is clearly defined to want to proceed with data collection and to worry about the analysis later. Some decisions about data analysis, of necessity, must be postponed. Nevertheless, it behooves the investigator to turn his attention to some questions about data analysis before collecting any data. Examples of such questions include the following:

1. Are only qualitative observations to be made, or can scores be quantified in some way?

2. Is it possible to arrive at reasonable estimates of the number of subjects required?

3. What assumptions are involved in the statistical techniques to be employed, and can data collection be designed to satisfy these assumptions?

4. Can the precision or the validity of the measurements be studied as the data are being collected?

5. How can quality control be studied and maintained during data collection?

6. Can data recording forms be designed or obtained to facilitate machine analysis of data?

SAMPLING

Ignorance or negligence in correct sampling procedures is probably responsible, more than any other single factor, for drawing incorrect conclusions in research. Space will permit only a brief treatment here. Additional references, which provide a more thorough coverage of the topic, are listed at the end of this chapter, p. 178.

Sampling Theory

An understanding of the concept of sampling and probability theory is indispensable in research. The notion of a "problem" population was mentioned. In sampling, this is referred to as the "universe" or the "population." This does not necessarily mean the number of individuals living in a particular place—for example, the population of Hawaii—but all of the elements (human beings, animals, or inanimate objects) which make up the entire group to which the results are to be generalized. Normally, we do not test or measure all elements in this universe. One can define a small universe so that all elements in it can be studied, but the application then becomes so limited as to render the research insignificant. Thus, we must work with a sample of the universe or population. Furthermore, even if one could examine or measure each element in the universe, the application of results would take place at some future time when the universe itself had changed. Hence, the data population is still a sample in this instance. To illustrate: one might be able to test every fourth grade boy in Minneapolis, but by the time the data were collected and analyzed, some of these children would have moved out of, and others into, the city. Therefore, for reasons other than economic ones, investigators work with samples which they hope are representative of a total universe or problem population.

Methods of Sampling

The selection of a problem and research design are discussed elsewhere in this text (Chapter 2, pp. 32–34 and Chapters 3 and 4). These earlier chapters have included such matters as sex of the subjects, which species of animals will be used, whether the subjects will act as their own control, etc. However, once the problem population (universe) has been identified, the question then arises as to how a sample will be selected. Naturally, a sample which is representative of the universe is desired. Although there is no way of knowing with certainty if a sample is representative without studying all of the elements in the entire universe, there are sampling methods which, while not insuring representation, nevertheless increase the likelihood of obtaining it. Also, mathematicians have provided methods that allow us to estimate this likelihood. These methods are related to probability theory, which, in its early history, developed out of the interest of such people as Chevalier de Mere in calculating gambling odds.

Random Sample

Although it is easy to define a random sample, obtaining one is frequently difficult. A random sample is one in which each element in the universe has an equal opportunity of being selected. Consider a box of black and white marbles, thoroughly mixed. If, then, without looking into the box, one draws out the first marble he touches and repeats this process, a random sample will result. On the other hand, if one were sampling from a bushel of apples of various sizes, repeating this procedure would not produce a random sample. The larger apples would have a better chance of being selected. Similarly, a random sample of a university's students would not be obtained by selecting every tenth student leaving the Student Union Building, since some students frequent this building more than others. A random sample of 10th grade girls in a high school would be unlikely to result if every 20th girl in the physical education classes were selected. Some girls may not be enrolled in physical education and, furthermore, they may be quite different in sports skill, physical fitness, etc., from those who are. The investigator must ask himself, "Does every element in the universe have an equal opportunity of being drawn into the sample?" Careful thinking at this point is time well spent.

In practice, there are several common ways of carrying out the sampling procedure. We could assign a name or number to each of the elements, type the names or numbers on uniform pieces of paper, mix the slips thoroughly in a box, and draw a sample as described above in the example with marbles. This could readily be done if, for example, we wished to divide at random 80 animals into four groups of 20 each. We could also roll a die or toss a coin to decide in which group a particular animal is to be placed. But generally it is easier to use a set of random digits. An abbreviated sample of such digits is shown in Table 1. This

TABLE 1. Table of Random Digits

```
26 06 24 52 95 01 65 30 06 10 84 92 93 22 20 56 57 72 57 99 25 70 69 43 98 43
06 09 38 25 04 65 17 20 75 07 69 63 96 10 37 31 44 66 12 39 85 54 52 02 82 33
95 03 87 65 81 03 86 59 16 03 62 88 19 19 63 32 93 05 72 94 52 78 13 63 91 30
61 94 07 43 67 25 66 92 74 77 97 32 69 76 58 25 79 15 44 55 02 38 73 19 96 62
56 81 76 05 32 62 69 99 94 05 05 85 17 10 73 59 62 22 60 68 44 93 55 92 48 59
86 72 78 41 95 08 67 30 65 95 44 50 04 29 08 65 67 45 27 81 33 16 96 58 09 52
54 75 26 06 31 52 40 70 99 71 63 18 52 50 09 02 24 57 12 03 02 10 54 75 26 06
38 94 08 93 95 38 06 71 72 80 30 74 21 08 10 91 85 70 90 68 03 75 10 86 10 78
07 80 46 11 90 58 89 94 97 21 12 25 05 73 71 32 03 11 66 37 44 29 42 75 75 76
88 50 51 24 19 33 41 09 86 10 94 70 74 99 39 58 64 53 70 07 09 62 50 56 67 81
15 97 57 96 75 56 68 65 97 29 19 47 17 22 81 21 35 81 94 46 23 41 39 54 26 78
54 79 88 81 42 21 91 38 47 51 36 25 79 78 24 43 12 59 38 22 80 04 56 74 65 66
75 85 66 33 52 21 89 44 90 49 26 74 40 83 67 37 14 74 66 61 70 22 58 66 18 53
00 13 21 22 16 00 98 72 65 81 58 01 73 67 19 36 06 65 54 55 11 24 37 30 06 11
71 94 55 21 12 81 23 78 46 98 03 40 97 49 61 26 54 35 65 65 37 05 82 24 82 15
57 58 60 36 59 97 02 01 71 64 37 67 03 17 93 92 15 20 68 65 27 44 28 04 80 37
79 79 71 49 24 15 99 69 00 36 20 23 01 29 94 54 29 66 23 66 69 26 29 88 91
47 98 26 41 63 08 11 99 04 76 38 61 88 05 66 44 54 92 10 89 39 17 60 78 97 71
05 64 93 40 12 20 75 35 34 63 96 36 93 43 64 14 19 36 54 78 91 51 63 94 01 71
00 84 17 34 41 10 40 47 60 98 94 26 10 54 59 05 66 26 27 72 65 43 49 18 93 76
18 65 50 05 76 03 82 95 54 20 92 77 57 54 38 45 01 73 64 62 05 58 11 51 22 20
60 60 76 75 12 92 87 53 75 19 93 06 08 57 15 31 56 44 15 33 46 44 15 33 46 55
17 67 54 91 82 94 59 46 43 98 77 30 34 89 98 64 61 28 27 25 69 28 71 14 07 16
74 13 15 78 81 02 98 91 18 06 86 15 37 27 96 71 62 44 42 89 89 70 38 37 66 92
32 93 57 33 80 92 07 48 75 39 95 93 81 04 03 75 56 18 67 25 28 08 71 75 01 04
```

table can be used as follows. The 80 animals should be numbered consecutively. Then a system of reading numbers should be selected: for example, to read from right to left and when one reaches the left, start again at the right on the next lower line. Then, without looking at the table, we select a starting point with a pencil. Suppose we picked "07," which is encircled on the table. Then the first 20 numbers from right to left and then downward would correspond to the numbers of the animals which form group one. The next 20 numbers would form group two, and so on. In our example, animal number 7 would be in group one, together with animal numbers 70, 53, 64, 58, and 39. The next number, 99, is ignored because it is larger than the total number of animals. We would continue with number 74 and since the next number, 70, has appeared already, it also is ignored. Continuing, we would have numbers 10, 9, 41, 33, 19, 24, 51, 50, 78, 26, 54, 23, and 46. This would comprise group one. Group two would begin with number 35.

If we wished to select 100 students from a total population of 2,000, the same procedure could be used except that a table of four digits would be needed. Since larger numbers are cumbersome to handle, machine procedures can be used to draw the sample. It is important *not* to rely on our "unbiased" nature. A simple example will illustrate. If a group of people are each asked to select "at random" a number from one to four, it will be discovered in tabulating the results that the numbers 1, 2, 3, and 4 are not selected with equal frequency. Number 3 will be selected much more often than the others.

The advantages of random sampling can be summarized briefly as follows: 1) nothing need be known about the characteristics of the universe being sampled, 2) most statistical techniques for analysis are appropriate when random sampling is employed, and 3) as the number of elements in a sample is increased, the likelihood that the sample is representative also is increased. More importantly, probability theory provides us with methods of estimating this likelihood. On the other hand, there are also disadvantages to this method of sampling: 1) the task of numbering every element in a large universe may be time-consuming, difficult, expensive, and, in some instances, impossible, 2) other sampling methods can use a smaller sample and still provide the same likelihood that the sample is representative, and 3) because the individual elements selected at random might be widely dispersed geographically, the measurement or interviewing of those selected might be prohibitively expensive.

Systematic Sample

Another method which provides a sample that usually approximates a random sample is called systematic sampling. The procedure involves selecting every k'th unit in a list or in an area. Selecting every 100th name on a registration list or every 5th house on an area map are examples. Sometimes a telephone list is used for this purpose but it should be remembered that families which do not have phones differ in many ways from those which do. Sometimes systematic sampling is used in conjunction with other sampling methods described below. An advantage of systematic sampling, particularly if a list of the elements is available, is that it is relatively inexpensive and rapid. It is also not difficult to train others to select the sample. Finally, a proportionate or stratified sample is easily obtained if there are separate lists for each strata.

Aside from the fact that one must be careful about what list is being used (i.e., whether or not the list was prepared in such a way as to bias the sample), the principal disadvantage to this sampling method has to do with estimating the values of various parameters in the universe (mean, standard deviation, etc). A good discussion is presented by Kish (8: Chap. 4).

Stratified Sample

As already indicated, random sampling is not the most efficient method of obtaining a sample. One way of increasing the chances of obtaining a representative sample is to use a stratified sampling. The population or universe is first divided into strata according to one or more characteristics. Then a random or systematic sample from each of the strata is taken. Thus, if one wished to determine the average strength in a large population of fourth grade children in a school system, it would be recognized immediately that age and sex might be important factors. Hence the children might be separated first on the basis of sex and then further divided into age subgroups. A random or systematic sample can then be taken of each sex-age group (i.e., 9-year-old boys, 9-year-old girls, 10-year-old boys, etc.).

If an estimate of the mean strength for the entire population were desired, one of two procedures could be followed. Within each stratum (i.e., age-sex groups) a random or systematic sample could be selected, with the number proportional to the percentage of children in the total population who fall in this category. When the various samples from the strata are combined, the percentage of subjects by age and sex in the sample will be the same as in the total population. In our example, suppose there were 8,000 fourth grade children in the school population (the universe) and we wished to test the strength of a sample of 400 of them (5% sample). Suppose also that 52% (4,160) of these children were boys, and that 30% (1,248) of these boys were 10 years of age. In our sample of 400 then, 52% (208) should be boys, and 30% (62) of these should be 10-year-olds. We would then select at random or systematically, 62 10-year-old boys from the total population. When this procedure is followed with the other age-sex groups, the proportion of boys and girls in the age-sex strata will be representative of these proportions in the total population. Of course, if we simply sample at random from the total population of 8,000, the percentages of children in the various age-sex groups in our sample will approach those in the population. But our sample in this case would have to be larger than 5% to achieve the same likelihood that it is representative.

Much the same result will occur if, in stratified sampling, we take samples of equal size from each stratum, calculate the mean scores for these strata, and then average these individual means, weighting each mean according to the percentage of this stratum in the total population. The first method (preceding paragraph) is called proportional stratified sampling; the second method, disproportional stratified sampling. Regardless of whether the first or second method is used, stratified random sampling requires more elaborate methods for estimating the various parameters in the total population (mean, standard deviation, etc.) than does simple random sampling. A discussion of this is not appropriate here. The interested reader should consult Kish (8).

Cluster Sample

In fairly large surveys random, systematic, or stratified sampling is expensive if the sampling units or elements (subjects) are separated geographically and/or if it is difficult to obtain an accurate list of the subjects. To circumvent these difficulties, cluster sampling is employed. In this technique, groups or clusters containing several or many elements are sampled instead of the individual elements. Then every element within the cluster sampled is measured or interviewed. An example will illustrate. Let us assume one wishes to determine the level of sports ability of third grade children in California. If a complete list of individual third grade children were available, a random or systematic sample (for example, 10%) could be obtained, perhaps at considerable time and expense. In this case, one or two children might be selected from this school, one from that, and so on. It would then be necessary to travel throughout the state, testing one or two children in almost every school, disrupting many classes—an indefensible procedure, both economically and in other respects.

Instead, in applying cluster sampling, one might obtain or develop a list of all third grade homerooms in the state and a random or systematic sample of these would be selected. Then all the children in a particular homeroom (including those absent on a particular day) would be tested. Assuming about 30 children per class, this would mean only about one thirtieth as many classes need be disrupted and only a fraction of the schools visited. There are somewhat more complicated and efficient methods for selecting clusters than this, but again, this is beyond the scope of this text. An example of a national survey in physical education in which cluster sampling was used is the study by Hunsicker and collaborators (6, 14).

Clusters of various kinds are employed: families, homerooms, census tracts, villages, etc. In the Tecumseh, Michigan Community Health Study (10, 13) sampling was by dwelling units. The entire list of dwelling units in the study population was sampled at random and all the persons living in a particular dwelling unit (cluster) were studied at one time.

Cluster sampling, when properly employed, generally provides a representative sample of the universe. However, this does not mean that one can select a homeroom and test only those children who are in school that day. It is likely that some children will be absent because of illness or other reasons. In fact, some children will purposely miss class to avoid being tested in physical fitness tests (9). The possibility exists that children absent from class on any given day may be different, on the average, in physical fitness, sports skills, etc., from those who are in class. The absent children should be tested at another time. Cluster sampling, just like other sampling methods, cannot compensate for a possible bias of this sort.

Although cluster sampling usually involves a considerable saving in cost and time, there are some disadvantages. The cost of statistical work is increased, though generally not a great deal. More importantly, the elements in a cluster are often more homogeneous than in a random sample. For example, it is not difficult to see that individuals in the same family can be expected to be more similar than individuals selected at random from a community. Similarly, children in a particular third grade, from a particular neighborhood in a particular part of the country resemble one another more than if randomly sampled from various parts of the country. This results in a larger estimated variance in the universe; hence, some precision is sacrificed. Modifications of the usual statistical formulae are necessary when using cluster sampling. It is preferable to have the clusters as similar as possible but with maximum heterogeneity within the individual clusters. The student contemplating the use of cluster sampling should consult a text which deals with this topic in depth before he proceeds.

Other Kinds of Samples

Variations of the methods described above are sometimes employed, but they are beyond the scope of this text. Sequential sampling, sometimes used in quality control, was developed to increase sampling efficiency and provide a basis for decision making as early in the experiment as possible. Applications in physical education are too rare to justify a discussion here.

Occasionally special sampling problems arise. Sampling from a finite universe is a case in point. In the community study previously mentioned (10, 13) it was of interest to know whether high school athletes in this community differed from other boys in the same population. The universe, in this case, is conceived as all the boys of the same age in the community. Usually one must estimate population parameters (mean, variance, etc.) from a sample. In this instance these parameters were known for the variables of interest: serum cholesterol, serum uric acid, blood pressure, etc. The high school athletes were included in the total population; hence the usual tests of significance had to be adjusted for sampling from a finite universe (11).

Size of Sample

Theoretical Considerations

One of the first questions a graduate student usually asks his advisor is "How many experimental subjects do you think I should have?" He wants to determine in advance how many animals are necessary, how many children in each grade must be tested, how many samples of shoulder padding must be studied, how many schools should be surveyed, etc. Unfortunately, no sample size can be specified with the assurance that it will provide definitive data; hence the investigator is faced with a dilemma.

Two questions must be answered before one can estimate the sample size needed. The first of these concerns the error tolerance that would be allowed. Suppose it were of interest to know whether reducing the teacher-pupil ratio in physical education from the present 1:60 to 1:30 would be desirable. The possible increased learning among the pupils must be weighed against the cost of doubling the staff size. Let us postulate that if a 30% increase in learning were achieved, it would be worth the additional expenditure. What would be our error tolerance? Would a 20% error be acceptable, i.e., an improvement of 24-36% in learning? Or do we hold to a 1% error, representing 29.7 to 30.3% improvement in learning?

Of course, one can't be sure that the sample we use in the experiment is representative of what would happen if other teachers and pupils were used. How much assurance do we wish to specify that our sample is representative? This is the second question we must answer. In order to estimate this we must know how much variation there is in the correlation of teacher-pupil ratio and learning in different samples of the universe of teachers and pupils. Often it is difficult to obtain even approximate answers to such questions.

Recently the writer was a member of a committee charged with the responsibility of studying the feasibility of a national investigation in which the effect of a program of regular physical exercise on coronary heart disease would be assessed. Two members of this committee, using reasonable approximations, were able to provide estimates of the number of subjects needed. Data were already available to provide approximations of the expected coronary heart disease incidence rate, probable drop-out rate, etc. The student is invited to study these calculations and estimates as an illustration of the problems involved (Remington and Schork, 15).

Some Practical Suggestions

In conducting surveys of various kinds, the number of cases required is usually smaller than one might guess. The method of sampling is generally more important than the numbers involved. A carefully selected and tested small sample is often adequate—certainly it is better than a large sample which forces one to do a poorer job of testing or in which a bias appears that could be avoided in a small sample. One could also argue that if a very large sample is needed to show a statistically significant difference or a relationship, the results are probably not very important.

Another practical point to keep in mind is that when estimating parameters or testing the significance of differences, precision increases in proportion to the square root of the number of subjects. For example, getting a standard error of the mean one tenth as large requires a sample 100 times as large.

Sometimes, of course, large numbers are needed, as for example in prospective studies of disease or injuries. For example, if a prospective study of knee injuries as a result of football is contemplated (i.e., the players are to be studied and tested before any injuries occur), large numbers are needed since it is not known how many injuries will occur and to which players.

Sampling in one sense is important even in historical studies. Is one justified in studying the history of one small segment of the population or the development of the recreational program in one city? How typical are these samples? Do the results have application to a larger population? In biographical studies how important is it to demonstrate that early childhood experiences contributed to the development of an outstanding leader in physical education? How representative is this of other leaders?

MECHANICS OF DATA COLLECTION

Observations

A group of people may be exposed to the same events but the observations and recall of these events will vary among the individuals. One's capacity to make observations, to attach significance to the events, and explain them reflects not only his awareness and sensitivity to details but also his training. A person trained in exercise electrocardiography can distinguish between artifacts and abnormalities. Only a historian trained in the general history of a particular time can appreciate the significance of sports or recreational developments of that era.

In making observations, particularly in the laboratory or the field, it is well to remember that every event has an explanation. Sometimes a gross error or an unusual but important event is explained too quickly as being caused by an equipment artifact. It helps to know the theory on which an apparatus operates in order to interpret such phenomena. A few years ago an experiment was conducted with three groups of rats. One group (sedentary animals) lived in small cages. Another group (voluntary exercise) also lived in small cages, but were allowed to exercise at will in the attached wheels which had automatic revolution counters. A third group (forced exercise) lived in the same small cages but were forced to swim two hours daily. In the early stages of the experiment one of the animals in the voluntary exercise group died, which at that time we thought could have been a chance event. However, when three more animals in this group died during the next few days, chance was not the likely explanation. The probability of all four animals which died being in this group was 1 in 81, a rare event. It was observed that the food cups in the cages of these animals were empty, and revolution counters all indicated an unusually large amount of activity. The explanation was then clear. When the animals became hungry, they began to run in the wheel and a vicious cycle developed causing their death. Large food cups prevented any more deaths.

Records and Notebooks

A scientist, early in his career, learns that memory is not very dependable and that he must *record* observations. If data are recorded on loose scraps of paper, sooner or later important information will be lost. In laboratory work there are many kinds of notebooks in use. It is generally agreed, however, that notebooks should be bound and the pages numbered. Some investigators recommend double pages with carbon paper between them so that at the end of the day the carbon copies can be removed and stored in another place, in the event that the notebook itself is mislaid or lost. If a carbon copy is desired, ink should be used, preferably a ball point pen. The notebook should be handy at all times. It is better to record, at the time, all details and observations; the irrelevant ones can be discarded later. The date of the observation and the investigator's or technician's name should always be a part of the record.

If calibration data on an instrument are to be graphed, the graph can be pasted into the notebook. From time to time, equipment or procedures may be modified. The date and nature of these modifications should be carefully recorded because sometimes it is necessary to correct data before making the modification. Basic data should always be recorded—not just the values calculated from them. A table of contents in the notebook is also helpful.

If certain data are being used routinely to identify records it is often wise and efficient to have a rubber stamp prepared so essential data will not be omitted. For example, when certain physiological data are being recorded on photographic paper, a rubber stamp can be prepared which prints the labels:

    Name _____　　　I.D. Number _____

    Date of Test _____　　Hour of Test _____

It is often expedient to use prepared forms, precoded for using punch cards. Figures 1 and 2 contain examples of forms used in collecting oxygen uptake data on over 1,200 subjects during treadmill tests which were conducted over a period of $2\frac{1}{2}$ years (2, 12). The technicians transcribed the information from notebooks and the photographic record onto the precoded forms. A second technician verified and also initialed the entries. The form was then used to prepare IBM punch cards which in turn were verified. Then, by means of a prepared computer program, oxygen uptake and related calculations were done automatically and printed out. (Figure 3 contains an example.) This last step avoids the many human errors which would have occurred in the $2\frac{1}{2}$ years of routine arithmetical work.

In some studies, particularly questionnaire surveys, printed forms are used in which the respondent marks the appropriate space and a machine "senses" these marks and prepares a punch card automatically. A variation of this is the use of partially punched cards in which the observer merely punches out the appropriate space and the card is used to prepare the usual data punch cards. These systems save considerable time, and since there is no intermediate record, no transcription errors will be made. On the other hand, it is time consuming and annoying for a respondent to read a question on one sheet and mark another. This may lead to a poorer response rate. Also, since the spaces for marking or punching are small, errors are frequent; some estimates run as high as 20%. There is, of course, no written record, so it is virtually impossible to locate errors or even know when they have been committed.

Some of the suggestions in this section apply not only to laboratory and field studies, but to the collection of historical and biographical data as well. As Woody (17) has stated, historical research is concerned with ascertaining facts as accurately as possible, and this objective is shared with all scientific investigations. It is hardly sensible, then, to record historical information on scraps of paper that will be lost or disorganized. If a card system is used rather than a notebook, the cards should be numbered or held together in a box or folder. Sometimes it is useful to record data on cards that can be hand-punched to facilitate sorting. One example of this kind of record is illustrated in Figure 4. A code can be established and the appropriate numbers along the edge punched as

Figure 1. Form for recording routine calibration of electronic gas analyzers. Tecumseh Community Health Study—calibration measurements for N_2, CO_2, and O_2.

COLLECTING DATA 157

Card Col.	1	2	3	4	5	6	7	8	9	10	11	12	13	14	15	16	17	18	19	20
Item		Deck No.					I.D. No.					Sex 1 M 2 F	Age last b'day		Code for Level 0 Only Date of Examination Day Month Year					
Entry	4	1	9	2																

Card Col.	21	22	23	24	25	26	27	28	29	30	31	32	33	34	35	36	37	38	39	40
Item	Weight (kg)			Bar. Press. (mm Hg)			Temp. (°C)		Code for Level 0 Only Water Vapor Tension sat (mm Hg)			Relative Humidity			Tread- mill Grade (%)			Time of Sample (After start on test) (min)		
Entry																				

Card Col.	41	42	43	44	45	46	47	48	49	50	51	52	53	54	55	56	57	58	59	60
Item	Total Time of Sample (min)			Volume (ATP) (liters)			Temp. (°C)	Resp. Rate				N_2 (%)			CO_2 (%)			O_2 (%)		
Entry																				

Card Col.	61	62	63	64	65	66	67	68	69	70	71	72	73	74	75	76	77	78	79	80
Item	Heart Rate			Blood Pressure (Systolic) (mm Hg)			Blood Pressure (Diastolic) (mm Hg)			Level No.		Total No. Levels			Total Length of Physical Exercise (min)			RFS *	TM Sp MPH	
Entry																				

Name_____
Sheet No._____
Total No. Sheets_____

Cols. 10, 11 and 80 Blank
All other cols must be coded
Code 9 when information unknown
*RFS col. 78

Code
0 Fatigue
1 HR 150 (age 60-69)
2 HR 160 (age 40-59)
3 Physician's request
4 Technical difficul-
   ties or equipment
   failures
5 Miscellaneous

Figure 2. Form for recording treadmill test data. Tecumseh Community Health Study exercise test (6/67).

RESEARCH METHODS

ID 09558, AGE 22, EXAM DATE 14-02-68   LENGTH OF TEST – 25 MINUTES

LEVEL	GRADE	V O2 L/MIN	V O2 ML/KG/MIN	V CO2	VE L	F	VT	R	O2 PULSE ML/BEAT	V EQ L/V O2	W KGM/MIN	V O2 ML/KGM	WT KG	FH B/MIN	BPS MMHG	BPD MMHG	RFS
00	0	.35	5	.29	9.8	15	.6	.84	3.9	28.18	0	.00	76	90	142	082	0
01	0	1.25	16	.97	29.3	25	1.2	.78	12.2	23.58	0	.00	76	103	160	080	0
02	3	1.33	17	1.17	33.6	25	1.3	.88	12.8	25.45	183	7.24	76	104	180	090	0
03	6	1.45	19	1.29	35.9	27	1.3	.89	13.0	24.83	367	3.96	76	112	180	082	0
04	9	1.78	23	1.65	43.9	30	1.5	.92	13.9	24.74	550	3.24	76	128	192	084	0
05	12	2.10	28	1.85	49.3	30	1.6	.88	14.7	23.61	734	2.86	76	143	200	070	0
06	15	2.39	31	2.16	56.9	32	1.8	.90	14.8	23.88	917	2.61	76	162	212	062	0
07	18	2.76	36	2.79	71.0	35	2.0	1.01	15.5	25.68	1101	2.51	76	178	212	070	0
08	21	3.02	40	3.16	86.0	42	2.0	1.04	16.2	28.38	1284	2.35	76	187	222	062	0
09	24	3.35	44	3.44	95.9	45	2.1	1.03	17.5	28.63	1468	2.28	76	191	230	060	0
10	0	9.99	9999	9.99	999.9	99	99.9	9.99	99.9	99.99	0	9.99	76	168	210	070	0
11	0	9.99	9999	9.99	999.9	99	99.9	9.99	99.9	99.99	0	9.99	76	119	180	060	0
12	0	9.99	9999	9.99	999.9	99	99.9	9.99	99.9	99.99	0	9.99	76	115	172	060	0
13	0	9.99	9999	9.99	999.9	99	99.9	9.99	99.9	99.99	0	9.99	76	109	170	080	0
14	0	9.99	9999	9.99	999.9	99	99.9	9.99	99.9	99.99	0	9.99	76	104	150	080	0
15	0	9.99	9999	9.99	999.9	99	99.9	9.99	99.9	99.99	0	9.99	76	104	132	080	0
16	0	9.99	9999	9.99	999.9	99	99.9	9.99	99.9	99.99	0	9.99	76	104	134	092	0

Figure 3. Computer printout – treadmill test data.

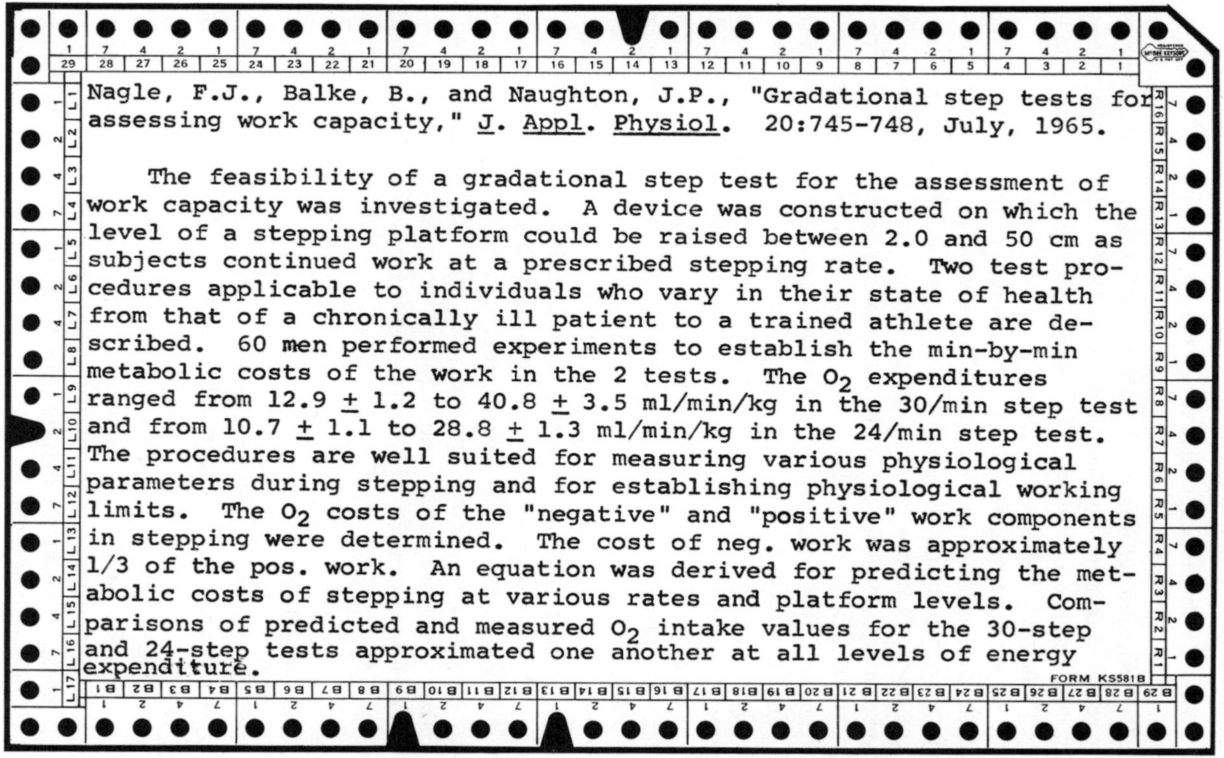

Nagle, F.J., Balke, B., and Naughton, J.P., "Gradational step tests for assessing work capacity," J. Appl. Physiol. 20:745-748, July, 1965.

The feasibility of a gradational step test for the assessment of work capacity was investigated. A device was constructed on which the level of a stepping platform could be raised between 2.0 and 50 cm as subjects continued work at a prescribed stepping rate. Two test procedures applicable to individuals who vary in their state of health from that of a chronically ill patient to a trained athlete are described. 60 men performed experiments to establish the min-by-min metabolic costs of the work in the 2 tests. The O_2 expenditures ranged from 12.9 $\pm$ 1.2 to 40.8 $\pm$ 3.5 ml/min/kg in the 30/min step test and from 10.7 $\pm$ 1.1 to 28.8 $\pm$ 1.3 ml/min/kg in the 24/min step test. The procedures are well suited for measuring various physiological parameters during stepping and for establishing physiological working limits. The O_2 costs of the "negative" and "positive" work components in stepping were determined. The cost of neg. work was approximately 1/3 of the pos. work. An equation was derived for predicting the metabolic costs of stepping at various rates and platform levels. Comparisons of predicted and measured O_2 intake values for the 30-step and 24-step tests approximated one another at all levels of energy expenditure.

Figure 4. Example of an abstract of an article on McBee punch card.

illustrated. Using a needle, one can sort a group of cards fairly rapidly; the punched cards fall out of the pack.

The availability of inexpensive equipment to reproduce letters, pages of books, and records of various kinds has made the task of the historian easier. Reproducing records can be done in a fraction of the time previously required to copy this information by hand. Additionally, errors of transcription are eliminated. The availability of inexpensive tape recorders has made feasible the collection of oral histories.

The importance of going to original sources in historical research cannot be overemphasized. Woody (17) includes as original sources implements of work and play, clothing, ornaments, food, architectural structures, oral traditions (legends, songs, family stories), testimony of survivors, letters, personal diaries, account books, genealogies, inscriptions, contemporary chronicles, newspapers, drawings, photographs, official journals, laws, court decisions, church records, charters, curricula, books, films, and recordings. Frequently secondary sources contain typographical errors, transcription errors, or errors of interpretation. Anyone familiar with genealogical research is aware of the frequency with which errors in dates of birth and death appear. A few years ago, the writer had occasion to trace the literature on the effects of physical training on breath-holding ability. An American physical educator had quoted an English reference that physical training greatly improves this capacity. The English writer, it turns out, was quoting a study originally published in Italian. A translation of this paper revealed that it was practice in breath holding that had resulted in improvement. This was quite a different matter. The words "practice" and "training" had been misinterpreted, to be then quoted and requoted incorrectly.

An excellent discussion of laboratory data collection may be found in Wilson (16).

Identification of Subjects

It is expedient in research with large numbers of subjects, be they human beings, animals, or objects, to number them serially. In the case of human beings, several subjects might have identical names so a number is essential. Furthermore, a number, rather than a name, requires fewer spaces on an IBM card, and sorting and other operations by data processing and computing equipment are facilitated.

It is usually imperative that animals be more or less permanently identified. In handling them, or treating them in groups, they are likely to be mixed up. Also, there is always the possibility that several will escape from their cages. There are several common methods of identifying animals. Mice, rabbits, pigs, and many other animals may be numbered by an ear punching system. Small inexpensive ear punches are available from equipment supply companies. This is almost painless to the animal (he can be punched without an anesthetic) and it in no way affects his health or performance. Other methods include removing toenails or color-coding the animals with dyes. Various colored dyes are available which react with the protein in the animal's hair and provide a fairly permanent mark lasting a month or two. If animals swim daily, the dye will need to be applied frequently. Both colors and areas on the animal's back have been used to develop a code. Dubin (3) has reported a simple numbering system for laboratory animals.

Environmental and Other Controls

In conducting laboratory studies or field tests it is frequently necessary to have reasonable control over the environment or to avoid testing under certain conditions. For example, heart rate response to exercise is a common measurement in physical education. If the ambient temperature is high (particularly with high humidity), the heart rate will be higher for a given work load. This is so because the cardiovascular system, beside delivering oxygen to the tissues and removing carbon dioxide, has a heat regulatory function. More blood will be shunted to the skin (hence, a higher heart rate) in a hot climate so that heat may be transferred to the environment.

A complete discussion of animal facilities is not possible here; only a few important points will be mentioned. Entire volumes have been published on animal facilities. An excellent reference has been published by the U. S. Public Health Service (4). In studies using small animals, it is usually easy to achieve reasonable environmental control. Temperature and humidity can be maintained within a fairly narrow range. Automatic light controls are available so that light exposure can be rigidly maintained. However, when animals are housed in racks of cages it is necessary to rotate them regularly to equalize conditions, particularly light exposure. It is a good idea to have a central warning control so that if there is a power failure in the laboratory, a light will appear 24 hr/day where maintenance employees are located.

When animals in one group are handled regularly, as for example in putting them on a treadmill, control animals should also be handled because it has been demonstrated that handling alone affects growth. Similarly, sham injections of isotonic saline or other appropriate material and sham operations should be performed on controls.

It is not appropriate here to list all of the control procedures which might be important in the various kinds of experiments with human beings and animals. The investigator, before collecting data, must try to anticipate what factors might affect the measurements and then plan either to control them or expose all subjects to the same influences.

Data Storage

Laboratory notebooks, if carefully bound, will last a long time provided they are stored where they will not be exposed to the elements. IBM and other punch cards absorb water and become damaged by handling and being passed through data processing equipment. They must be replaced from time to time. It should also be mentioned that errors have a way of creeping into duplicated decks, so each new deck should be verified or checked in some way.

Decks of punched cards in large studies require considerable space. One round of examinations in the Tecumseh Community Health Study alluded to earlier (10) generated more than 200,000 IBM cards. For this reason and for greater ease in analysis, data are often transferred to magnetic tape. However, these tapes vary in quality and permanency. When basic data are transferred to cards or tapes, these should not be stored in the same place as the folders or notebooks containing the original data, lest both be lost or destroyed.

Photographic recordings also vary in the length of time they may be stored satisfactorily. Records using the rapid development process usually deteriorate faster than those in which the usual development process is used. Various duplicating processes also vary in the permanency of the copy.

Procedure Manuals

It is important to describe in detail in a laboratory manual exactly how certain procedures are carried out. In addition, abbreviated steps or checklists can be attached to the apparatus or posted on the wall in full view of the operator. These manuals serve several purposes. They contribute greatly to the standardization of procedures from day to day and eliminate the necessity to rely on memory for recalling details of procedure. This applies to questionnaire or interview studies as well as to laboratory investigations. One does not know in what way or how far in the future data will be utilized, or if another investigator may want to duplicate parts of the experiment. Recently the writer reviewed a paper for *Human Biology* based on anthropometric and other data collected by Dudley Sargent at Harvard. Who could have anticipated that these data would be utilized in a longitudinal study years after his death?

Not only in the actual collection of data, but in the coding of it, detailed description is necessary, particularly when subjectivity is involved. Code books for data on cards or tapes should be maintained and kept up-to-date.

Rehearsal of Experiments

In complicated experiments, rehearsals are usually necessary to develop a smooth operation. If a team effort is involved, it is especially desirable to have one or more dry runs so everyone will become familiar with his job and, it is hoped, the jobs of others. To achieve standardization in directions given to subjects, a tape is sometimes prepared. Playing the tape insures that each subject will receive identical instructions and that no important details are omitted.

Rehearsals often reveal problems with equipment. Even field testing of skills or physical fitness should be preceded by rehearsals with other subjects taking the tests, preferably subjects of the same age and sex.

In questionnaire and interview studies it is equally important to rehearse and test the procedures. Usually after a preliminary sample is tested (a pilot study), the questionnaire or interview procedures will have to be revised and another trial run conducted. Vocabulary, sentence structure, etc. are very important if the subjects are to make the proper interpretations and provide meaningful data. Sometimes several revisions are required.

Practical Suggestions

During the actual collection of data, computations should not be done, or at least they should be minimized. In the first place, the investigator can use his time to better advantage by making observations and recording basic data. In the second place, during the excitement or confusion of data collection, errors in calculations are apt to occur. If at all possible, computations should be delayed until later when there is no time pressure and the work can be done quietly without distractions. Better yet, perhaps a computer program can be written to do the calculations routinely, as illustrated in Figure 3 (p. 158) and discussed previously in the section on Records (pp. 154–155).

Whenever possible the procedures should be automated, provided accuracy is not sacrificed and it is economically feasible. For example, in the oxygen uptake study described above (Tecumseh Community Health Study, p. 155) an automatic lift raised the treadmill angle 3% every 3 min. The technicians then did not need to worry about this step. Similarly, the electric clock started automatically when the experiment began. When the treadmill was stopped, the clock stopped and another started. A buzzer was built into the circuit to warn the technician at crucial periods in the test, and a precise one-minute mark automatically appeared on the written records at certain times to facilitate record measurements. For a $2\frac{1}{2}$-year period, such alterations in the equipment are more than justified.

It is a good practice, particularly in large investigations, to analyze and study some of the data as soon as practicable. Otherwise, problems in the data collection resulting in errors may not be detected until all the data have been collected and it is too late to correct the equipment or procedure. Also, it sometimes becomes apparent when a sample of the data is analyzed that a procedure could be changed or added to provide additional important data. It is tempting to wait until all the data have been collected before doing any analysis, but the slight expense and effort expended early in data collection are generally worth it.

ERRORS IN MEASUREMENT

Whenever a measurement is taken, the recorded value is not 100% accurate and precise. (See pp. 82–83, 115–116.) Even a simple measurement of body height (stature) has its limitations. If the subject is fatigued and slumps a bit, his full stature will not be recorded. If the measurement is taken with a yardstick measured to the closest 1/4 in, then the precision is limited to about the closest 1/8 in. The true stature may be a little above or below what is actually recorded. Absolute precision and accuracy are not required in research but we must be able to estimate the probable limit of the error or be able to correct for it in some way. In the following section, errors have been grouped into several kinds and discussed separately for the sake of convenience.

Random Errors

Lack of precision results in random errors. For example, if the length of a room were measured several times to the closest millimeter using a tape measure, it is unlikely that each measurement would be precisely the same. Sometimes it would be a little longer, sometimes a little shorter. The length of the room, of course, does not vary significantly, but our ability to measure it does. The mean of a large number of such measurements, provided the tape is accurate, would be very close to the true length. Similarly, in repeatedly measuring a person's chest circumference with a tape, there will be some variation. In this case, the situation is more complicated because, in addition to variations in our technique, there will be actual variations in the subject's chest circumference depending on his posture, volume of air in his lungs, etc. However, if a number of measurements were taken, the values would be uniformly distributed above and below the mean. These are examples of random errors, sometimes called chance or variable errors. Fortunately the distribution of such errors is known, as mentioned earlier under Methods of Sampling (pp. 146–148). We can, therefore, estimate quite accurately the increase in precision to be expected if the measurement is repeated two, three, four or more times and averaged.

Although an investigator is not obligated to measure things with absolute precision (which is not possible anyway), he should know the variability in the measurement. This can be learned from other studies on populations, but it is always preferable to determine it by repeating the measurement on the population under study, or a sample of this population. Precision is frequently expressed as a standard error of measurement, a reliability coefficient, an intraclass coefficient, or in the form of a scatter diagram.

A few examples will illustrate these concepts. Several years ago the relationships between exercise habits and serum cholesterol and uric acid were being studied. We were considering having the serum determinations done at a commercial laboratory. Although commercial laboratories are generally not known for their precision, this one was very highly recommended. Nevertheless, the precision was investigated by drawing a blood sample from a number of subjects. The serum from each sample was split into two samples, a fictitious name attached to each of the pair. When the serum cholesterol values were received from the laboratory, they were uncoded and paired values compared. The correlation coefficient describing the relationship among the paired values was close to zero. Needless to say, this laboratory was not engaged to do the cholesterol determinations.

In a similar way, the serum samples were split to study the reliability (precision) of the uric determinations which were being made by one of the coworkers in the project. These results are shown in Figure 5, which illustrates good reproducibility. The small deviations between paired determinations represent random errors. This coworker, of course, did not know we had split the samples and would not have cared in any case. A careful scientist never objects to his work being checked.

In measuring oxygen uptake in a large population (see Tecumseh Community Health Study pp. 155–158) some of the subjects were asked to return a week or two later for a retest (12). The results of the two tests are shown in Figure 6. In this instance, the situation was a little different. The errors scattered around the line of identity in Figure 6 represent not only random errors in measurement technique but also changes in the subjects' oxygen uptake capacity (random errors) from day to day. These could also be a systematic error, but this seems not to have been the case since the second test gave results that were not uniformly higher or lower than the first test.

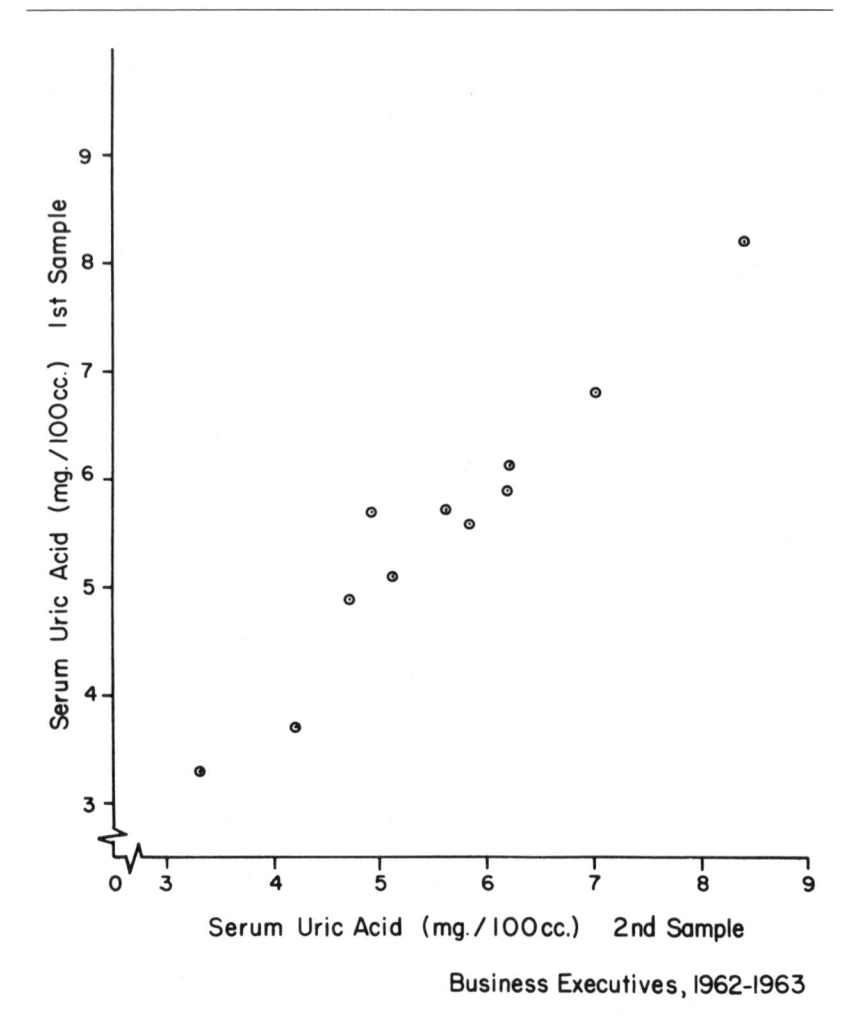

Figure 5. Comparison of split-sample urid acid determinations.

Random errors in themselves do not produce a bias or systematic error, but they make the task of testing a hypothesis more difficult. For example, if one took the cholesterol values as determined above with poor precision and correlated them with physical activity, it would be difficult to demonstrate a correlation even if one existed. Poor precision tends to vitiate the correlation. In comparing group means, it is similarly difficult to show significant differences when the measurements have poor reliability.

Space does not permit a discussion here of how precision (reliability) in measurement can be improved, but many tests and measurement texts

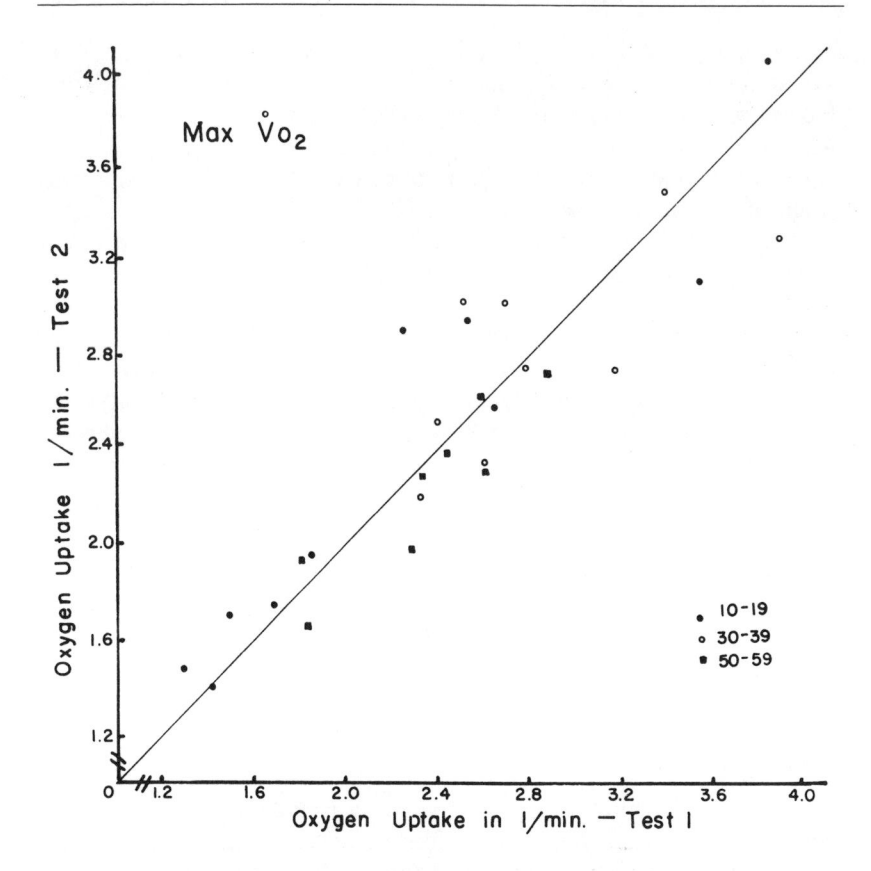

Figure 6. Reproducibility of maximal oxygen uptake on treadmill test.

in physical education cover this topic—at least with regard to the sports and physical fitness tests with which physical educators are often concerned.

Systematic Errors

There are errors of another kind that cause difficulties in research. Suppose the tape used in measuring the circumference of the chest in the measurements described above contained an error in the markings so that all measurements appeared to be ½ inch shorter than the true circumference. The recorded measurements would thus contain two kinds of errors: the possible random error due to imprecision in our technique and variations in the subject, plus the constant systematic error causing everyone's recorded circumference to seem ½ inch less than it really is. A constant systematic error is sometimes not difficult to detect and correct (see pp. 82 and 115–121). In any case, a constant error, if present, would not affect the correlation of this measurement with other variables. However, if one compared the mean chest circumference of this group with one in which a different tape were used, the $\frac{1}{2}$-inch error, if not corrected, would produce an apparent statistically significant difference when one actually did not exist.

Systematic errors may be always in the same direction but not of equal magnitude. This would occur, for example, if height were measured with the subjects wearing shoes. In this case, everyone's height would be overestimated but to a different amount, depending on the height of the heel. This kind of error affects both correlation problems and those in which groups are compared. If children are tested on a shuttle run such as the one used in the AAHPER Youth Fitness Test, a slippery floor introduces a systematic error causing the scores to be poorer. If some children took the test wearing their stockings but no shoes, the effect of the floor would be greater because of the poor traction in attempting to reverse direction. The systematic error in this case, also, would not be constant. One can think of hundreds of such possible sources of systematic errors. When an instrument is responsible for errors, they can usually be detected by careful calibration. But the investigator must be alert to the more subtle sources of error as well.

Psychological Bias

A scientist embarking on a research project usually has a hypothesis he wishes to test; hence, he probably has a bias. He must therefore design the experiment in such a way that his bias will not have an opportunity to affect the results. It is not a question of honesty, but the investigator might unconsciously see what he expects to see or wants to see. Frequently, therefore, when data are being collected, knowledge is sometimes withheld from the observer so that his observations will be objective. (See previous example concerning uric acid determinations, pp. 165–166.)

An investigator learns very early not to trust his intuition in many instances. A frequently quoted problem will serve to illustrate. Consider the question: how many people must be present before the odds are better than 50–50 that there are at least two persons with the same birthday? Generally, individuals will estimate that 100 or even 365 are necessary. When there are only 23 persons present, the odds are greater than 50–50 that two or more persons will have the same birthday. With 40 persons present, the odds are better than 8 to 1.

In research it is also necessary to guard against a bias on the part of the person being tested. It is well-known that when an athlete in training is given a particular nutrient (vitamin, for example) because it might improve his performance, it may well do so simply because it is expected to, hence the use of placebos (substances that look and taste like the substance being tested). If one is studying the effects of breathing oxygen-rich mixtures on performance, it is necessary to conduct some experiments in which the subject breathes air, but believes it to be the oxygen-rich mixture. This is called a blind study. However, if the observer knew when the subject was breathing a high oxygen concentration he might unconsciously motivate the subject to greater performance. Therefore, an assistant should select the gas mixture on a given day without informing the observer. This, then, becomes a double-blind study. (Someone facetiously defined a double-blind study as one in which neither the subject nor the investigator knew what he was doing!)

In repeating tests, particularly performance tests, it is important that the subject not be told how he is doing with respect to the first performance. Otherwise, this procedure would not measure the reproducibility of the test as we commonly understand it.

Quality Control

In research that continues for a relatively long period of time, it is especially important to build in methods of quality control. An example will illustrate. In the previously discussed study of oxygen uptake in over 1,200 people, which required $2\frac{1}{2}$ years, electronic apparatus was employed to measure the concentration of O_2, N_2, and CO_2 in exhaled air. A sample of exhaled gas from every fifth subject was taken for chemical analysis to be compared with simultaneous electronic determinations. The results were plotted weekly. Had there been any change in the equipment during the period of the study, the breakdown would have appeared in the quality control plot. A portion of the oxygen concentration plot is illustrated in Figure 7.

As a second accuracy check, when the computer program was written for calculation of oxygen uptake and related measurements (Figure 3), it also included a scatter diagram of oxygen uptake plotted against heart rate at the various exercise loads (Figure 8). A fairly straight line should result, and if a transcription or measurement error was made it could usually be detected. The plot was inspected for each subject within a week or two after the data were collected. It is important to do this promptly so that the technician can still recall details.

Concluding Statements

A frequent problem in surveys of various kinds has to do with nonreturns. In the section under sampling, an experience in the Tecumseh

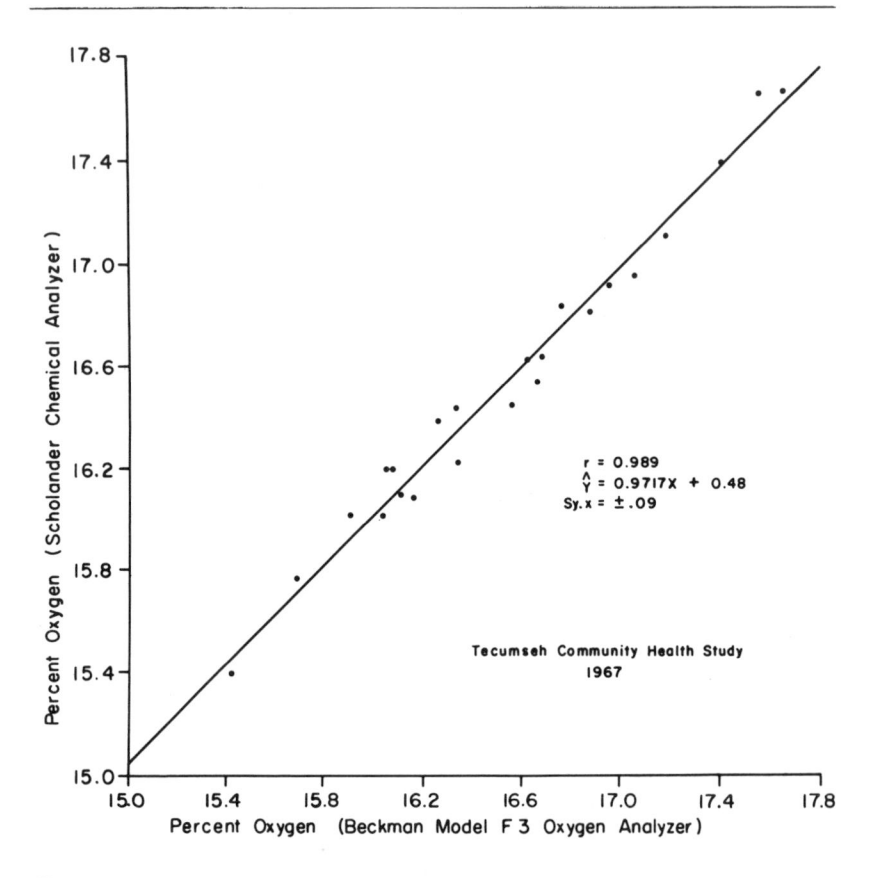

Figure 7. Comparison of percent of oxygen in exhaled air—electronic vs. chemical analysis.

Community Health Study was mentioned in which the AAHPER Youth Fitness Tests were administered to students, fourth grade through senior high school. Because students who are not in class on a given day are very likely to be different in fitness from those who are present, it was necessary to return to the same schools a number of times in order to obtain data on over 99% of the population.

When questionnaires are sent out, 100% return is almost never obtained. It is probable that the individuals, schools, etc. which did not return the questionnaires are different, but since data on them are not available, what bias, if any, exists cannot be studied. Some investigators circumvent this difficulty by interviewing or visiting a *sample* of those who made no returns. Certainly it is better to obtain data on 100% or almost 100% of a smaller sample than to work with 50, 60, or 70% return of a larger sample.

OXYGEN UPTAKE (ML) VS. HEART RATE (BEATS/MIN)—ID 09558

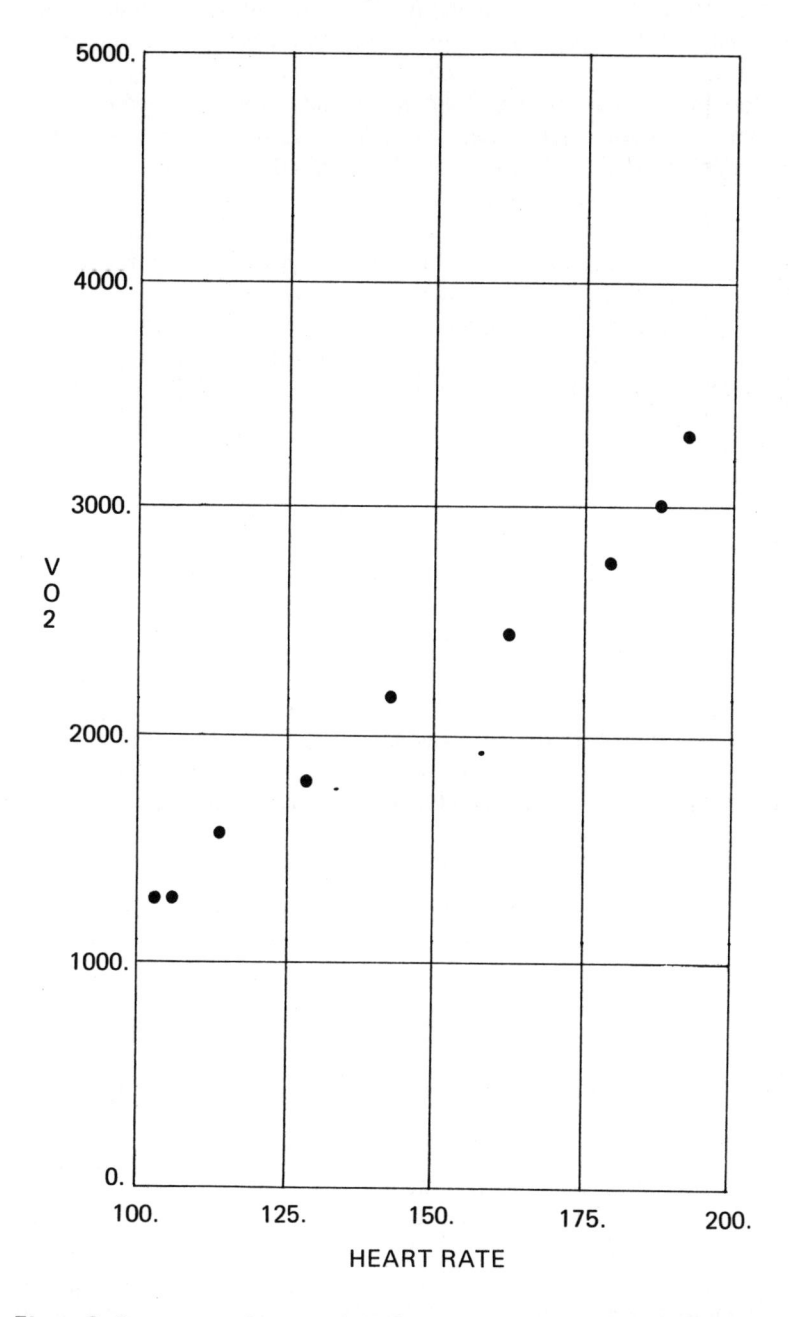

Figure 8. Computer printout—plot of oxygen uptake against heart rate.

Similar problems exist in longitudinal experimental studies. If subjects (human beings or animals) in several groups are matched, and one of a pair or trio drops out of an experiment, a bias is introduced. There is no satisfactory way to overcome this bias. Dropping the other subject(s) in the pair or trio is an inadequate solution because the first dropped out for a particular reason related to that individual, the experiment, or both. When the paired individual is eliminated, this is done more or less at random, so a bias conceivably still exists. Of course, if the number of such instances is small, no important effect will result.

Another question frequently arises concerning the replication of measurements. If three determinations were to be done on the same blood sample, and two of them agree quite closely, should one reject the discrepant value and average the other two or average all three? Of course, one could replicate the determinations further, if this were possible, to determine if the discrepant value truly represents a poor determination. But if this is not possible, and there is no other evidence that the discrepant value represents an erroneous score, it is probably better to average all values. Henry's discussion (5) and our data on stopwatch-timing support this view (1).

Another problem, usually less important, involves the method of rounding off figures. If it is decided to use a specific number of digits and the next one is always dropped, a bias in the mean or other measure of central tendency will result. Standard procedures for avoiding this bias are to: never round serially from the right, drop any remainder less than one-half, round upward any remainder more than one-half, and drop a remainder of exactly one-half if the last digit to be significant is even or round upward if that digit is odd. A few illustrations:

$$16.4 = 16 \qquad 21.72 = 21.7$$
$$12.8 = 13 \qquad 28.17 = 28.2$$
$$15.49 = 15 \qquad 14.345 = 14.3$$
$$17.50 = 18 \qquad 19.950 = 20.0$$

PERSONAL RELATIONS AND ETHICAL CONSIDERATIONS

Between Investigator and Subjects

Before collecting data, it is sometimes necessary to raise questions of ethics and personal involvement of the subjects. Before financial support is granted to research involving human beings, the National Institutes of Health and some other agencies now require that the research proposal be reviewed by a committee at the institution where the proposal originates. Researchers and institutions are legally responsible for the health and safety of human subjects. Institutions normally require appropriate safety precautions and medical supervision. They also require "informed consent" if any experimental procedures may be potentially hazardous or injurious. Subjects or their legal guardians must be fully informed of *both* the possibility and probability of injury from any potentially harmful procedures before signing a release or consent form. Subjects should be told the general nature and purpose of the experiment. Disclosure need not be made of nonhazardous aspects that might compromise the research design, such as whether a subject is in the experimental or control group.

Research in physical education or recreation not uncommonly involves some risk. This might be the risk of accidental injury or, with older subjects, the risk of cardiac arrest or other complications. The investigator is obligated to anticipate these difficulties, if possible, and take means to prevent them. It may be necessary to have a physician present. Arrangements for emergency care should be made in the event that some untoward incident occurs. The Nuremburg Code or the Declaration of Helsinki should be familiar to all investigators, including students. The latter is reproduced here.

Recommendations from the
DECLARATION OF HELSINKI

I. BASIC PRINCIPLES

1. Clinical research must conform to the moral and scientific principles that justify medical research and should be based on laboratory and animal experiments or other scientifically established facts.

2. Clinical research should be conducted only by scientifically qualified persons and under the supervision of a qualified medical man.

3. Clinical research cannot legitimately be carried out unless the importance of the objective is in proportion to the inherent risk to the subject.

4. Every clinical research project should be preceded by careful assessment of inherent risks in comparison to foreseeable benefits to the subject or to others.

5. Special caution should be exercised by the doctor in performing clinical research in which the personality of the subject is liable to be altered by drugs or experimental procedure.

II. CLINICAL RESEARCH COMBINED WITH PROFESSIONAL CARE

1. In the treatment of the sick person, the doctor must be free to use a new therapeutic measure, if in his judgment it offers hope of saving life, reestablishing health, or alleviating suffering.

If at all possible, consistent with patient psychology, the doctor should obtain the patient's freely given consent after the patient has been given a full explanation. In case of legal incapacity, consent should also be procured from the legal guardian; in case of physical incapacity the permission of the legal guardian replaces that of the patient.

2. The doctor can combine clinical research with professional care, the objective being the acquisition of new medical knowledge, only to the extent that clinical research is justified by its therapeutic value for the patient.

III. NON-THERAPEUTIC CLINICAL RESEARCH

1. In the purely scientific application of clinical research carried out on a a human being, it is the duty of the doctor to remain the protector of the life and health of that person on whom clinical research is being carried out.

2. The nature, the purpose and the risk of clinical research must be explained to the subject by the doctor.

3a. Clinical research on a human being cannot be undertaken without his free consent after he has been informed; if he is legally incompetent, the consent of the legal guardian should be procured.

3b. The subject of clinical research should be in such a mental, physical and legal state as to be able to exercise fully his power of choice.

3c. Consent should, as a rule, be obtained in writing. However, the responsibility for clinical research always remains with the research worker; it never falls on the subject even after consent is obtained.

4a. The investigator must respect the right of each individual to safeguard his personal integrity, especially if the subject is in a dependent relationship to the investigator.

4b. At any time during the course of clinical research the subject or his guardian should be free to withdraw permission for research to be continued.

The investigator or the investigating team should discontinue the research if in his or their judgment, it may, if continued, be harmful to the individual.

Health and safety are not the only ethical considerations. Sometimes data collection is offensive to the subjects. Informed consent of the subjects and propriety on the part of the investigating team should guide the researchers in these instances. The confidentiality of personal data should be maintained when necessary, and plans for this should be formulated in advance. For example, in the Tecumseh Community Health Study, involving a relatively small community (10,000 persons), the policy was established before field work began that no one living in the community was to be employed in the project to avoid furnishing subject matter for town gossips.

The investigator should always be mindful in animal experiments of the importance of comfort and humane treatment. Pain and discomfort should be avoided whenever possible. They may be used only if absolutely essential to the experiment and then only if the significance of the results to human welfare and understanding can be clearly seen. An animal, unless anesthetized, suffers pain and this might be even more stressful than in humans because lack of communication prevents an explanation to the subjects. Some guidelines in the care and use of experimental animals, as approved by the Council of the American Physiological Society, follow:

Only animals that are lawfully acquired shall be used in this laboratory, and their retention and use shall be in every case in strict compliance with state and local laws and regulations.

Animals in the laboratory must receive every consideration for their bodily comfort; they must be kindly treated, properly fed, and their surroundings kept in a sanitary condition.

Appropriate anesthetics must be used to eliminate sensibility to pain during operative procedures. Where recovery from anesthesia is necessary during the study, acceptable technique to minimize pain must be followed. Curarizing agents are not anesthetics. Where the study does not require recovery from anesthesia, the animal must be killed in a humane manner at the conclusion of the observations.

The postoperative care of animals shall be such as to minimize discomfort and pain, and in any case shall be equivalent to accepted practices in schools of veterinary medicine.

When animals are used by students for their education or the advancement of science, such work shall be under the direct supervision of an experienced teacher or investigator. The rules for the care of such animals must be the same as for animals used for research.

Between Investigator and Other Personnel

There is a tendency for some investigators, probably because they are deeply involved in the theoretical aspects of their work, to forget that technicians, secretaries, and students are human beings and need encouragement and understanding. The investigator must develop a sensitivity to this. It is often helpful, for example, to explain to the technical personnel the scientific principles on which an instrument operates and even the significance of their observations. Usually it is wise for them to attend research seminars in the laboratory or department.

It is also well-known that if an investigator is careful about details in his work, the technical workers and students also will be concerned about details.

A scientist is often so strongly motivated in his work that he ignores or is oblivious to discomfort and boredom. But other personnel cannot be expected to be as strongly motivated. Hence, the senior investigator should provide for the comfort of his staff insofar as possible. While the investigator may only make occasional laboratory determinations of a particular kind, the student or technician may be required to do this routinely and continuously, so breaks of some kind are needed to interrupt the monotony.

Finally, to a senior investigator with a long list of publications, the mention of a name in a footnote appears trivial. However, this may be very rewarding and satisfying to a dedicated, hard-working person who never becomes a coauthor. Students should remember this in the publication of their theses and dissertations.

Among Investigators

To the beginning student in research, this section may appear less important. Usually he is working with a major professor. But even in this case, misunderstandings do occur, particularly with regard to the publition of results. Various major professors view the joint publication of theses and dissertations differently. At one extreme is the professor who considers his salary as recompense for working with graduate students, and regardless of the extent of his own participation in data collection, he declines to have his name included as a coauthor. On the other hand, there are professors who insist that they be included as coauthor regardless of how the problem originated and regardless of the extent of participation of either party in the collection of the data. Most major professors function somewhere between these extremes; that is, if the student originates the problem, collects the data with minimal participation from others, and writes the manuscript, most major professors would suggest the student publish the results under his own name only. On the other hand, if the chairman or other members of the student's committee participate actively in data collection or work is in his laboratory under his supervision, it is natural that he be included as a coauthor. A coauthor must always be given an opportunity to read the various drafts of the manuscript before it is submitted for publication.

Sometimes a large investigative effort is involved and the student participates as a member of the team or uses a portion of the results for his thesis or dissertation. In these cases there are often numerous coauthors on the reports. The ultimate publication of results in such cases should be understood *before* the student becomes involved. Team investigations usually provide wonderful learning opportunities but the senior investigator should make certain the role of the student does not become that of a technician. He must be involved in the planning and analysis. A very interesting, amusing, but provocative discussion of the relationship of professor and student in research is a paper entitled "Percy T. Diorets" (steroid spelled backwards) by a well known endocrinologist-philosopher, Dwight Ingle (7). A student should always clear the final manuscript through his major professor even if the student is sole author. There may be supporting funds or other considerations involved which require acknowledgement in the publication.

There are several advantages to team investigations. They often provide for more efficient use of particular talents and specialities, and they often are more enjoyable, particularly if they include periodic "skull sessions" for the exchange of thoughts. On the other hand, team efforts can be inefficient and the source of discontent and bitterness. The latter can usually be avoided if it is made clear from the start who is in charge and who the coauthors of the final publications are to be.

One last point should be mentioned. Most investigators are individualistic and need a laboratory or space they can call their own, even though they may have to share major facilities. They need to know a piece of equipment will be there the next morning. A few years ago this was not so important in physical education because a department usually had only one investigator doing a particular kind of laboratory work. The situation has changed and administrators planning buildings should provide for individual research and teaching laboratories.

REFERENCES

1. Beck, Buford and Montoye, Henry J. On the use of the mean and median in stopwatch timing. *Research Quarterly* 25: 201–209, May 1954.
2. Cunningham, David A.; Montoye, Henry J.; and Welch, Hugh G. An evaluation of equipment for determining oxygen uptake. *Research Quarterly* 40: 851–856, Dec. 1969.
3. Dubin, S. A method for numbering laboratory animals using a binary number system. *Laboratory Animal Care* 18: 574–576, 1968.
4. *Guide for Laboratory Animal Facilities and Care.* Rev. ed. Washington, D.C.: U.S. Public Health Service, 1965.
5. Henry, Franklin M. The loss of precision from discarding discrepant data. *Research Quarterly* 21: 145–152, May 1950.
6. Hunsicker, Paul A. and Reiff, Guy G. *A Survey and Comparison of Youth Fitness, 1958–1965.* Cooperative Research Project No. 2418. Washington, D.C.: Department of Health, Education and Welfare, 1965.
7. Ingle, D. J. Percy T. Diorets, endocrinologist—A fable. *Endocrinology* 67: 139–145, July 1960.
8. Kish, Leslie. *Survey Sampling.* New York: John Wiley & Sons, 1965. 643 pp.
9. Marmis, Cary et al. Reliability of the multi-trial items of the AAHPER youth fitness test. *Research Quarterly* 40: 240–245, March 1969.
10. Montoye, Henry J. and Epstein, F. H. Tecumseh Community Health Study. *Journal of Sports Medicine and Physical Fitness* 5: 127–131, Sept. 1965.
11. Montoye, Henry J.; Howard, G. E.; and Wood, J. H. Observations of some hemochemical and anthropometric measurements in athletes. *Journal of Sports Medicine and Physical Fitness* 7: 35–44, March 1967.
12. Montoye, Henry J. et al. Laboratory methods of assessing metabolic capacity in a large epidemiologic study. *American Journal of Epidemiology* 91: 38–47, Jan. 1970.

13. Napier, J. A. Field methods and response rates in the Tecumseh Community Health Study. *American Journal of Public Health* 52: 208–216, Feb. 1962.
14. Reiff, Guy; Kish, Leslie; and Harter, Jean. Selecting a probability sample of school children in the coterminous United States. *Research Quarterly* 39: 409–414, May 1968.
15. Remington, R. and Schork, M. A. Determination of number of subjects needed for experimental epidemiological studies of the effect of increased physical activity on incidence of coronary heart disease—Preliminary considerations. In *Physical Activity and The Heart,* edited by Martin J. Karvonen and Alan J. Barry, pp. 311–319. Springfield, Ill.: Charles C. Thomas, Publisher, 1967.
16. Wilson, Edgar B. *An Introduction to Scientific Research.* New York: McGraw-Hill Book Co., 1952. 373 pp.
17. Woody, Thomas. Of history and its method. *Journal of Experimental Education* 15: 175–201, March 1947.

SELECTED READINGS

Cochran, W. G. *Sampling Techniques.* 2d ed. New York: John Wiley & Sons, 1963. 413 pp. A fairly good knowledge of elementary statistics is needed to read and profit from this text.

Deming, W. Edwards. *Some Theory of Sampling.* New York: Dover Publications, 1966. This, too, is a rather advanced treatment not recommended for the student with no background in mathematics or statistics.

Kish, Leslie. Selection of the sample. In *Research Methods in the Behavioral Sciences,* edited by Leon Festinger and D. Katz, pp. 175–239. New York: Holt, Rinehart & Winston, 1953. A mathematical background is helpful but much valuable information can be obtained from this excellent reference without it.

―――. *Survey Sampling.* New York: John Wiley & Sons, 1965. 643 pp. The author is head of the sampling section of the Institute for Social Research at the University of Michigan. This is a comprehensive treatment. Some mathematics is desirable.

McCarty, P. J. Sample design. In *Research Methods in Social Relations: Part II, Selected Techniques,* edited by Marie Jahoda, M. Deutsch, and S. W. Cook, pp. 643–680. New York: Dryden Press, 1951. A background in statistics is helpful but not essential.

Parten, Mildred B. *Survey, Polls, and Samples.* New York: Cooper Square Publishers, 1950. 624 pp. Somewhat technical. A knowledge of statistics is helpful but not essential.

Slonim, Morris. *Sampling in a Nutshell.* New York: Simon & Schuster, 1960. 144 pp. This is a very readable, nontechnical, and useful reference.

CHAPTER 9 UNDERSTANDING STATISTICS

Alfred W. Hubbard
University of Illinois
Urbana, Illinois

STATISTICS UNDERGIRD SCIENTIFIC RESEARCH with numerical facts derived from data. An isolated observation (datum) is less stable than an average, so all statistics are averages of some sort. The procedures for analyzing and synthesizing data are collectively called statistics. But the products of data processing which summarize and describe data also individually are called statistics. The basic purposes of these individual statistics, and thus also of statistics collectively, are to determine on the average the magnitude, variability, relationship, and fit of data to various mathematical models. Sorting statistics according to these basic purposes indicates why each is computed.

Nature of Statistics

Statistics is a branch of applied mathematics dealing primarily with animate objects. This subject matter introduces some special problems that will be dealt with later. The intimate procedure-product relation results from the mathematical practice of defining a product in terms of the essential elements and operations required to produce it. Having the relation expressed in symbolic shorthand as a formula generates deciphering problems for the uninitiated. Definition formulae provide precise verbal descriptions if you substitute the right words in the right order. But their simplicity is deceptive when one or more essential elements must be derived before performing the operations. Operational formulae starting from the basic data and specifying all the operations sequentially and symbolically become highly complex. They are difficult to decipher and the starting point is obscure. They also differ depending on whether the data will be processed by hand, desk calculator, or computer. They may also incorporate ingenious detours around computational problems and shortcuts which treat the data as though various operations have been performed when they actually have not. The multiplicity of methods may leave you wondering which purpose you were headed toward initially, whether you got lost on a detour, where a shortcut leads, or when, whether, and where you have arrived.

Statistical procedures and products represent for the uninitiated a monumental and mysterious mathematical maze with four possible exits. You must initially gird yourself with some elementary mathematical principles. These are logical, reasonable, and essentially simple once you understand them. Things look different as you travel out through the breaking apart (analysis) and travel back through the putting together (synthesis). One way to avoid getting lost is to look back, so look back occasionally when you feel uncertain. But the mystery may be resolved further on, so keep moving ahead even though the going gets sticky and the mystical meaning should become manifest.

THINGS AND GAMES

Things in nature of different kinds and amounts are classifiable and measurable. The right combination of necessary and sufficient conditions causes events to occur, like the expansion of metals with heat. Things may also vary concomitantly without one causing change in the other. Human weight tends to increase with height but increased weight cannot cause increased height, and increased height as such cannot increase the attraction of gravity. Measuring requires scales and tests. A scale is a graduated standard with equal increments. A test is a combination of specified conditions for obtaining a score. A measurement or score is a datum. Measurements and scores are data. A statistic is a numerical fact derived from data. A statistic is also a standard procedure for deriving a numerical fact. Using the same label for a process and a product seems confusing, but products result from processes and different processes can produce different products from the same material or data so understanding statistics requires understanding the processes for treating data. Statistics are numerical facts, but statistics is also the science of collecting and processing data to establish numerical facts and to determine causal and concomitant relations as a basis for making inferences and drawing conclusions which solve problems and answer questions. You must state a problem to solve it, or ask a question to get an answer. Statistics have meaning only in terms of the questions being asked of the data.

Models for Things

Statistical procedures depend on mathematical models. Mathematics treats quantity, form, arrangement, and magnitude logically with precise definitions and consistent rules. Mathematics is as Stevens (27:1) stated, "...a formal, logical, symbolic system—a game of signs and rules." Mathematics has many games, three of which are finite (completely determinable). Arithmetic is the number game. Algebra is the letter game. Geometry is the diagram game. Essentially, arithmetic depends entirely on addition. But you can add in the opposite direction (subtract). You can add a number some number of times (multiply). You can add in the opposite direction some number of times (divide). Arithmetic, algebra, and geometry deal basically with the same ideas in what seem like different ways. Legitimate operations in one form are legitimate in the other two forms so their rules are isomorphic. Figure 1 is an elementary example of their similar processes, or isomorphic operations.

$(a + b)^2 = a^2 + 2ab + b^2$
$(6 + 2)^2 = 36 + 24 + 4$

Multiply a and b separately by a and then by b. Combine the identical terms, ab.

$(a - b)^2 = a^2 - 2ab + b^2$
$(8 - 3)^2 = 64 - 48 + 9$

Each $-ab$ includes b^2 so the $-2ab$ removes b^2 twice— which is once too many times.

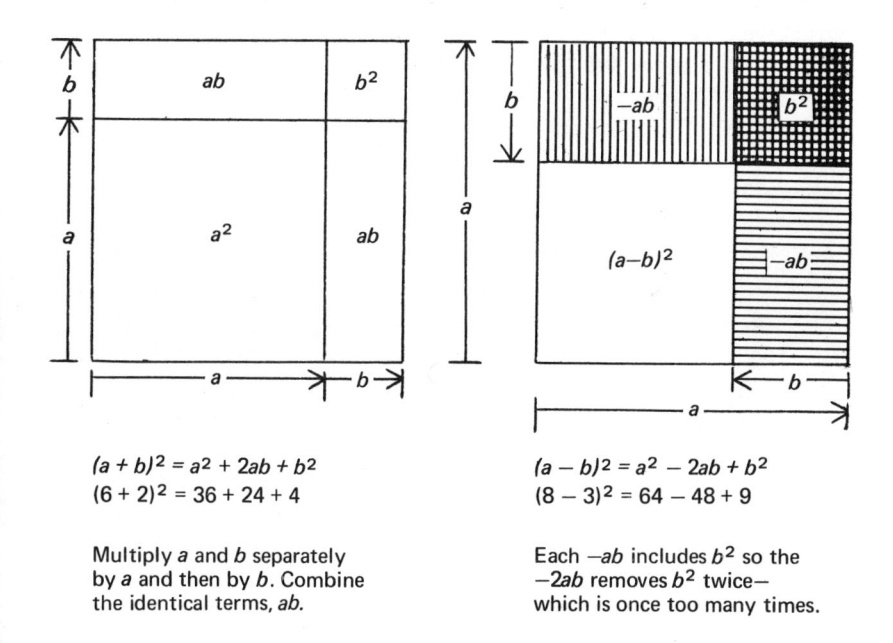

Figure 1. Isomorphic operations.

The left side of Figure 1 shows the components of $(a + b)^2$ when a and b move in the same direction or are "added." You can see that the parts of $(a + b)^2$ are $a(a + b) + b(a + b) = aa + ab + ba + bb = a^2 + 2ab + b^2$. You multiply $a + b$ by a and then by b and then add the parts. The right side of Figure 1 shows the parts of $(a-b)^2$ when a includes b, and $-b$ means move in the opposite direction or "subtract." The parts of $(a-b)^2$ when we multiply as before are $a(a-b) - b(a-b) = aa - ab - ba + bb = a^2 - 2ab + b^2$. Each $-ab$ includes the b^2 area, so $-2ab$ removes b^2 twice, which is once too many, hence the addition of b^2 at the end. The binomial (two-term) squared formulae can be used to find the squares of two-digit numbers by mental arithmetic. For example, $67^2 = (60 + 7)^2 = 3600 + 840 + 49 = 4489$, or $67^2 = (70 - 3)^2 = 4900 - 420 + 9 = 4489$. You can show algebraically that $(a+b)(a-b) = a^2 - b^2$ by multiplying the parts and then adding. Showing this graphically is tricky.

Inspection of Figure 1 should make the essential similarity (isomorphism) of arithmetic, algebraic, and geometric operations obvious. We squared a binomial sum and difference. We could use the same procedures with a polynomial, or n-term combination where n is more than two, but the graph would be more complex. We *squared* the binomial which generated a *plane*, or two-dimensional figure with four equal sides and equal (right) angles. The similarity holds for any rectangle (generalizing) and also for plane figures with unequal angles *if* you reduce them to *independent* dimensions. Independent is synonymous with rectangular or orthogonal. All three words mean basically that moving along one axis, dimension, or continuum involves *no* movement along another axis, dimension, or continuum. However, you would be surprised how many times algebraic proofs in statistics involve quadratics (squares) and how many times these things are basically $a^2 + 2ab + b^2$ or $a^2 - 2ab + b^2$. For example, $s_{\bar{x}_1}^2 + s_{\bar{x}_2}^2 - 2rs_{\bar{x}_1}s_{\bar{x}_2}$ is basically a square of a difference even though you do not know what it means yet.

Human measurements and scores (data) occur as "wholes" which presumably represent combinations of independent parts. So we try to get the component parts out of the whole with mathematical models which seem analogous. Nothing in nature is perfectly square, round, or any other form. Human ingenuity has made the geometric models and their algebraic or arithmetic counterparts available, so we pick the model that seems to fit best and use it. Mathematical models and their statistical counterparts do not rule the universe by some mystical power. They help us reduce nature, human nature, and data to some systematic form *if* we pick the right model and understand what the operations do to the data.

From Nothing To Infinity

Primitive people collected and bartered cows, goats, shells, and wives. Having more goods let them use or trade more without running out.

But primitives stopped when they got down to nothing (0), or turned to stealing and fighting. Having one of something did not permit trading as though you had two, since borrowing one was like stealing. The idea that 0 operated like any other number was a major mathematical discovery. Having 0 located between having one (1) and owing one (−1) permitted starting with 1, moving back 1 to 0 and back 1 more to −1, so $1 - 2 = -1$. The difference between having one and owing one is −2. Emergence from the before-zero era made borrowing, owing, credit, and deficit spending possible. Your relative importance in civilized society depends partly on how much you have, but primarily on how many people you owe. However, including 0 in a consistent number system requires that 0 operate like any other number. Consistent operations with 0 lead to the logical progressions in Table 1.

Parts *a* and *b* of Table 1 should cause no trouble if you think in terms of a linear scale with negative numbers to the left, 0 in the middle, and positive numbers to the right. Then moving to the right (in the + direction) or to the left (− direction) from a given point, 0 distance leaves you where you were, i.e., at 2, or any other given point. In parts *c* and *d*, multiplying 2, or any other number, leads progressively to 0, and dividing 0 by 2 or any other number leaves you with nothing (0). We are generalizing when

TABLE 1. Operations with 0

a) $2 + 2 = 4$ $2 + 1 = 3$ $2 + 0 = 2$	b) $4 - 2 = 2$ $3 - 1 = 2$ $2 - 0 = 2$	c) $2 \times 2 = 4$ $2 \times 1 = 2$ $2 \times 0 = 0$	d) $4 / 2 = 2$ $2 / 2 = 1$ $0 / 2 = 0$
e) $2 / 2 = 1$ $1 / 1 = 1$ $0 / 0 = 1$	f) $1 / .1 = 10$ $1 / .01 = 100$ $1 / .001 = 1000$ $1 / .0001 = 10000$ $\ldots 1 / 0 = \infty =$ infinity	g) $10 / .1 = 100$ $10 / .01 = 1000$ $10 / .001 = 10000$ $10 / .0001 = 100000$ $\ldots 10 / 0 = \infty$	

we say, "or any other number," but the generalizations seem reasonable as far as we have gone. In part *e*, any number divided by itself equals one, so having $0/0 = 1$ makes 0 operate consistently and seems reasonable—but rather odd. The logical progressions in parts *f* and *g* show that as we divide a number, either 1 or 10, by progressively smaller numbers, we get progressively larger numbers. Continuing indefinitely (...) to an "unlimited" limit leads both progressions to a common point, infinity or (∞). We can generalize that any number divided by 0 equals infinity. We have now left the realm of finite mathematics, which in terms of arithmetic, algebra, and geometry seem analogous to tangible things in nature. We have moved to an unfinite or infinite realm where counting definite things seems as unrealistic as counting grains of sand. What do we do? We shift to the "pebble game."

The Pebble Game

To prove may mean to demonstrate beyond a shadow of doubt, but it also means "to test," as in the adage, "The proof of the pudding..." Mathematical proofs test the model and find it sound. Statistical models have primarily algebraic proofs which are simple once you understand defining terms, summation, substituting identities, and the basic rules in the number game. Plane geometry also treats rectilinear and angular relations neatly, but curvilinear relations create a problem and, like some treatments of numbers, get us into the pebble game, or the infinitesimal calculus. The normal curve represents frequencies (numbers of cases) at different distances from the mean and is an ever-changing, bell-shaped curve. One nice round pebble will not fill the bell, so more, smaller pebbles must be used. Using more approximates fills the space better. We could use progressively smaller pebbles until they get infinitesimally small like the finest grains of sand. This would fill the space better, but counting them at different distances from the mean would become an infinitely tedious (and gritty) problem, so we had better stop when we have a reasonable approximation. The infinitesimal calculus provides a method for reaching reasonable approximations.

Let us see quickly how the infinitesimal calculus operates. The formula for a straight line is $Y = a + bX$, where a is the Y-intercept (where the line crosses the Y axis when $X = 0$), and b is the slope of the line, or the rate of change of Y with respect to X. The formula tells us that Y changes proportionately with X ($Y:X$). If $a = 0$ and the slope, $b = 1$, then the line is a 45° diagonal through the intersection of the X and Y axes. Some regularly curved lines can be treated essentially as straight lines (10:Chap. 5). Other curves require the calculus to determine the rate of change of Y with respect to X. The calculus consists of *differentiation*, the analytical portion, and *integration*, the synthesizing or putting together portion. All curves can be graphed, but the calculus starts from algebra—and so must we.

We start with a curve in which $y = x^2$, so y increases with respect to x in an ever-changing 1:1, 4:2, 9:3, 16:4, etc., proportion. We let Δx represent an increment (difference) to be added to x, and Δy an equivalent increment by which y has to change, so our constant relation is:
$$y = x^2$$

We add equal increments to each side: $\quad y + \Delta y = (x + \Delta x)^2$

We square the right hand member: $\quad y + \Delta y = x^2 + 2x\Delta x + \Delta x^2$

We subtract the original equation: $\quad -y \quad = -x^2$

Subtracting leaves equal remainders: $\quad \Delta y = 2x\Delta x + \Delta x^2$

Dividing both by Δx leaves them equal: $\quad \Delta y/\Delta x = 2x + \Delta x$

Our operations thus far have been purely algebraic and strictly legitimate in the finite rule realm. This brings us to the infinitesimal calculus.

If we make the increment by which x changes (Δx) infinitesimally small, it approaches 0, and at the limit it is 0. With $\Delta x = 0$, the Δx in the right hand member becomes 0, so it drops out. Then the instantaneous rate of change of y with respect to x becomes $\Delta y/\Delta x = 2x$. On the left side we have $\Delta y/\Delta x$. You might think that when $\Delta x = 0$, $\Delta y = \infty$. A little knowledge is a dangerous thing. We started with Δy and Δx changing *proportionately*, so *the ratio remains constant*. We have thus *differentiated* $y = x^2$ and gotten $\Delta y/\Delta x = 2x$. This retains the important constant ratio, but it removes the infinitesimally small but previously gritty bit— the Δx on the right side—by reducing it to the limit (0). Substituting on the left side dy/dx indicates that differentiation is completed, so the *derivative* of $y = x^2$ is $dy/dx = 2x$. Eliminating the exponent (the 2 in x^2) makes the ratio linear. You might deduce that differentiation involves simply shifting the exponent (the 2 in x^2) to a coefficient (the 2 in 2x). This is almost right and therefore wrong. However, if $y = x^n$, the derivative of y with respect to x is *always* $dy/dx = nx^{n-1}$. Differentiation can obviously become much more complex, but the operation basically grinds up and sifts out the inconsequential pebbles that would otherwise make the solution impossibly gritty. Peters and Van Voorhis (22: Chap. 1) presented a sound and simple explanation of the pebble game. Having now shown that 0 (nothing) can operate consistently in the calculus, we might generalize that nothing operates consistently in human operations also.

You might try visualizing differentiation. The algebraic operations in differentiation resemble those on the left side of Figure 1. You can consider the distance a on the horizontal axis (abscissa) as equal to x and the abscissa portion b as equal to Δx, or an increment of x. The vertical distance a (ordinate) could represent y, and the ordinate portion b would represent Δy, or the proportionate change in y. Then as the respective b portions (increments) become infinitesimally small, the ab at the right and the ab at the top approach a line with 0 width, and the b^2 in the upper right corner approaches a point with 0 dimensions. If you consider the two lines reduced to one dimension as still "something" and the dot (with 0 dimensions) as essentially "nothing" relative to the two lines, then the two ab portions remain appreciable but the b^2 disappears. Thus as Δy and Δx both approach 0 in a constant ratio, we have left when they reach 0 what started as $2ab$ but becomes $2a$ with no "b" dimension. Since we started by having $a = x$ (and its corresponding y), our visualized differentiation results in $dy/dx = 2x$. You can dump the two ab's into nothingness, if you think in terms of a times 0 equals 0. But if you approach the brink remembering that the ratio $\Delta y/\Delta x$ remains constant, you may jump to the derivative and avoid the quicksand.

Complex curves must be differentiated in parts. Coefficients of x (like the n in nx) are included in differentiation. If $y = 2x^3$, then $dy/dx = 6x^2$. But constants like the y-intercept (the a in $Y = a + bX$) are disregarded in differentiation since you cannot differentiate what does not vary. *Integration* is the reverse of differentiation. The symbol for integration (*S*) is an ancient "s" meaning summate (add). In one sense you add the derivatives with the inconsequential and gritty bits discarded. But you must actually reverse the differentiation process by generating *integrals* with proper coefficients and exponents before adding the parts. Integration is tricky but books on the calculus contain many standard integrals generated by previous calculators. So you pick the appropriate integrals and add them algebraically. All integrals end with "$+c$," which reminds you to add any constants that you disregarded in differentiation. The result is a reasonable approximation without the inconsequentials. Any error in differentiation-integration results in a curve that does not run as it did before. Any child can take a clock apart to analyze it, but putting it together (or synthesizing) it so it runs is tricky. The lost part may be what made it run.

RECIPES FOR RELATIVES

Novices view formulae as mathematical messes for bugging people. Formulae seem formidable, but they really define ideas in shorthand and provide recipes for combining constants and variables systematically to get what you want. Formulae consist solely of constants, variables, and operational symbols. Constants are conversion factors for changing units on one scale to units on another scale, like 1 meter = 39.37 inches, or 1 inch = .0254 meter, or the a and b in $Y = a + bX$ which provide a linear conversion of X to Y. For example, we have Fahrenheit (F), Centigrade (C), and Kelvin (K) scales for temperature. Fahrenheit set up a tube with convenient gradations (degrees) and found that water froze at 32°F and boiled at 212°F, so the difference was 180°F. The French wanted decimal (or base 10) scales for their metric system. One hundred was a convenient number of degrees between the freezing and boiling points of water, so they set the freezing point at 0°C and the boiling point at 100°C. Kelvin wanted an absolute temperature scale with 0°K representing the point at which molecular motion stopped and he used

Centigrade units. He found that absolute zero was approximately $-273°$C. The ratio of Fahrenheit to Centigrade units is $F/C = 180°/100° = 9/5$, and the units cancel when you divide, so this is a "pure ratio." (The reverse ratio is $C/F = 5/9$.) We have a constant difference in the 0 points and a constant ratio for degrees. The conversion is linear so $Y = a + bX$ defines it.

We can substitute $F°$ for Y and $C°$ for X and $Y = a + bX$ becomes $F° = 32° + (9/5)C°$. This formula converts Centigrade temperature to Fahrenheit. The reverse operation, going from $F°$ to $C°$, requires reversing the formula. In algebraic terms, this involves solving $Y = a + bX$ for X. Omitting the steps, this gives $X = (Y - a)/b$. Substituting as before, $Y = F°$ and $X = C°$, the formula becomes $C° = (F° - 32°)/(9/5)$. With the fraction $(9/5)$ in the denominator, we must invert it and multiply, so the formula becomes $C° = 5(F° - 32°)/9$. Normal body temperature is 98.6°F. Substituting this for "F°" gives body temperature in Centigrade degrees (37°C). Adding 273° gives us 310°K, which we could convert back to 98.6°F, if we wished. The F to C and C to F conversion formulae look different because the ratio must be inverted and the order of operations must be reversed. The *last* step in getting $F°$ is adding 32°, which requires first converting $C°$. The *first* step in getting $C°$ is subtracting 32° from $F°$, and then you convert to $C°$. The formula and the constants remain basically the same. They merely look different depending on which way you want to go.

Definition Formulae and Statistical Recipes

Definition formulae are precise, shorthand descriptions of ideas and operations. They are easily read and remembered if you get the right words in the right places and know what they mean. We must first define some terms:

X = any score of a particular kind, a datum.
Y = another particular kind of score, another datum.
$\bar{X}, \bar{Y}$ = a mean or average of X or Y.
x, y = a deviation score, $x = X - \bar{X}$, $y = Y - \bar{Y}$.
n = the number of scores, $(n - 1)$ represents a "degrees of freedom (df)."
r = correlation = a Pearson product-moment correlation.
s = the standard deviation.[1]

---

[1] *SD* often is used to represent the standard deviation.

z = a standard score; z_x, z_y = standard scores from X and Y.
Σ = summate, add.
$/$ = divide.
$\sqrt{\ }$ = extract the square root.

These specify the ingredients of recipes for finding and defining statistics.

Recipes	Definitions
$\bar{X} = \Sigma X/n$	The *mean* is the arithmetic average.
$s_x = \sqrt{\Sigma x^2/(n-1)}$	The *standard deviation* is the root mean squared deviation.
$z_x = x/s_x$	A *standard score* is a deviation score divided by the standard deviation.
$r = \Sigma z_x z_y/n$	A *correlation* is the average product of paired standard scores.

The $\bar{X}$ recipe defines the mean. The s, z, and r recipes are defined relative to the mean or in terms of deviations from the mean. These recipes for relatives provide a family of statistics originating from the mean. Much of elementary and advanced statistics depends on the ideas inherent in these definition formulae. The reasons for using the mean as a base and treating data relative to the mean will be explained later. These definition formulae are wonderfully simple. They seem simply wonderful until you try using them for computations. For example, computing a correlation with the formula, $r = \Sigma z_x z_y/n$, requires computing successively $\bar{X}$, $\bar{Y}$, x's, y's, s_x, s_y, and then z's for each X and Y in order to get the standard score products ($z_x z_y$) to plug into the formula. Computational errors increase with the number and complexity of operations. Means are rarely whole numbers. Retaining decimal fractions for accuracy complicates calculations. Rounding differences to whole numbers introduces rounding errors (e), and $(x + e)^2$ is obviously greater than x^2. The wonderfully simple definition formulae precipitate the uninitiated into a mathematical mess. Much of the confusion and frustration engendered in beginning statisticians arises from defining things in one way and then computing them in a different way so the ideas are lost in the computations.

Computations

Operational formulae simplify computations, avoid rounding errors, and confuse the uninitiated. Computation is simpler and more accurate if a base other than the mean and an average correction for the error of origin is used. Table 2 illustrates this commonly used device. Computing the standard deviation requires determining the appropriate Σx^2. This is simple in part A because the mean is a whole number, 3. The $\Sigma x = 0$ indicates that the mean is the point about which the deviations sum to zero. Squaring and summing gives $\Sigma x^2 = 10$. Parts A, B, and C start with identical scores and arrive at the same $\Sigma x^2 = 10$. Part B uses the raw score 0 as the base. Squared deviations from the wrong base require an average correction for the error of origin, the $-(\Sigma X)^2/n$ portion. Part C involves subtracting a constant (−5) from each score, and then the same operations as in part B give the same answer for the Σx^2. The procedure seems roundabout but it is simpler and more accurate regardless of whether or not the mean is a whole number.

TABLE 2. An Average Correction for the Error of Origin

A) Using $x = X - \bar{X}$			B) Squaring Raw Scores		C) Using $X' = X - \bar{X}$		
X	x	x^2	X	X^2	X	X'	X'^2
5	2	4	5	25	5	0	0
4	1	1	4	16	4	−1	1
3	0	0	3	9	3	−2	4
2	−1	1	2	4	2	−3	9
1	−2	4	1	1	1	−4	16
$\Sigma X = 15$			$\Sigma = 15 \quad 55$		$\Sigma = 15 \quad -10 \quad 30$		
			$\Sigma x^2 = \Sigma X^2 - (\Sigma X)^2/n$		$\Sigma x^2 = \Sigma X'^2 - (\Sigma X')^2/n$		
$\Sigma x = 0$			$= 55 - (15)^2/5$		$= 30 - (-10)^2/5$		
			$= 55 - 45$		$= 30 - 20$		
$\Sigma x^2 = 10$			$\Sigma x^2 = 10$		$\Sigma x^2 = 10$		

One can show by algebraic manipulation that $\Sigma x^2 = \Sigma X^2 - (\Sigma X)^2/n$, so it works with numbers also. Algebraic manipulation can be used to convert the formula for correlation to a simple and accurate basis for computation, $r = \Sigma z_x z_y/n = \Sigma xy/\sqrt{(\Sigma x^2)(\Sigma y^2)}$. You know how to compute Σx^2 simply and accurately. You compute the Σy^2 by the same procedure, except of course, from the Y scores. Then the $\Sigma xy = \Sigma XY - (\Sigma X)(\Sigma Y)/n$. This is the same formula, except that it involves a product rather than a square. Using an average correction for the error of origin thus provides a legitimate shortcut from raw scores—X's or Y's—to their standard deviations, s_x or s_y, and from paired X's and Y's to their correlation, r_{xy}, without the unnecessary intervening steps. You can write the operational formula for r by substituting the equivalents for Σxy, Σx^2, and Σy^2 in the formula above. The result is formidable as you write it or find it in a statistics book. The cookbook recipes for statistical computations look hard. One key to understanding them is to recognize anything that looks like "$-(\Sigma X)^2/n$" is simply an average correction for the error of origin.

Two Statistical Families

We refer to the mean, standard deviation, standard scores, and correlation ($\bar{X}$, s, z, and r) as a family of statistics using the mean as their reference point. This family does things to data relative to the mean and treats data in terms of the *distance* of each score from the mean, or as deviation scores (x's and y's). Several people may get the same score, so the data consist of various frequencies of "same scores" at different distances from the mean. The term "moment" (mass times distance) is used in mechanics and was borrowed in statistics to mean frequencies times distances from the mean. Statistics based on the mean are called "moment measures." Some other statistics belong to this family.

A cruder family of statistics depends on arranging or ranking scores in order as a basis for locating points in the distribution above and below which specific proportions of the cases fall. Differences between adjacent scores are disregarded after they are ranked. The "point measures" are proportionate points in the distribution usually expressed as percentages. Proportions (p) are parts of a whole and sum to 1.00. Percentages (%) have a base of 100 so the percent corresponding to a given p equals $100p$. The central point is the median or middle score above and below which half of the cases fall, or the 50% point where $p = .50$. Other common point measures are the quartiles, Q_1 and Q_3 (the 25% and 75% points), the deciles, D_1 to D_9 (the 10% to 90% points), and the centiles, C_1 to C_{99} (the 1% to 99% points). Point measures have a frugal formulary. All are computed with the same formula which is using P as the desired point and p as the corresponding proportion:

$$P = l + [(pn - \Sigma f_b)/f_w]i$$

You have to start inside the parentheses and then move to the brackets which are more inclusive parentheses.

This formula resembles $Y = a + bX$ since it is basically a linear interpolation formula. You arrange whatever number (n) of cases or scores you have in ascending order or in step intervals of equal size (i). You pick the desired point (P) and multiply by the corresponding p to get pn, the proportion of cases or scores below that point. Then you locate the pnth score or the interval in which it falls, subtract the cumulative frequency, or all scores below that interval (Σf_b), and divide by the frequency within that interval (f_w). This indicates how far up the interval the pnth case or score falls. Multiplying by i converts the ratio to raw score units. Adding this to the lower limit (l) of the interval gives the raw score equivalent to the desired P (by linear interpolation).

Finding the centile (C) that is equivalent to a specific raw score is the reverse of finding the raw score that corresponds to a desired point measure. Each score occupies an interval in the distribution, either alone or with other scores that are the same. You consider each score as being at the middle of its interval (or itself). Each score represents $100/n$ percent of the total number (n). Then the centile equivalent (C) of any score is the percent of scores exceeded plus one-half the percent of the scores equalled. The formula in terms of the symbols above is:

$$C = 100(\Sigma f_b/n) + 100(.5 f_w/n), \text{ or simply } C = 100(\Sigma f_b + .5 f_w)/n$$

The two formulae are identical but the second is easier to use—if you start inside the parentheses.

The formulae for P and C start with the same thing, Σf_b and f_w, but lead to different results. This can be confusing. The key for the operations is to start inside the parentheses. The key for understanding is to know where you are going and how to get there. P is going toward a raw score equivalent to a desired percentage of the distribution. C is going toward a percentage (centile) corresponding to a specific raw score. P and C both start from a frequency distribution but disregard any gaps between adjacent scores. P leads to a raw score. C leads to a percentage. You arrive at a point corresponding to the one you started from but on different scales. Statistical operations can lead to a cul de sac or confusion unless you know what you want, can pick the right shortcuts, and can locate the secret doors without falling in the moat.

Proportions: How Much From Where

Temperature is measured from three different reference points in two different units. Absolute zero was set where molecular motion stops by Lord Kelvin to make expansion of gases and metals directly commensurate (proportional) with temperature. Geographic elevations are measured from an arbitrary zero set at mean low tide level. Human height and weight start from absolute zeroes. Other human measurements and test scores have arbitrary units and arbitrary zeroes. Thus the difference between the lowest score and zero depends simply on the units of measurement and what the poorest performer did on the test. The arbitrary zeroes and differing units make the different kinds of human data highly incommensurate and ambiguous. They need a common reference point (or 0) and common units to have any standard meaning.

The mean of a fairly large and representative sample tends to be stable. Considerable ambiguity can be removed from data by using the mean as the reference point, or as 0. This does not solve the units problem. Human measures and scores still appear highly variable if the units are small, and relatively invariable if the units are large. Measuring the same thing in inches or millimeters makes them appear more variable than measuring in feet or meters. Measures also differ depending on how variable people are in the same units. Standing height is much more variable than the length of the forearm or the width of the head *in inches*. The best assumption is that people are equally variable regardless of the units used in measuring or scoring. The standard deviation (s) can be used as the standard unit of variability, since it has a definite meaning. Then a difference from the mean ($x = X - \bar{X}$) divided by s gives a *standard score*, or z score ($z = x/s$). This is a pure ratio, since x and s are in the same units and the units cancel in division. Thus z, or standard scores, have the same meaning regardless of the units of measurement. You may remember that a correlation can be computed without actually computing each $z_x z_y$, but the data are treated as though both measures were in standard score units. This does *not* mean that $z_x = z_y$ however. Using the mean as the base and the standard deviation as a standard unit solves the how-much-from-where problem for human data. Standard scores make human data relatively meaningful.

Humans create another problem. No one wants to be average, and no one is in all things. People dislike getting zero, and the half with –z scores like even less being obviously subnormal. People also dislike computations with negative numbers and decimal fractions. So z scores are generally converted as a concession to people. Such conversions set $\bar{X} = 50$ units. A common conversion sets z or $s = 10$ units. The range from 0 to 100 units then equals $10(z)$ or $10(s)$. Having 10 units for each z or s and a 10 z or s range provides a "10-based" or T score. Then a linear conversion of raw scores can be made by using $T = 50 + 10(z)$, or $T = 50 + 10(X - \bar{X})/s$. Other conversions differ in the coefficient (multiplier) for z. Note the $Y = a - bX$ type of formula.

Some distributions of human data are skewed, with scores bunching at one end and tailing off markedly at the other end. Using a logarithmic (base-10) scale will sometimes normalize the distribution—make it look like a normal curve. Any distribution, regardless of its shape, can be normalized by converting the scores to centile equivalents, then to z scores, and then to T scores (10:65–69). These are sometimes called "McCall's T scores." This conversion is nonlinear in that the raw score increments and z increments are not proportional over the range of scores. This normalizes any distribution, which is sometimes useful, although having two types of T scores is confusing.

VARIABILITY

People, data, and statistics generally vary. Individuals obviously differ from each other, or exhibit *inter*individual differences. Individuals also change, or exhibit *intra*individual differences. Inherently invariable and never erratic individuals cannot adapt or learn and remain imbeciles. Individuals may develop relatively consistent performances but still exhibit some random or chance variation, although persistent unadaptive inconsistency is spasticity. We are told frequently that we must consider individual differences, and assured dogmatically that something must be done about them. Those who vociferously advocate taking individual differences into consideration practically never specify which type presumably demands our immediate and exclusive consideration. Failure to specify leaves uncertain whether we should accept, reject, maximize, minimize, or merely consider among-people, within-people, and chance variability.

Scientists and statisticians have been working with, if not always doing something about, interindividual (among people), intraindividual (within people), and random (chance) variability for decades. Their work has tended to bifurcate (follow forked paths), depending on whether their primary concern was the causes of changes within people or the relationship of differences among people. This bifurcation has led to what seems a "forked tongue" approach until you determine which path they have followed. The key to the bifurcation is relatively simple—once you understand some mathematical models for variability and their utilization in statistical operations.

The Normal Curve Model

Extensive empirical evidence has shown that many kinds of human data and some statistics tend to distribute in a bell-shaped, normal curve form. The normal curve is basically a random error curve where the probability (P) of an event or error occurring is .5 and the improbability (Q) is also .5. Expanding $P + Q$ to the nth power, or $(P + Q)^n$, generates coefficients of PQ like the 1, 2, 1 in $1a^2 + 2ab + 1b^2$. When $n = 10$, the coefficients are: 1, 10, 45, 120, 210, 252, 210, 120, 45, 10, 1. The coefficients change systematically as n increases. The first and last are always 1. The second and next to last are always n. The rest are maximal in the middle, symmetrical, and progress in nonlinear steps toward the tails. Deriving a continuous function requires the calculus. The frequently quoted formula for the height of the ordinate (y) of the normal curve at any distance (z) from the mean looks elegant mathematically (10:189). But it is difficult to interpret. An inelegant formula with three easily interpreted factors is: $y =$

$(ni/s)(1/\sqrt{2\pi})(1/\sqrt{e^{z^2}})$. This also looks formidable, so we start inside the parentheses to see how it works.

The first factor (ni/s) is a constant for any distribution having n scores, a step interval (i), and a standard deviation (s). This first factor is customarily omitted, but you need it to compute expected frequencies ($\tilde{Y}$'s) for actual distributions. The remaining factors define the "unit normal curve" which has $n = 1$ and $s = 1$ (although s is replaced with σ, since this is a "population" standard deviation). The second factor, $(1/\sqrt{2\pi})$, is a constant (.3989). This represents the height of the ordinate (y) at the mean. This occurs because $z = 0$ (at the mean), so in the third factor when $z = 0$, $z^2 = 0$. Anything to the zero power equals 1 (including e), so the third factor reduces to $1/1 = 1$ at the mean. This makes the ordinate at the mean of the unit normal curve, $y = .3989$. The third factor $(1/\sqrt{e^{z^2}})$ actually generates the curve and is less formidable than it looks. The e is another constant, 2.7183, which is the base of Naperian or "natural" logarithms and has some special virtues in the calculus. Consequently, what actually makes y change is the z^2 under the radical. The relation is inverse, so y decreases as z increases. The ordinate (y) begins its descent slowly and then accelerates downward, while z is fractional and approaches 1.00, where $y = .2420$. This portion of the curve is concave downward, like an umbrella. The curvature changes to convex downward beyond $z = 1.00$ and continues asymptotically to infinity (approaching but never reaching 0).

Computing the normal curve ordinates (y) at specific standard score distances (z) is easy with logarithms, but unnecessary since most statistics books contain the ordinates tabled in .01 (z) increments. They also list the corresponding areas ($\propto$) from the mean to each z and from the z to the end of the infinitely long tail. The areas indicate the proportion of cases one would expect from the mean to z, or beyond it in the tail. Half (.5000) of the cases fall on either side of the mean, so the mean is equal to the median *in a normal curve*, although they differ numerically in actual distributions. A quarter (.2500) of the cases fall between the mean and .6745(z), so $Q_1 = \bar{X} - .6745(s)$ and $Q_3 = \bar{X} + .6745(s)$ *in a normal distribution*. The proportion of cases from the mean to 1.00(z) on either side is .3413, so .6826 falls between $\pm$ 1.00(z) or $\pm$ 1.00(s). Beyond 1.96(z) you find .0250 of the cases in the tail; beyond 2.58(z) you find .0050, and beyond 3.00(z) you find .0013 (13 in 10,000).

The normal curve is basically a random error curve. It has become a statistical holy figure with pseudo-miraculous powers and the relations of P to z have become holy numbers simply because they are useful. You might remember 1.96 and 2.58 because you will see them shortly. More important, remember that the chance probability (P) *decreases* as the distance from the mean (z) *increases*. All tests of significance, of which z

is the prototype, operate on the principle that the chance probability decreases as the significance test statistic increases.

Student's *t* Model

An ingenious amateur statistician (28), using the pseudonym "Student" to keep his business associates unaware of his hobby, became interested in the distributions of small samples. He found that the distributions became more platykurtic (lower and broader like a duck-billed platypus) as the number of cases decreased. The progressively lower and broader distributions with decreasing cases upset the normal curve probabilities associated with z distances from the mean. So he invented a new statistic, t, and prepared tables of t corresponding to selected probabilities. These are similar to z in that P decreases as t increases, and they converge at infinity where the probability of cases in the tail is .0250 for z or $t = 1.96$, and .0050 for z or $t = 2.58$. But as the sample gets smaller the value of t for any specific P, such as .0250 or .0050, *increases*—slowly at first and then rapidly when the sample gets very small. This produces a two-way stretch—t increases as P decreases, and t must also increase as the sample size decreases. Thus z is the limit of t, and t for a specific P is always larger than z except with an infinite number of cases.

You need the *degrees of freedom* (df) to enter the t table. The degrees of freedom represent the opportunity of data to vary—an accurate and ambiguous definition. You would expect heads (H) and tails (T) half of the time by chance in flipping a coin, so the probability of each is .5. Using H and T for the sides of one coin and H' and T' for the other, flipping the pair together gives an equal probability of getting HH', HT', TH', and TT', or $P = .25$ for each. The total is 1.00 or certainty, and the probability in four flips is 1 for both heads, 2 for mixed H and T, and 1 for both tails, like the 1, 2, 1 coefficients of $(P + Q)^2$. Flipping the pair 20 times would give the *expected* combinations as illustrated below. You

	H	T	Total
H'	5	5	10
T'	5	5	10
Total	10	10	20

might not actually get 5 of each combination, but the border totals of 10 H and 10 T for each coin should remain the same if the coins are unbiased. We will impose the reasonable restriction of equal border totals. Copy the table with the border totals but *without* the cell entries (the four 5's). Put any number (n) between 0 and 10 in *one* cell. You must then put $10 - n$ in the other column or row cell, and n in the diagonal cell if the row and column sums (border totals) are to remain the same. Having four empty cells makes it appear that the four n's might vary, or as though you had four degrees of freedom in choosing n's. But the restriction of equal border totals reduced the degrees of freedom in this 2×2 table to one. The degrees of freedom in $n \times n$ tables are $(k-1)(r-1)$, using k for columns and r for rows. You can try this with a 3×3 table and you will find that four entries determine the other five *if* the border totals remain constant.

Returning to t, using the mean ($\bar{X}$) as a constant (parameter) in computing the standard deviation (s) puts one restriction on the opportunity of the data to vary. A *parameter* is a limiting constant or a population statistic. You lose one degree of freedom for each parameter (constant) that you use in computing a statistic. Thus in using $\bar{X}$ as a constant in computing s, you lose a degree of freedom, so Σx^2 is divided by $(n-1)$ to get the root mean squared deviation. In another sense, an s from a sample tends to underestimate the population standard deviation (σ) and using $(n-1)$ in place of n tends to correct for this, so s becomes a better estimate of σ. If $n = 100$, dividing the Σx^2 by 99 rather than 100 has little effect, but the effect of the reduced divisor increases as n decreases. You must have at least two measurements to compute a mean and standard deviation and with $n = 2$, the $df = 1$. Formulae usually indicate the correct degrees of freedom (in parentheses containing n).

The t model is basically the normal curve with z adjusted upward for samples of any size, however small. Using the normal curve (via z) for comparing means required large samples until Student defined the t distribution and gave some representative value in 1908. He refined the proof and gave t values for df from 1 to 20 in 1925 (29). Fisher extended the table for df (labelled "n") up to 30 (12:139), when he advocated using "efficient" and "sufficient" statistics for precise estimates of chance probability (P) from small samples. Using t in place of z for estimating P removed the large sample limitation and accelerated experimental research tremendously. Now we need to see how this is done.

Standard Errors

Statistics are numerical facts derived from data which are in turn derived from samples. A population is all people of the same kind. Measuring a population is virtually impossible. Every individual in the population has an equal opportunity to appear in a random sample. Difficulty sometimes arises in locating all subjects in a random sample and getting their cooperation. The mean of a random sample ($\bar{X}$) and standard deviation (s) may approximate the population mean (μ) and standard deviation (σ). But selecting a second random sample gives a different $\bar{X}$ and s. You might draw 100 random samples of the same size and get a distribution of means and standard deviations. Averaging the $\bar{X}$'s and s's would give a better approximation of μ and σ. The standard deviation of the $\bar{X}$'s and s's would indicate how much these statistics varied by chance, or sampling. We could call the standard deviation of the means the *standard error of the mean* ($s_{\bar{x}}$) and that for the standard deviation the standard error of the standard deviation (s_s) since this would indicate how much they varied, or were in error, by chance. We would not know what the parameters μ and σ were, but we would know how much our sample statistics varied—by an extremely tedious process. We already know that data and statistics vary and that random variables tend to distribute normally, or according to the more platykurtic t distribution if they are small samples. We might try another approach.

In the absence of anything better, the best estimate of a parameter is the statistic in hand. The best estimate of variability is the obtained s, which is numerically large or small depending on the units of measurement and how much the thing measured on people varies in these units. The means of random samples should vary proportionately with our "best estimate," or with s. We would expect greater differences by chance between sample means when s is large than when s is small, simply because we measured in relatively small units. Thus having standard error of the mean proportional to s, or $s_{\bar{x}}:s$, seems reasonable. This does not mean that $s_{\bar{x}} = s$, however.

The probability of getting a single score on one side or the other of μ is $1/2$, and the probability of n scores all on one side of μ is $(1/2)^n$. If we take $(1/2)^2 = 1/4$ and $(1/2)^4 = 1/16$, we see that the relation of probable unlikelihood of all from one side is inverse and exponential—P quadruples as n doubles. We might resort to the calculus, but we might use some backward logic: if squaring n quadruples the unlikelihood, taking the square root of n should double the unlikelihood. So means of samples four times as large should be half as variable, or $s_{\bar{x}}:1/\sqrt{n}$. Combining $s_{\bar{x}}:s:1/\sqrt{n}$ gives $s_{\bar{x}} = s/\sqrt{n}$. We thus arrive by mathematically inelegant methods at the actual formula for estimating the variability of means of successive samples of the same size based on the s and n of the sample in hand. The estimate *is* legitimate mathematically and very convenient.

We can generalize that estimation of the chance variability of a statistic is possible on the basis of the variability of the data on which the statistic depends and the number of cases. We call these estimates standard errors and designate them with a variability symbol (s) and a subscript representing the particular statistic. The formula for the standard error of the mean is sometimes given as $s_{\bar{x}} = s/\sqrt{n-1}$ rather than $s_{\bar{x}} = s/\sqrt{n}$. You use $\sqrt{n-1}$ in estimating the standard error if you found s by the formula $s = \sqrt{\Sigma x^2/n}$, rather than $s = \sqrt{\Sigma x^2/(n-1)}$. You can also find the standard error of the mean directly, since $s_{\bar{x}} = \sqrt{\Sigma x^2/n(n-1)}$. Correlation ($r$) can be separated into a proportion of the variance of one test related to, or explained by, the other (r^2) and a proportion of unrelated or unexplained variance ($1 - r^2$). The standard error of a correlation is $s_r = (1 - r^2)/\sqrt{n-1}$. You use a correction for the sample size, $n - 1$, in the denominator because r is computed without the correction originally. The standard error of a standard deviation is $s_s = s/\sqrt{2n}$. You use $2n$ because n is involved first in computing s from the data and again in computing the standard error, or because someone found that this gave the best estimate of the variability of s. Statisticians have generated standard errors for most statistics, and all of them depend on an estimate of random error and the number of cases.

The Confidence Interval

The confidence interval has also been called the fiducial limits. We do not know what the population mean (μ) might be. We know what our sample mean is ($\bar{X}$). We can estimate how much it varies by chance ($s_{\bar{x}}$). The t distribution describes the random fluctuation of means of samples with various degrees of freedom. We use this information to estimate the interval or limits within which we would expect the population mean to fall by working backward from what we know. We select a probability of 1 in 20 (.05) or 1 in 100 (.01). Some tables list these under $P = .025$ and .005. These are "one-tailed" tables, or give the area in one tail of the curve. If you want to use $P = .05$, you look at the bottom of the table for ∞ and use the column above 1.96 (1.95996), or 2.58 for $P = .01$. You take the t in the desired column and in the row for the degrees of freedom (df). You multiply this by the $s_{\bar{x}}$ which converts it to raw score units. Then you add the product, $t(s_{\bar{x}})$, to $\bar{X}$ and subtract it from $\bar{X}$. The $\bar{X} - t(s_{\bar{x}})$ gives the point *above* which you would expect μ to fall, and the $\bar{X} + t(s_{\bar{x}})$ gives the point *below* which you would expect μ to fall 5% (or 1%) of the time by chance alone. In other words, you have found the confidence interval.

This is easier to understand if you make yourself a visual aid. Draw a horizontal line about 3 inches long and label a point in the middle $\bar{X}$ to represent the obtained mean. About 1.5 inches either side of $\bar{X}$, erect vertical lines about an inch high. Then draw a half of a bell-shaped curve from each vertical toward $\bar{X}$ so the curves intersect above $\bar{X}$ and a small part of each curve, the "tail," is beyond $\bar{X}$ on each side. Consider each tail as representing .025 (or .005) of the area under each half-curve. Label the left vertical μ_1 and the right vertical μ_2. The verticals then represent limits within which you would expect μ to fall .95 (95%) of the time (or .99 = 99% of the time) on the basis of chance alone. This does not determine what the population mean (μ) is, but it indicates the limits within which you could expect it to fall with some specified confidence—95 or 99 times in 100 simply by chance.

CR and t

The heading sounds like the name of a railroad. The preceding material presumably got you on the track to move statistically. Suppose you measure two samples of subjects and compute $\bar{X}_1$, $\bar{X}_2$, s_1, and s_2. Having $\bar{X}_1 = \bar{X}_2$ is extremely unlikely. You might wonder whether they were random samples from a homogeneous population or samples from different populations. You might select two groups, preferably randomly, give one some treatment and the other no treatment, and then measure both groups. You would then face the question of whether the means of the two groups differed simply because of sampling error, or whether the treated group seemed to represent a sample from a different population because of the treatment. In other words, did the treatment produce a sufficient change within the treated subjects on the average to make them appear different from the untreated (control) group? The alternative is that the apparent difference resulted from sampling error. You have the ingredients for making a sound judgment statistically; now you need the recipe.

The Critical Ratio (CR) was defined long ago as a mean difference divided by the standard error of the mean difference, or as a recipe: $CR = (\bar{X}_1 - \bar{X}_2)/s_{\bar{x}_1 - \bar{x}_2}$. The CR was formerly used with large samples and the normal curve probabilities by way of z. The same formula is now used with the t distribution which corrects for sample size. Computing the numerator, $\bar{X}_1 - \bar{X}_2$, is a simple matter of subtraction. The standard error of the mean difference in the denominator, $s_{\bar{x}_1 - \bar{x}_2}$, presents a problem—fortunately solvable. We can estimate the random variation of each mean by computing its standard error from s_1 and n_1, and s_2 and n_2. But a standard error is a square root quantity, $s_{\bar{x}} = \sqrt{\Sigma x^2/n(n-1)}$. Combining square root quantities requires squaring them, adding them, and taking the square root. But rather than actually computing $s_{\bar{x}_1}$ and $s_{\bar{x}_2}$, and then squaring, adding, and extracting the root, you can add $\Sigma x_1^2/n_1(n_1 - 1)$ and $\Sigma x_2^2/n_2(n_2 - 1)$, and extracting the square root gives $s_{\bar{x}_1 - \bar{x}_2}$, the standard error of the mean difference. A correction is necessary if the two samples are different in size ($n_1 \neq n_2$), and we have skipped some other intricacies. However, you divide the mean difference by the standard error of the mean difference. Then you enter the t table with $df = n_1 + n_2 - 2$, since you lost a degree of freedom by using each mean as a parameter (constant). If the obtained t exceeds the table value at the .05 level (or .01), the probability of a mean difference this large occurring simply from sampling error is less than .05 (or .01), so you say that the difference was significant at the .05 (or .01) level. Being "significant" means that a difference this large would result from sampling error 5% (or 1%) of the time, so it seems relatively unlikely.

Having an obtained t exceed the table value indicates that its occurrence by chance was unlikely, but unlikely occurrences still occur 5% of the time at the .05 level and 1% of the time at the .01 level. Rejecting the hypothesis of no difference except chance (or null hypothesis) permits accepting the alternative hypothesis that the treatment had a real effect. Rejecting the null hypothesis when it is true is a "Type I" error. Failure to reject it when it is false is a "Type II" error. Either logical error is possible in testing hypotheses. Redoing (replicating) the experiment with other samples provides more assurance, provided the results are similar.

The full formula for the standard error of the mean difference is

$$s_{\bar{x}_1 - \bar{x}_2} = \sqrt{s_{\bar{x}_1}^2 + s_{\bar{x}_2}^2 - 2r s_{\bar{x}_1} s_{\bar{x}_2}}.$$

This is basically a square of a difference $(a^2 - 2ab - b_2)$. But computing a correlation (r) is impossible if the two samples are independent, since r depends on paired scores. The best assumption with independent groups is that r = 0 and thus $2r s_{\bar{x}_1} s_{\bar{x}_2} = 0$. But if the same subjects are tested before and after a treatment, you have paired scores—an X_1 and X_2 for each subject—and the full formula applies. If $s_{\bar{x}_1} = s_{\bar{x}_2}$, and $r = 1$, then $s_{\bar{x}_1}^2 + s_{\bar{x}_2}^2 = 2r s_{\bar{x}_1} s_{\bar{x}_2}$. You can substitute any number (preferably between 2 and 9 to keep the arithmetic simple) for both $s_{\bar{x}}$'s and you will find, for example, that $3^2 + 3^2 - 2(9) = 0$. So if $r = 1.00$, $s_{\bar{x}_1 - \bar{x}_2} = 0$, and any mean difference, $\bar{X}_1 - \bar{X}_2$, divided by 0 equals ∞, or $t = \infty$. And with $t = \infty$, the probability of finding a t this large on the basis of sampling error is zero. In other words, if a treatment affects all subjects in exactly the same way and by exactly the same amount and you have no measurement error, then $r = 1.00$. If $r = 1.00$, then you have left the realm of sampling error and your best prediction would be the certainty that this treatment would affect *any* person in the same way and by the same amount. This is an ideal condition which can only be approximated in experimental work.

Computing the full formula for paired scores would be extremely tedious, except for a convenient shortcut. If you let the difference between any pair of scores = D, then $\bar{D} = \bar{X}_1 - \bar{X}_2$, or the mean difference equals the difference between the means. Then if you let $d = D - \bar{D}$, or the difference of any paired score from the mean difference, you can simply compute ΣD and ΣD^2 and use the error-of-origin correction, so $\Sigma d^2 = \Sigma D^2 - (\Sigma D)^2/n$. Then

$$s_{\bar{x}_1-\bar{x}_2} = \sqrt{\Sigma d^2/n(n-1)} = \sqrt{s_{\bar{x}_1}^2 + s_{\bar{x}_2}^2 - 2rs_{\bar{x}_1}s_{\bar{x}_2}}.$$

This may seem amazing but algebraic manipulation shows that it is sound. However, if the treatment reversed the relative position of the subjects on the second test, the test would be maximally unreliable and the $-2rs_{\bar{x}_1}s_{\bar{x}_2}$ would become positive, double the radicand, increase the standard error of the mean difference, and make finding t significant extremely improbable.

The standard error of the mean difference is in the same units of measurement as the mean difference, so the t ratio is a "pure" ratio independent of the units of measurement. The diagram for the confidence interval with changed labels is a suitable visual aid if you want to see how the t ratio works. Label the left vertical line $\bar{X}_1$ and the right one $\bar{X}_2$ to represent the two obtained means. The two half-bell shaped curves represent the respective estimated distributions of means of samples of the same size. The overlapping tails represent the "two-tailed" probability. Moving the means apart, with the curves fixed, reduces the overlap of the two tails and reduces the probability of the mean difference resulting from sampling error.

The virtue of *tests of significance*, like the "critical" and t ratios, lies in the fact that random or chance variation in statistics, such as $\bar{X}$ and s, *tend* to distribute normally, or according to the t distribution when sample size is considered. The means and standard deviations tend *strongly* to distribute according to t even though the data or population distributions are skewed. Thus t provides a sound model and as Box (3, 4, 5) and Boneau (2) put it, a "robust" model for testing small sample statistics IF the subjects are randomly assigned to treatments. But t has limited utility. With n groups given different treatments, including one no-treatment (control) group, you have $n(n-1)/2$ mean differences. Testing each mean difference separately with t runs considerable risk of finding two means significantly different simply because the variability about these means (s within these groups) happens to be minimal. Pooling the within-group variability on which the estimate of error variance is based helps avoid artifacts, or spurious facts. The method with pooled error variance is analysis of variance, commonly called ANOVA.

ANOVA

You should know by now that s, $s_{\bar{x}}$, and $s_{\bar{x}_1-\bar{x}_2}$ can be computed without actually computing a mean. Means can be computed later using $\Sigma X_a/n_a$,

$\Sigma X_b/n_b$, etc. if you need them. Analysis of variance, or ANOVA, provides a method of testing for significant differences between two or more means simultaneously without actually computing the means being tested. Another advantage, aside from the shortcut, is that a pooled, within-group variance is used as the estimate of error variance, which tends to avoid the artifact previously noted. Testing mean differences without actually determining the means sounds mysterious, but it is a simple idea if you look at it the right way. The visual aid is Figure 2.

```
Treatment
                        X̄_t                    X̄_t
                         :                      :
    A           ........:..X̄..........    .....:..........X̄...
                         :                      :
    B           ..........X̄.:...........    ......:..X̄...
                            :                      :
    C           ..........X̄..:........      ...X̄..:..
                             :                     :
    D    .........X̄..........:        ...X̄...     :
                        X̄_t                    X̄_t

               Nonsignificant                Significant
```

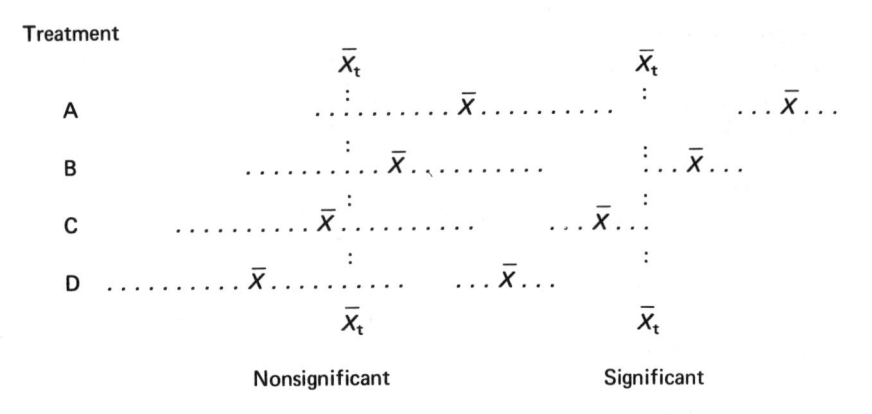

Figure 2. Effect of within-group variance on significance.

Figure 2 represents two possible outcomes of applying three experimental treatments (A, B, C) and no treatment (D) to randomly selected groups. The distribution of scores in each group is represented by dots. The difference in the length of the lines merely indicates that within-group or random variance is large on the left side and small on the right side. The means of the four groups ($\bar{X}_a$, etc.) are equally spaced on the left and right side, so the mean differences are identical. But the within-group variance on the left has considerable overlap, while that on the right has relatively little. The mean differences on the left have so much overlapping random (error) variance that they seem to originate from sampling error, so we labeled them "nonsignificant," or probable on the basis of chance. The same mean differences on the right have so little error variance that they seem to have resulted from the different treatments, so we called them "significant," or highly improbable on the basis of sampling error.

That is a lot to see in one little figure. But the basic ideas are: 1) that means represent the effect of treatments, so mean differences represent the differing effects of treatments; 2) that raw score mean differences provide no sound basis for determining whether the differences might have resulted from sampling error or whether the treatments made the groups appear to come from different "populations;" and 3) that this decision depends on *both* the mean differences *and* the random (error) variation within the groups. These ideas are basic to analysis of variance and also to experimental research. Experimental research with people involves treating groups in various specified ways to determine whether sufficient within-people changes result so the data act as though the groups come from different populations. ANOVA answers the sampling-error versus different-population question.

The vertical line $\bar{X}_t$ in Figure 2 represents the total mean or the mean of all the scores. This provides a base for computing the total sum of squared deviations, SS_T or Σx_T^2. This SS_T is separated into two parts (in a one-way ANOVA), a sum of squared deviations of the treatment means about the total mean, or a sum of squares between (i.e., "among") groups, SS_B, and a sum of squared deviations of the subjects within the groups about their treatment means, SS_W. The basic formula for a one-way ANOVA is:

$$SS_T = SS_B + SS_W \text{ or } \Sigma x_T^2 = \Sigma x_B^2 + \Sigma x_W^2$$

The total sum of squares in more complex ANOVAS is separated into more parts, but the basic equation above simply means that a total sum of squares can be separated into an effect of treatments portion (SS_B or Σx_B^2) and a within-groups or among-subjects portion (SS_W or Σx_W^2). The treatments produce changes within subjects, or average "within-people" changes, and the "within-groups" or "among-people" variation about the treatment mean is the source of "error" variance—as you will see shortly. A *variance* is a sum of squared deviations about a mean divided by the appropriate degrees of freedom, such as SS_B/df_B, SS_W/df_W, and also s^2.

The formulae for a one-way ANOVA in Table 3 are the recipes for computing the mean squares or variances for the situation graphed in Figure 2. The subscripts, *a, b, c, d*, represent the groups having treatments A, B, C, D, with 10 subjects per group. You should note that *all* of the formulae depend basically on sums of raw scores, ΣX, sums of squared raw scores, ΣX^2, and sums of raw scores squared, $(\Sigma X)^2$—along with the appropriate n's. All of the formulae contain an error-of-origin correction (similar to "$-(\Sigma X)^2/n$") because the sums and squares are from the "wrong base." The Total and Between sums of squares (SS_T and SS_B) use the *same* correction because their base is the "total mean." The Within SS uses the same formula as the Total SS, but the error-of-origin corrections for *each* within-group SS differ because each within-group SS uses the mean of *its* group as the base. The Within SS is the source of the "pooled error variance" after it is divided by the degrees of freedom (df). If you compare the formulae, you will find that the separate within-group, error-of-origin quantities are summed to get the "raw-score" Between (treatments) SS before the total error-of-origin correction is subtracted. The reason for this peculiar operation is that a sum of scores acts like its mean because $\bar{X} = \Sigma X/n$, so $n\bar{X} = \Sigma X$, except that you have to use an error-of-origin correction.

TABLE 3. One-way ANOVA Formulae

Variance Source	Sum of Squares, SS	Degrees of Freedom, df	Mean Square MS
Total	$\Sigma x_t^2 = \Sigma X_t^2 - (\Sigma X_t)^2/n_t$	$n_t - 1 = 39$*	
Between	$\Sigma x_B^2 = (\Sigma X_a)^2/n_a + ... + (\Sigma X_d)^2/n_d - (\Sigma X_t)^2/n_t$	$T - 1 = 3$**	SS_B/df
Within	$\Sigma x_W^2 = \Sigma X_a^2 - (\Sigma X_a)^2/n_a + ... + \Sigma X_d^2 - (\Sigma X_d)^2/n_d$	$n_t - T = 36$	SS_W/df

* Using $n_a = n_b = n_c = n_d = 10$; so the total number $n_t = 40$.
** Using four treatments, so Treatments $= T = 4$.

ANOVA computations depend basically on computing the sums of scores and the sums of squared scores *for each group separately*. This generates a major labeling and identification problem in complex ANOVAS. The next step involves combining the various sums of scores and squares in different ways to get the various corrected sums of squares you want. This is a complex mental maze—with pitfalls if you mix your labels or get confused about how the recipe combines ingredients. If you can avoid the pitfalls of operational and computational mistakes, you come out with various sums of squares (SS) which are divided by their corresponding degrees of freedom (df) to get the respective mean squares (MS) or variances. So what? The basic purpose of any ANOVA is to separate a meaningless total variance into its component parts. A simple one-way ANOVA separates the total variance into a between ("among") treatments component and a within-groups (or among-people within groups) component. The "Between" (MS_B) component represents the effects of the treatments, and the "Within" (MS_W) component represents random (among-people) variation, which is used as "error variance." You want to determine whether or not the treatments made the people on-the-average appear to come from different populations, so you divide the "treatment effect" (MS_B) by the "error variance" (MS_W) and you get a "variance ratio."

A variance ratio, such as MS_B/MS_W (or s_1^2/s_2^2), can be evaluated with the F distribution. Technically, $F =$ Larger MS/Smaller MS, and is "one-tailed," since such a ratio would always be equal to or greater than 1.00. But if the error variance (MS_W) in an ANOVA is greater than the treatment effect (MS_B), then any mean differences are obviously the result of sampling error. So the treatment MS is usually divided by the error MS and any fractional F is obviously not significant, or the result of sampling error. You enter the F table with the df of the numerator (3 in the example) and go down that column until you come to the row with the df of the denominator. You find two numbers at the intersection of the column and row. The smaller number is the value of F probable from random variation .05 of the time; the larger number is the value by chance .01 of the time. An obtained F larger than the table value is *less* probable by chance and thus considered significant at the .05 or .01 point.

We used a one-way ANOVA with four treatments as an example in Figure 2 so the basic formulae in Table 3 and the basic principles could be kept reasonably simple. One of the treatments was a no-treatment or control situation. Using progressive levels of the same treatment with none as the lowest level would make this a *functional* design where the question is *how* successive levels of the same treatment affect performance. Figure 2 shows a perfectly rectilinear trend of the means, which would be unlikely in actual data. A curvilinear trend is possible. Submaximal treatments might improve performance but maximal treatments might be significantly worse than no treatment. Further analysis of the partitioned variance could be made to determine whether the mean trend, or progression of means, was rectilinear or curvilinear. This is called *trend analysis*. The appropriate methods and formulae may be found in Edwards (9:148–152) and Winer (37), as well as in many other sources. The basic question in trend analysis is whether a mean trend differs sufficiently from rectilinearity to be considered curvilinear (quadratic). Oddly enough, trend analysis, like the basic analysis of variance, does not require actually computing the means. But you can see the mean trend if you compute and graph the means. You might even try curve fitting (10: Chap. 5).

A four-treatment design with "none" as a control condition might involve two experimental factors (two different types of treatment) and a two-way design with two levels of each treatment on each axis. We might represent the two treatments as A and B, with no treatment as A_o and B_o for the control and with some amount of each treatment as A_s and B_s. Then the two-way design with two levels of each treatment would form a 2×2 table with four cells representing combinations of treatments, like this:

Levels	A_o	A_s	Sums
B_o	A_oB_o	A_sB_o	$B_o.$
B_s	A_oB_s	A_sB_s	$B_s.$
Sums	$A_o.$	$A_s.$	

The four randomly assigned treatment groups consist of a "control" with none of either treatment (A_oB_o), two experimental groups with some of one treatment and none of the other, (A_sB_o and A_oB_s), and one experimental group with some of both treatments (A_sB_s). This is a *factorial* design where the basic question is *whether* a treatment is a factor affecting performance, or in this case, whether the two factors affect performance.

We would start this analysis as before by getting the ΣX and ΣX^2 for each cell (A_oB_o, etc.) *separately*. We would combine these as before to get the total sum of squares, SS_T or Σx_T^2. We would still proceed as before in using sums with the error-of-origin correction to compute the "between" sums of squares, except that we have *two* "between treatments" SS, so we must compute them separately. The column sums of scores are represented as A_o. and A_s. The period means "summed over" and A_o. and A_s. are both summed over both levels of B (B_o and B_s). And the row sums, B_o. and B_s. are both summed over both levels of A (A_o and A_s). The basic procedures and formulae are the same as in the one-way, four-treatment problem, except that you treat the two-column and the two-row sums separately. The "within-groups" or within-cells SS is computed exactly as before using the mean of each cell (without computing it) as the base. But something is missing; our partial sums of squares will not add to the total sum of squares, so $SS_T \neq SS_A + SS_B + SS_W$. We must find the missing element.

We had better use the "think first, do later" principle. We used two different types of treatment or two factors. Do you suppose they could interact? A basic condition (or assumption) for analysis of variance is that the treatments are *additive*. Could some of one treatment add something else, and some of both treatments add more? They could. But the some-of-both might also negate each other, so A_sB_s could be similar to (not significantly different from) A_oB_o. The missing element was the *interaction*—the combined effect of two or more factors. Interactions are usually represented as $A \times B$. In a three-way analysis you would have $A \times B$, $A \times C$, $B \times C$, and a three-way interaction, $A \times B \times C$. However, the sum of partial SS must equal SS_T, so $SS_T = SS_A + SS_B + SS_W + SS_{A \times B}$. With four known parts and one unknown we can find the unknown by subtraction: $SS_{A \times B} = SS_T - (SS_A + SS_B + SS_W)$. Any partial SS determined by subtracting the sum of all but a missing part from the total SS is a *residual* SS. Residuals can be tricky, since any error in computing the other parts makes the residual SS wrong; a residual may contain two or more inseparable sources of variance, and a residual SS is sometimes used as the best approximation of "error variance" when the real among-subjects within-treatments SS cannot be separated. Computing the component SS independently provides a check on the computations—if their sum equals SS_T.

You might wonder about the degrees of freedom (df), mean squares or partial variances ($MS = SS/df$), and F's (MS_A/MS_W, MS_B/MS_W,

$MS_{A \times B}/MS_W$) in the two-way, factorial ANOVA. Using 10 subjects per cell, the respective df are: $A = 1$, $B = 1$, $A \times B = 1$, $W = 36$, and the total = 39, or one less than the number of scores. Thus the df are the same as for the one-way, except that the between groups df (3) is separated into three parts—one each for the factorial treatments and their interaction.

ANOVA has many ramifications and can be highly complex. Winer provides a comprehensive coverage of the various types of ANOVA (37). However, you always sum raw scores and square raw scores for the separate parts, use the error-of-origin correction for the corrected SS, divide by the appropriate degrees of freedom, and then divide treatment variance (MS) by error variance to get variance ratios (F's) from which the probability of obtaining mean differences that large on the basis of sampling error indicates whether or not the F is significant. Having found F improbable by chance (significant), you might wonder which means differed significantly from which other means. This requires computing the treatment means, which was not required in computing F. Tukey (36), Duncan (7, 8), Newman (18), Kuels (16), and Scheffé (23) have all provided methods of testing for significant differences among treatment means. The methods differ in details but they all use the pooled estimate of error variance as a basis for determining significance between treatment means.

ANCOVA

Analysis of variance requires random assignment of subjects to treatments. This introduces sampling error since the means of random samples vary by chance. Groups may be equated to have essentially equal means and standard deviations, but equating on more than one variable becomes progressively more difficult. A way around these difficulties is to use analysis of covariance or ANCOVA. Analysis *of* covariance implies that covariance is analyzed. But covariance is actually used to adjust or correct the partitioned sums of squares and thus to treat the data *as though* the groups were equated initially. Analysis *with* covariance would be more appropriate.

All subjects must be tested before and after the experimental treatments since covariance requires paired scores. The initial test or covariate (X) may be the same as the final test (Y), a closely related test, or any test on which you wish to treat the final data as though the experimental groups had been equated initially. Having groups with equal n's simplifies computation. The initial step is to compute the ΣX, ΣX^2, ΣXY, ΣY, and ΣY^2 *separately* for each group. The X and Y data could be tested separately with ANOVAS, but this is unnecessary since ANCOVA removes any initial inequality of the covariate means. Removing this inequality depends on the *cross products* derived from the paired XY's. The total and within groups sums of cross products in deviation score form (Σxy_T and Σxy_W) are derived in basically the same way as the corresponding sums of squares. The formulae in Table 3 are modified by substituting ΣXY for ΣX^2 and $(\Sigma X)(\Sigma Y)$ for $(\Sigma X)^2$. The total sum of cross products is then $\Sigma xy_T = \Sigma X Y_T - (\Sigma X_T)(\Sigma Y_T)/n_T$. The last member on the right is basically identical to $(\Sigma X)^2/n$ and thus the "error-of-origin correction." The sum of cross products within groups (Σxy_W) is obtained with this same formula used separately for each group and then summed over all groups.

Using the total and within-groups cross products (Σxy_T and Σxy_W) to correct the corresponding sums of squares on the final test (Σy_T^2 or SS_T and Σy_W^2 or SS_W) involves the formula for a straight line, $Y = a + bX$. This becomes $y = bx$ in deviation score form since the Y-intercept (a) becomes 0 when the axes intersect at $\bar{X}$ and $\bar{Y}$. The slope of the regression line (b) represents the average rate of change of Y with respect to X, and $b = \Sigma xy/\Sigma x^2$. Subjects tend to maintain the same relative position on both tests, so regression tends to be similar (homogeneous) and appreciable. Homogeneity of regression must be tested before you proceed. The formulae are too complicated for inclusion here but they may be found in Edwards (9) or Winer (37). Using o for "observed" and c for "corrected" in the subscripts, the total and within-groups sums of squares (SS_T and SS_W) are corrected with the formulae $SS_{T_c} = \Sigma y_{T_o}^2 - (\Sigma xy_T)^2/\Sigma x_T^2$ and $SS_{W_c} = \Sigma y_{W_o}^2 - (\Sigma xy_W)^2/\Sigma x_W^2$. The last member on the right is the "covariance correction" which treats the posttreatment (Y) SS as though the groups had equal means on the covariate (X). It resembles the formula for b, except that the numerator is squared. A covariance correction is not used on the between-treatments sum of squares (SS_B). This is obtained as a residual by subtraction: $SS_{B_c} = SS_{T_c} - SS_{W_c}$. Figure 3 should help you visualize how ANCOVA treats the posttreatment data as though the groups were equated initially.

The pretreatment means in Figure 3 ($\bar{X}_A \ldots _D$) were evenly spaced for convenience. Their spread relative to the variability within the groups would probably make them differ significantly. Equating the groups would make them coincide with the total pretreatment mean ($\bar{X}_T$), but ANCOVA would then be unnecessary. The dots represent the paired pre- and posttreatment (X,Y) scores. The crosses represent the paired means. The groups of dots have homogeneous regression. The relative position of the uncorrected posttreatment means ($\bar{Y}_A \ldots _D$) depends partly on the treatments and also partly on the initial differences among the groups. The covariance correction treats the data as though the groups were equated initially. This corresponds graphically to moving the crosses parallel to the common regression line (diagonally up or down) until they

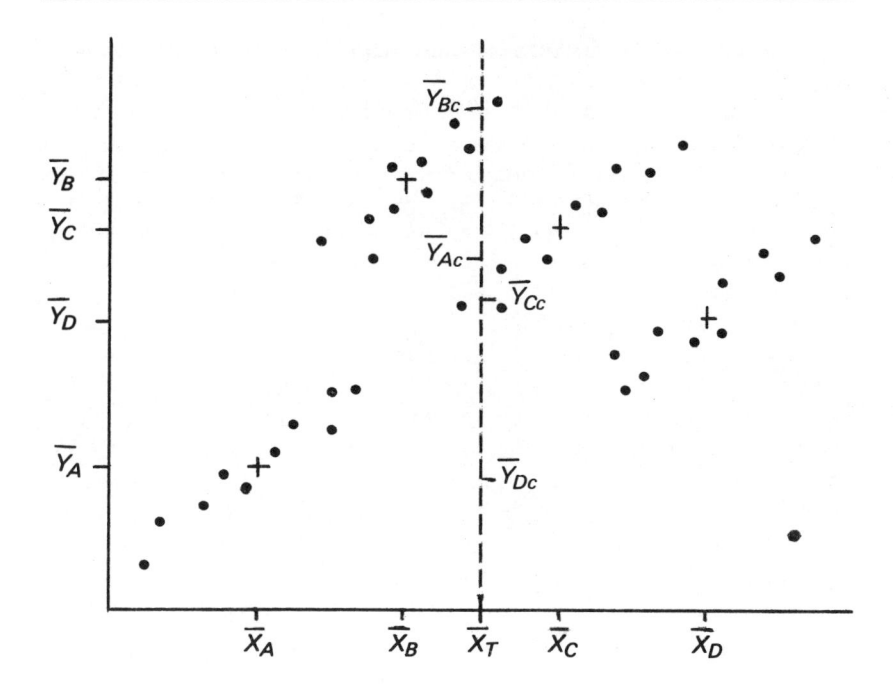

Figure 3. Posttreatment means corrected for covariance.

reach the positions of the corrected posttreatment means ($\bar{Y}_{A_c \ldots D_c}$) above $\bar{X}_T$. Equating or holding constant the pretreatment differences thus makes $\bar{Y}_{A_c}$ and $\bar{Y}_{C_c}$ essentially equal, but $\bar{Y}_{B_c}$ rises slightly and $\bar{Y}_{D_c}$ lowers considerably. Such results could occur if A to D represented none (control), some, more, and a lot of a treatment with reflex effect. Thus some (B) is beneficial, but more (C) acts like none (A), and a lot (D) is a detrimental overdose. Plotting the corrected $\bar{Y}$'s over their corresponding $\bar{X}$'s would show the reflex effect.

The paired scores for four groups of 10 each in Figure 3 provide 40 data points. Our primary concern is the posttreatment (Y) sums of squares (SS) and mean squares (MS). The degrees of freedom (df) for the uncorrected SS are 39 for SS_T, 3 for SS_B, and 36 for SS_W—just as in ANOVA. Using the covariance correction, a second parameter, on SS_T and SS_W reduces their df's by one each, leaving 38 for SS_T and 35 for SS_W. But the corrected SS_B was obtained by subtraction, rather than by correction, so the df remains 3 for SS_B. Then the MS_B, MS_W, and $MS_B/MS_W = F$ are computed and interpreted exactly as in ANOVA. The formulae are involved and the operations seem mysterious because simplifying computation obscures ideas. The basic idea is simply that treating posttreatment variance with covariance provides treatment effects free of sampling bias.

Chi Square, χ^2

We mentioned previously that we would expect by chance equal frequencies of HH', HT', TH', and TT' combinations in flipping pairs of coins. Equal probability of events occurring or not occurring was also the basis for the normal curve. The probability of getting only pairs of heads (or tails) in 10 flips is $(1/2)^{10} = 1/1024$, which is pretty unlikely. If you want to gamble by matching coins, insist on flipping the coins and letting them hit the floor. Experts can catch a coin on a full or half turn and can also make either side come up on the back of the other hand. Avoid matching coins with the catching coin-flippers, unless you want to pay to learn. However, we might ask equal numbers of men and women whether they would eat in restaurants with topless waitresses. We would expect an equal number of both sexes to favor and disfavor this gustatory diversion unless some factor related to sex biased their answers. But we would not expect the frequencies to be exactly equal. The question is how much deviation from an expected frequency can occur before we abandon the premise that the results are simply random sampling error and seem to represent real differences? All tests of significance ask the same basic question. The answer depends on someone having determined the appropriate chance, or random sampling, distribution. The sampling distribution for frequencies was determined by Pearson [20] in 1900 and labelled χ^2.

Chi square compares observed (o) and expected (e) frequencies. We are interested in the discrepancy, $o - e$, which, as the name implies, is squared, $(o - e)^2$. We would expect larger discrepancies and thus squared discrepancies when e is large, so we reduce these to a comparable base by dividing by e, $(o - e)^2/e$. Our coin flipping problem and the topless waitress counterpart generate a 2 × 2 contingency table, so we would get a chi square from each cell. The chi squares from the separate comparisons are additive, so the formula for χ^2 in easily remembered form is $\chi^2 = \Sigma(o - e)^2/e$. We determine the expected frequency, determine the discrepancy, square the discrepancy, and divide by the expected frequency before summing. Then we go to the χ^2 table. We would expect larger $(o - e)^2/e$ less frequently by chance, so as χ^2 increases, P decreases, exactly like z, t, and F. But χ^2 is additive, so it increases, somewhat but not exactly proportionately, with the degrees of freedom (df). You need the df to enter the table. Then you find the table value *next smaller* than your obtained χ^2 and at the top of that column you find P for its occurrence by chance. If P is less than .05 or .01, you say your χ^2 is significant (unlikely by chance) 5% or 1% of the time.

Chi square is useful in any situation where you have observed frequencies and can determine the expected frequencies, such as determining the goodness of fit of observed distributions to the normal curve. Chi square is also interesting historically. Pearson originally, in 1900, determined P and thus the significance of χ^2 from the number of separate chi squares involved in the sum, *i.e.*: four for a 2 × 2 table. Fisher, in 1922 (11), showed that any single entry in a 2 × 2 table determines the other three if the border totals remain constant. This restriction reduced the opportunity for things to vary (degrees of freedom, *df*) from four to one. Fisher subsequently (12) advocated using the *df* in entering any probability distribution to determine whether a statistic was significant. The degrees of freedom for any contingency ($n \times n$) table are rows minus one times columns minus one, or $(r-1)(k-1)$. In testing goodness of fit of obtained distributions to the normal distribution, the *df* are the number of step intervals minus 3. You lose one *df* each for using $\bar{X}$, s, and n as parameters (limiting constants) in fitting the curve. You also run into an important limitation of χ^2 in curve fitting. Suppose you have the observed frequency, $o = 2$, when the expected frequency, $e = .5$ is in the tail of the curve. You will find by using the formula, that $\chi^2 = 5.50$ for that step interval alone. Adding this abnormally large χ^2 distorts the sum, so you combine frequencies in the tails until e equals at least 5. In general, you should not use χ^2 when e is less than 5.

You may not be able to determine a priori probabilities, but you might want to determine whether comparable sets of frequencies differed significantly. In this case you essentially combine the sets of frequencies to derive an "average" expected frequency for each cell. You "combine" them by using the border totals. The expected frequency in a specific row and column (e_{rk}) is the product of the row total (Σf_r) and the column total (Σf_k) divided by the number of observations (n), or $e_{rk} = (\Sigma f_r)(\Sigma f_k)/n$. You probably noticed that using a sum because it acts like a mean makes χ^2 in a way similar to ANOVA. Tests of significance are all basically similar. They look different simply because they are designed to be used with different types of data.

Nonparametric Tests

The mathematical models for tests of significance have assumptions with formidable labels. Normalcy, or a basically normal distribution, is relatively intelligible. Homogeneity of variance simply means like-variability within groups. Homoscedasticity is similar and means simply like-"skedaddle" (scatter) in rows and columns. Rectilinearity of regression means that the best fit is a straight line. These assumptions are considered limiting factors (parameters) in using the models. One difficulty is that, to my knowledge, we have no satisfactory way of determining whether a sample with $n = 10$ or 20 is or is not normally distributed, except that the scores tend to bunch toward the middle. These assumptions present a real dilemma for the uninitiated. But assumptions must be taken on faith; you cannot test them directly, although you can make various assumptions and see which seems to fit the facts best. If you can test them, they are hypotheses. However, means of random samples tend to distribute normally, or according to the t distributions and, as Box (3,4,5) and Boneau (2) found by systematically violating the assumptions, F and likewise t are relatively "robust." Even though the underlying assumptions are violated rather grossly, F and t provide reasonably sound estimates of chance probability, especially if the number of cases per group is 25 or over. Perhaps violating sacred assumptions is an anathema to the statistical purist. But you cannot do much with data concerning people if you strive to be too pure. Your inference will be wrong if you violate the assumptions grossly, but they may be wrong anyway because laboratory situations are only partly analogous to life.

Siegel (24) collected and advocated using a variety of nonparametric statistics. Nonparametric means no assumption is made about the shape of the underlying distribution, or they are distribution and assumption free. This apparently grants statisticians new freedom in not being bound by the traditional (archaic) assumptions. However, mathematical models must be based on something, and the "something" must be the old assumptions. Nonparametric tests of significance round the value to be reached for a specified P upward to avoid finding an obtained value "significant" when it is borderline. They avoid assumptions by being less sensitive. Parametric and nonparametric tests applied to the same data generally result in the same inferences based on P except in borderline cases. The esoteric advantage of avoiding assumptions is at least partially offset by built-in precautions against Type I errors—rejecting the hypothesis of no difference except chance (null hypothesis) when it is true.

Experimentation

People interested in cause and effect relations treat randomly selected groups in various ways, including a no-treatment control group, to determine whether the treatments make the groups appear to be samples from different populations. The treatments produce changes within people and the mean change is the best index of the treatment effect, so mean differences are compared. Comparison of means requires that the means be of the same kind. You cannot compare height in inches and weight in pounds, nor apples and oranges, except qualitatively. You may have noticed throughout this section that scores, means, standard errors, and mean squares were of the same kind, or basically from the same test. Variation among people within groups is considered random (chance) fluctuation and provides an estimate of error variance. Analysis *with* covariance may seem an exception, since the same test may be given before and after the treatments or a different test may be used as the covariate. The tendency of human test results to vary together (covary) is used to correct the final results or to control the situation, so the data are treated as though all groups started from a common mean initially. Test results may covary without either causing changes in the other. Analysis of the covariance of tests with each other is the topic of the following section. The fact that means are compared after the data are corrected with covariance does not mean that covariance was analyzed, as the name "analysis *of* covariance" implies. The misnomer is confusing, but we will probably have to live with it.

A key to the bifurcated pathways in data analysis leading to an apparent "forked tongue" approach was promised earlier. Half of the key is that the experimental method depends basically on *one test* or one measure. This means that the data must be from one measurement scale or one combination of specified conditions in order for means to be compared. One test does not mean that people are tested once. The experimental design may require that the same types of measures or score may be obtained several times. Various tests and measures may be used, but they must be treated separately and analyzed one at a time. Producing changes within people (other than by chance) and using variability among people (within groups) are common and reasonably distinctive characteristics of group experimental methods used on humans and other animate organisms.

COVARIABILITY

Parents cause children, but unsystematic mating, small litters, long gaps between generations, scanty records, and inaccurate memories of living relatives made testing Gregor Mendel's laws with human data a monumental task. Galton (13) accepted the challenge; he recognized a need for reducing various measures to standard units (standard scores). He found relatively early that children of extremely tall or short parents tended to revert, or regress, toward average height. The idea "flashed upon him" in 1877 of using the concomitant variation (covariability) of measures from parents and children as a basis for establishing genetic causal relations. He used r (from regression or reversion) as an index of the co-relation and included an estimate of the error (standard error) involved.

Pearson sought an appropriate mathematical model for "regression" (correlation) and reported in 1896 that the formula $r = S(xy)/N\sigma_1\sigma_2$, developed by Bravais in 1846 (6), was most appropriate because the

"... $S(xy)$ corresponds to the product-moment in mechanics ..." (19:265). The two standard deviations in the denominator also converted the cross products (xy) to standard scores. Pearson developed the formula for partial correlation in 1897, for chi square in 1900 (20), for tetrachoric correlation in 1901 (21), for the mean square contingency in 1904, for the correlation ratio in 1905, and for biserial r in 1907. These made possible determining the net relation between two variables with a third held constant, between two dichotomies, for curvilinear relations, and between a variable and a dichotomy. The new statistical methods were developed originally for studying genetic relations from the covariability of parent-child data, where the causal relation was obvious. They were applicable to any paired scores where inferences of a causal relation might be purely gratuitous, or even ludicrous.

Taller people tend to weigh more and also to earn more, on the average than shorter people. Height and weight tend to increase together, or covary appreciably, because humans have similar structure, although increases in a single dimension cannot cause weight increases. Income increases, on the average, with height, but the successive mean increases are small relative to the variation in income at each weight. Height obviously does not cause income or vice versa. Various other measures or scores covary to the extent that individuals occupy similar positions relative to a group on both scales. Position relative to the group depends on differences among people (*inter*individual). No experimental treatment is applied to alter individuals and produce *intra*individual differences. Relations based on covariability provide a basis for predicting or estimating a group's position on one measure relative to another measure, to the extent that the covariations are appreciable and consistent.

Andrews (1:17) used the term "differential" to distinguish analyses based on differences among people from those using experimental treatments to induce changes within people. Differential has general, but not universal, acceptance. Semantic impasses develop between those who do and those who do not distinguish between differences produced within (intra) and those occurring among (inter) individuals. Differential analyses always involve correlation, which requires paired scores from one group. Therefore, "correlational" is an adequate operational label. The analysis of covariability via correlation is a *one-group* approach for studying relations as they occur, in contrast to the *one-test* experimental approach. Differential or correlational analyses provide the other fork for studying relations.

Studying relations as they occur in a group by differential or correlational analysis was a novel approach for traditional cause-and-effect oriented experimentalists who considered correlation an unorthodox "statistical" method. The experimentalists considered themselves scientists, so the correlationalists must be nonscientists. Correlationalists frequently abetted this aberration with gratuitous inferences of causal relations based on correlations. The experimentalists amused themselves periodically by generating nonsensical correlations to make the "statisticians" (people using correlations) appear idiotic. For example, husbands and wives are paired in the sight of God and the assembled congregation. You can correlate the ages of husbands and wives. The correlation will be reasonably high. Trying to explain how either can "cause" the age of the other in our society without incest makes correlation, and hence "statistics," appear to be an incestuous form of data processing. The joke is that ecclesiastical and legal pairing does not provide "paired scores" in statistical terminology (two scores for each subject). Confusion concerning causation resulted initially from extensive use of correlation in a special case where the paired parent-offspring data had an obvious hereditary causal relation. Correlational or differential analyses always start with paired scores, but inferences concerning causation are gratuitous without additional evidence.

Correlation: *r*

A force producing rotation is a moment and the torque increases with distance from the axis. A body is balanced when the product of its masses (m) times their distances (d) from the axis sum to zero (when $\Sigma md = 0$). Separate measures or scores have equal weight, or "mass." The mean ($\bar{X}$) is the point in a distribution about which the deviations ($x = X - \bar{X}$) sum to zero, or $\Sigma x = 0$. The mean is the balance point in a distribution, or the "first moment." The inertia, or kinetic energy, of a body depends on the average product of the separate masses times their distances squared, $\Sigma md^2/n$, or with equal masses, simply $\Sigma d^2/n$. Extracting the square root reduces this to a linear distance at which the masses act as though they were concentrated. This is the moment of inertia, or "second moment." The root mean squared deviation, or standard deviation (s), is analogous to the second moment.

The Pearson product-moment correlation (r) is basically an average of the product of paired standard scores, $r = \Sigma z_x z_y / n$. Reducing the paired X and Y scores to standard scores (z_x and z_y) puts both sets of scores in equivalent units, or makes the "moments" on both axes equivalent, and also explains the "product moment" label. You could define correlation as the average product moment. Computing r with this formula is very complicated. You can compute r directly from raw scores with a formula which is algebraically equivalent, $r = \Sigma xy / \sqrt{(\Sigma x^2)(\Sigma y^2)}$. Computing Σxy, Σx^2, and Σy^2 with their appropriate error-of-origin corrections involves no new operations and is relatively simple. But the shortcut masks some basic relations which are essential in understanding correlation and correlational analysis.

Correlations are frequently computed from scattergrams, with vertical columns representing successive levels of X and horizontal rows representing successive levels of Y. Tallying each pair of scores in its proper pigeonhole provides a graphic indication of the correlation. Tallies that scatter widely up and down the columns and across the rows produce a low or zero correlation. Tallies concentrating along the diagonal produce a high correlation. Correlation is maximal (1.00) if all tallies fall in diagonal pigeonholes with Y increasing as X increases, or -1.00 with Y decreasing as X increases. Correlation increases as the paired scores tend to approximate a straight line. Procedures for preparing scattergrams and computing correlations from them are described adequately in many statistics books, so we can omit them.

Correlation indicates how well paired scores fit a straight line, or the degree of rectilinear relationship. The formula for a straight line, $Y = a + bX$, defines Y in terms of the *slope* of the line (b, or the rate of change of Y with respect to X) and the *Y-intercept* (a, or the point where the line crosses the Y axis, when $X = 0$). Paired scores that do not fit a straight line exactly (so $r = 1.00$ or -1.00) may approximate a straight line. As correlation (r) decreases, the average trend of Y values with respect to X (or slope) tends to regress toward the mean of Y. The average trend of X values with respect to Y also tends to regress toward the mean of X, so we have two *regression lines*. Correlation increases as the two regression lines approach each other; so $r = 1.00$ when the two regression lines coincide, and $r = .00$ when the angle between the regression lines is 90°. Thus r varies as the cosine of the angle between the regression lines. Determining the angle from r is easy, but determining r from the angle is extremely complicated.

The five lines in Figure 4 represent three different pairs of regression lines associated with three correlations, but with the tallies, or paired data points, omitted. LL, MM, and NN represent three different average rates of change (regressions) of Y with respect to X. $L'L'$, $M'M'$, and $N'N'$ represent the corresponding regressions of X with respect to Y. Standard score scales (z_x and z_y) and hypothetical raw score scales (X and Y) are on the abscissa and ordinate. Regression lines always cross at the mean of X and Y where $z_x = 0$ and $z_y = 0$. The formula for the Y-intercept is $a = \bar{Y} - b\bar{X}$. Substituting the standard score equivalent of $\bar{Y}$ and $\bar{X}$ makes $a = 0$ in standard score units. The slope of the line is required for determining the Y-intercept. The slope, or regression coefficient, in raw score units is commonly labelled b, $b_y = \Sigma xy/\Sigma x^2$ and $b_x = \Sigma xy/\Sigma y^2$. The ratios with a common denominator in Figure 4 are standard score regression coefficients, commonly labelled β (beta). Each pair of regression lines has the same β because the average rate of change of Y with respect to X, and of X with respect to Y, is identical in standard score units. Raw score regression coefficients are never equal, except accidentally.

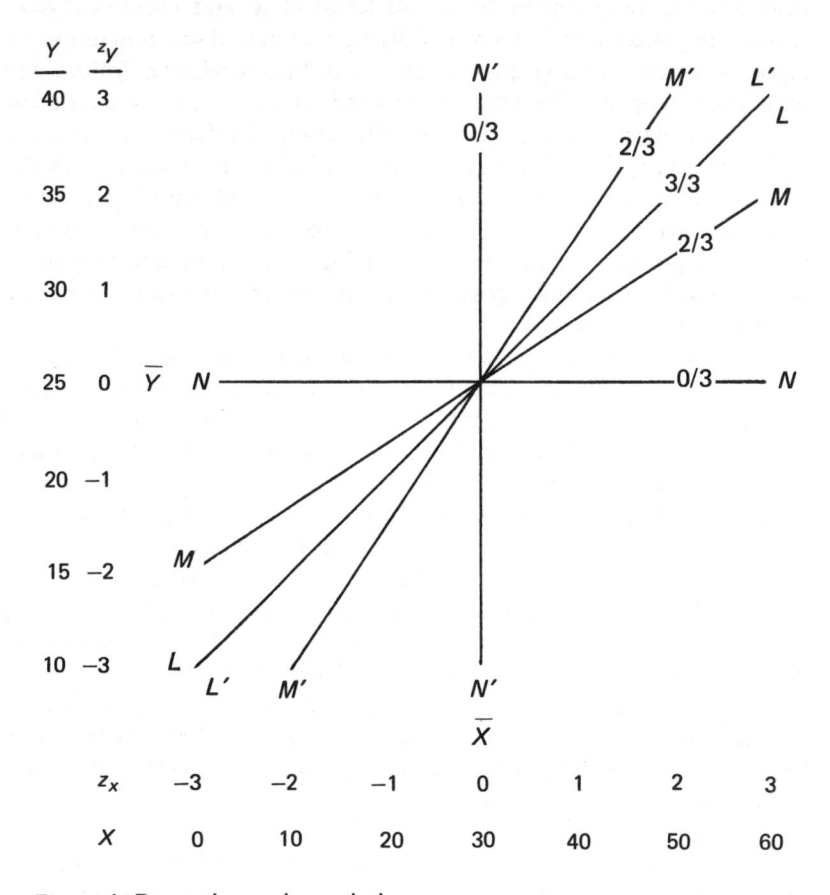

Figure 4. Regression and correlation.

The pair of regression lines that coincide in Figure 4, LL and $L'L'$, represent the upper limit of correlation where $r = 1.00$, because all paired scores fall on a straight line. The same situation but with high scores on one test paired with low scores on the other would give $r = -1.00$. The slope of LL in standard score units is $\beta_y = 3/3 = 1.00$, since $z_y = z_x$ so $z_y/z_x = 1.00$, and also for $L'L'$, $\beta_x = z_x/z_y = 1.00$. Thus in standard score units $r = \beta_y = \beta_x$, or both standard score regression coefficients equal the correlation. This identity holds regardless of the size of the correlation. The next pair of regression lines, MM and $M'M'$, diverge. This represents a situation in which the paired data tend to spread or scatter in the rows and columns but, on the average, Y tends to increase with X, as does X with Y. Since $r = \beta_y = \beta_x$, the correlation is 2/3, or approximately .67. In comparison with LL and L'L', MM moves toward the mean of Y or regresses toward NN, and M'M' regresses toward N'N' as r decreases. The last pair of regression lines, NN and N'N', represents a situation in which the paired scores scatter equally in all columns about Y and also in all rows about $\bar{X}$, or scatter indiscriminately in a circle. Thus $r = .00$ and the best estimate of the value of Y for any value of X is the mean of Y, or $\bar{Y}$, and conversely for any value Y is $\bar{X}$, since X and Y are mutually independent when $r = .00$.

The basic relations underlying correlation are identical in standard score and raw score units, but having X and Y in different units requires adjusting the formulae. We found a convenient identity in $r = \beta_y = \beta_x$. Squaring all terms makes $r^2 = \beta_y^2 = \beta_x^2$ but this does not change the identity. Now watch what happens when we square the raw score formula for correlation:

$r^2 = (\Sigma xy)(\Sigma xy)/(\Sigma x^2)(\Sigma y^2) = (\Sigma xy/\Sigma x^2)(\Sigma xy/\Sigma y^2)$. The raw score regression coefficients are $b_y = \Sigma xy/\Sigma x^2$ and $b_x = \Sigma xy/\Sigma y^2$, so now $r^2 = b_y b_x$ because the X and Y units differ. Additional algebraic manipulation would show that $b_y = r(s_y/s_x)$ and $b_x = r(s_x/s_y)$. A difference of one standard score always equals a difference of one standard deviation, so $s_x = 10$ and $s_y = 5$ in Figure 4. We can now determine the slope of line MM, $b_y = r(s_y/s_x) = (2/3)(5/10) = 1/3$, or .33 rounded. The slope of line M'M' is $b_x = r(s_x/s_y) = (2/3)(10/5) = 4/3$, or 1.33 rounded. The raw score regression coefficients are not identical. Substituting in $r^2 = b_y b_x$ gives $r^2 = (1/3)(4/3) = 4/9$ and then taking the square root makes $r = 2/3 = .67$, so r remains the same. We now have the raw score regression coefficient (b_y) for line MM so we can substitute this (as b) in the formula for the Y-intercept, $a = \bar{Y} - b\bar{X} = 25 - (1/3)(30) = 15$—as is readily apparent in Figure 4.

Algebraic manipulations are confusing, but correlation makes it possible to estimate or predict one score from another. The estimates are exact only when $r = 1.00$ (or -1.00) and the errors in prediction increase exponentially as r decreases. Predicted scores lie on a regression line. Actual scores vary about the regression lines. A predicted Y score is usually identified as $\widetilde{Y}$, so the formula becomes $\widetilde{Y} = a + bX$. Correlation provides a convenient basis for partitioning the variance of both tests (s_y^2 and s_x^2) into a mutually related portion, r^2 or the coefficient of determination, and an unrelated or independent portion, $1 - r^2$ or the coefficient of nondetermination. Each test "accounts for" rather than actually "determines" (produces) the r^2 portion of the variance of the other.

The basic assumption underlying r is rectilinearity of regression, or straight regression lines. Interpreting r also depends on having homoscedasticity,—equal scatter (skedaddle)—in the rows and columns, and normalcy—normally distributed scores—on both axes. Unequal scatter increases r artificially, since data in rows and columns with minimal dispersion fit the regression lines better. Skewed distributions also increase r artificially, since abnormally long tails lengthen the line to be fitted and reduce the apparent dispersion. Lack of rectilinearity, homoscedasticity, and normalcy are readily apparent when paired scores are graphed.

Significance of r

We frequently read that a correlation is significant or highly significant. This means that the probability (P) of finding an r this large by chance would be .05 or .01. We start by assuming that $1 - r^2$ represents the proportion of variance attributable to chance, or the error variance, and compute the standard error of the correlation using $s_r = (1 - r^2)/\sqrt{n - 2}$. We then assume that the true correlation is 0 and compute t, using $t = (r - 0)/s_r$, or more directly, $t = (r\sqrt{n - 2})/(1 - r^2)$. We then find the P of an r this large occurring by chance from a table of t, entering the table with $df = n - 2$, since n is the number of subjects or paired scores and two regression lines were used as limiting constants (parameters).

The significance of a correlation can be determined without computation if a table like Table VI in Edwards (10:426) is available. You enter the table with $df = n - 2$ and go across the row to the last value smaller than or equal to the obtained r. The P is at the top of that column and you must double it, since this is a "one-tailed" table and we are using a "two-tailed" test. Values from this table can be used for some inferences. With 25 subjects ($df = 23$) an r of .505 would be "highly significant," since $P = .005$, or .01 when doubled. With 102 subjects ($df = 100$) an r of .254 would be "highly significant." Thus having about four times as many subjects makes an r half as large equally unlikely by chance. But since r^2 represents the proportion of explained variance, $(.505)^2 = .255$ and $(.254)^2 = .065$. These "highly significant" correlations account for about 1/4 and 1/15 of the variance of either test. Highly significant correlations may have very little predictive value, especially if n is large. Nonsignificant correlations are probably actually zero—and may be useful in estimating other variables. "Fisher's z" (12) should be used in averaging or comparing correlations.

Partial Correlation: $r_{ab \cdot c}$

Data from any number (n) of tests on the same group permit $n(n - 1)/2$ intercorrelations or zero-order correlations, with subscripts identifying the tests involved, such as r_{ab}, r_{ac}, r_{bc}, etc. Common factors presumably underlie the test data. Two tests correlate or covary to the extent that they measure one or more factors in common. Partial correlation seeks to identify the factor or factors common to two tests by removing, partialling out, or holding constant another factor or other factors. First-order partial correlations represent the *net* covariability of two tests, with the covariability of these tests in common with a third test partialled out or held constant. Higher order partial correlations get the net-related variance between two tests by removing successively the portions of their variance related to two or more other tests. Partial correlation resembles holding factors constant experimentally, but differs in that common factors may cause test data to covary but neither test causes the variance of the other

Partial correlation starts by obtaining a first-order partial correlation from three zero-order correlations with the formula:

$$r_{ab \cdot c} = (r_{ab} - r_{ac}r_{bc}) / \sqrt{(1 - r_{ac}^2)(1 - r_{bc}^2)}$$

This is read, "The partial correlation between tests A and B with C held constant equals (whatever results)." The period in $r_{ab \cdot c}$ separates the two net-related tests (A and B) from any held constant (C in this case). The numerator subtracts the product of the two correlations involving C from r_{ab}, whose net relationship is sought. The denominator is the root of the product of the coefficients of nondetermination involving C, the test partialled out. Products, roots, and ratios of decimal fractions are tricky. However, letting $r_{ab} = r_{ac} = r_{bc} = .50$ makes $r_{ab \cdot c} = .333$, so the net relation between A and B reduces with C partialled out. Letting the three zero-order correlations equal .80 makes $r_{ab \cdot c} = .445$, so the relative amount partialled out increases as the correlations increase together. Letting $r_{ab} = .80$ and $r_{ac} = r_{bc} = .50$ makes $r_{ab \cdot c} = .734$; therefore little reduction results when A and B are highly related even though the relation of C with A and B is moderate. But letting $r_{ab} = r_{ac} = .50$ and $r_{bc} = .80$ makes $r_{ab \cdot c} = .196$, so the net related variance of A and B decreases markedly when the correlation of either with the test held constant (C) is high.

Higher order partial correlations use the same basic formula except that the next lower partial correlations are substituted on the right side. This makes the procedure progressively more complex and confusing, but not necessarily more productive, since holding more tests constant erodes the net relation between the tests without determining the factors underlying either test.

Multiple Correlation: $R_{a \cdot bc}$

Multiple correlation (R) uses the related (r^2) and unrelated ($1 - r^2$) parts of the variance of two or more tests to account for the variance of one test. Variance common to the two or more tests is partialled out, so their net-related variance with the one test remains. Since partialling out makes the two or more tests independent of each other, they are commonly called "independent variables" and the test which has its variance accounted for is commonly called the "dependent variable." Using terms long associated with experimental procedures in connection with correlational or differential operations is confusing. Experiments seek causal relations based on evidence that varying amounts of an "independent" factor precede and produce varying amounts of a "dependent" factor. Tests may covary or correlate because of some underlying common factor (or cause), but either test may be given before (precede) the other and the variance of neither test produces or results in the variance of the other. An inference of causal relation from correlation is gratuitous in the absence of direct evidence that one thing both preceded and produced the other. As a standard against which things are judged or evaluated is a "criterion"; this label seems appropriate for the test whose variance is being accounted for or explained. Multiple correlation also provides a basis for estimating or predicting criterion scores from other test scores, so "predictors" seems to be an appropriate label for those other tests. The latter tests are independent predictors because their common variance is partialled out; they are not independent variables in the sense that they can be varied systematically to produce the criterion.

M. H. Doolittle devised an ingenious solution for any number of linear equations about 1857. This was later adapted for computing R (14:393, 22:226). We shall start with the formula for the minimal situation involving three tests (A, B, and C) and three intercorrelations:

$$R_{a \cdot bc}^2 = (r_{ab}^2 + r_{ac}^2 - 2r_{ab}r_{ac}r_{bc}) / (1 - r_{bc}^2)$$

The subscript for the criterion (a) precedes the period and the subscripts for the predictors (b and c) follow it. The numerator on the right is a transposed and complicated form of $(x - y)^2$. The denominator $(1 - r_{bc}^2)$ is the unrelated, or independent, variance of the two predictors. The subscripts follow a simple pattern. The square root must be extracted to obtain R, which is interpreted like r.

Some simple manipulations will show how multiple correlation operates. Let us first assume that the predictors B and C are independent, so $r_{bc} = .00$, and substituting this in the formula makes $R_{a \cdot bc}^2 = r_{ab}^2 + r_{ac}^2$. The mutually independent variances are directly additive. Then letting $r_{ab} = r_{ac} = .50$ and $r_{bc} = .00$ makes B and C account separately for .25 of the variance of the criterion (A), but they account for .50 when added. Taking the square root makes $R_{a \cdot bc} = .707$. Combining the mutually independent covariances increases the multiple correlation. How r_{bc} partials out the related variance of B and C when this is not zero is obscure, since r_{bc} alters both the numerator and denominator. However, we can assume that $r_{ab} = r_{ac} = r_{bc}$ and then substitute successively .50, .60, .70, .80, and .90 for all three correlations. This makes R successively .577, .671, .759, .843, and .923. Each R is larger than the corresponding r for a single predictor, but the increase from the second predictor becomes progressively, and also increasingly, smaller as r_{bc} increases. More common variance among the predictors reduces their collective net-related contribution to the criterion, although R is greater than any of the separate correlations with the criterion. We might go to the limit and assume that $r_{bc} = 1.00$, but this makes $1 - r_{bc}^2 = .00$ in the denominator—which presents a problem. However, having $r_{bc} = 1.00$ means that B and C measure exactly the same thing; therefore both would have to correlate equally with the criterion and neither could account for any variance not accounted for by the other.

Multiple correlation increases with more predictors to the extent that they are related to the criterion and independent of each other. Tests correlating highly with the criterion tend to correlate with each other so using more tests tends to increase their common variance. Gains in R generally become inconsequential after four or five predictors.

Multiple Prediction

Multiple prediction is a by-product of multiple correlation. It extends the principle of using test covariability as the basis for estimating one test score from another to estimating a criterion score from the net-related variance of any number of independent predictors. The common variance among the predictors is partialled out so their net-related variance with the criterion accounts for the proportion of its variance equal to R^2. The independent predictors operate as mutually perpendicular axes or dimensions. Visualizing more than three mutually perpendicular axes is difficult or impossible. But if we move a specified distance along one (partial) regression line, then turn a right angle and move a specified distance along a second independent regression line, and keep repeating this process, we approach the criterion score closer than we could by moving only along one regression line. Multiple prediction equations are simply linear regression equations, like the formula for a straight line, except that they involve more factors.

The general raw score formula with test A as the criterion and tests B, C, ..., N as predictors is:

$$\tilde{Y}_a = a_{a \cdot bc \cdots n} + b_b X_b + b_c X_c + \ldots + b_n X_n$$

The subscript a in $\tilde{Y}_a$ identifies test A as the criterion and the other subscripts identify specific tests. The first factor on the right, $a_{a \cdot bc \cdots n}$, corresponds to the Y-intercept (a) and adjusts the scales of the predictors to the criterion scale (identified by the subscript a before the period). The remaining factors are products of the raw score partial regression coefficients (b's) and the raw scores (X's) of the corresponding predictors. The subscripts of the partial regression coefficients (b's) should be written, for example, as $b_{ab \cdot c \ldots n}$ to indicate the net regression between the criterion (A) and that predictor (B) with the covariance in common with the remaining tests partialled out, but b_b is simpler. The appropriate raw score partial regression coefficients and corresponding raw scores are substituted to estimate the raw score of the criterion. A regression coefficient is negative if the correlation was negative.

Multiple prediction or multiple regression equations are sometimes written in standard score form with β's in place of b's, z's in place of X's, and *no* added constant (a) corresponding to the Y-intercept, since using standard scores moves the origin of all tests to their means where $z_y = z_x = 0$. The lack of an added constant distinguishes them immediately from raw score regression equations. We noted previously that $r_{xy} = \beta_y = \beta_x$ in zero-order correlations. This identity holds for standard score partial regression coefficients, except of course that they equal the *partial* and not the zero-order correlations.

Multiple correlation and prediction depend basically on administering a battery of tests to the same group. Whether the same relations and predictions apply for a second group is an open question which can only be answered by replication (trying it again). Multiple correlation and prediction also require measuring the criterion. You might wonder why anyone would use such an involved procedure to estimate what can be measured. R^2, like r^2, represents the proportion of the variance of the criterion accounted for, or explained by, the independent predictors, and $1 - R^2$ remains unexplained. Thus multiple correlation helps to identify the various independent dimensions, or factors, underlying one test and to determine how much each part contributes to explaining the variance of the whole. Multiple correlation also provides a convenient method for using several simple and easily administered tests to estimate another measure which is very difficult to obtain. Multiple correlation concentrates essentially on explaining the variance of one test (the criterion). Partialling out the common variance among predictors, in essence, discards other possible sources of covariability in the battery of tests. Procedures for seeking out several possible sources of covariability among the tests in the battery would be more desirable than discarding them.

UNDERLYING FACTORS

Early psychologists viewed human mental ability as consisting of a large number of specific faculties—association, attention, judgment, memory, etc. This implied that tests of a specific mental faculty should correlate perfectly, barring measurement errors, and tests of different faculties should correlate essentially zero. But tests of supposedly different faculties frequently correlated higher than tests presumably measuring the same faculty. Either the human mental faculties were not discrete or the tests were not measuring what they were supposed to (invalid). This raised the dual question of what the tests were actually measuring and what common factors might possibly underlie their collective covariability.

Two Factors

Spearman analyzed correlations among mental ability tests and stated as his major conclusion (25: 284) that "... all branches of intellectual ability have in common one fundamental function (or group of functions), whereas the remaining or specific elements of the activity seem in every case to be wholly different from each other." Spearman reported additional evidence in 1914 (26) that correlations formed a hierarchy with those between tests measuring mostly the general (g) factor at the top and those between tests measuring specifics (s) at the bottom. Thus tests A, B, C, and D should intercorrelate in proportion to their common g factor even though their specific factors (s_a, s_b, s_c, and s_d) differed. A ratio between two correlations, such as r_{ab}/r_{ac}, tended to cancel anything specific to test A (s_a). A second ratio, r_{db}/r_{dc}, tended to cancel s_d. Then the proportion $r_{ab}/r_{ac} = r_{db}/r_{dc}$, with s_a and s_d cancelled should be equal if tests B and C measured a common factor. Proportions are equal when the product of the extremes equals the products of the means, for example, $2/4 = 3/6$ since $(2)(6) = (3)(4)$, and transposing, $12 - 12 = 0$. Such proportions of four correlations formed a *tetrad*. Having the *tetrad difference* approximate zero satisfied the criterion of proportionality. The tetrad difference might not be exactly zero, since tests have some unreliability. Four tests provide $n(n-1)/2 = 6$ correlations. Testing for proportionality among the six correlations requires three tetrads and the four tests presumably have a common g factor if the three tetrads approximate zero. Deriving these tetrads provides an introduction to, and some practice in, matrix algebra.

A *matrix* is a rectangular array of similar data or statistics. The correlation matrix in Table 4 has tests A to D in the same order as column and row headings. The cell entries are correlations of each test with every other test, so that corresponding columns and rows contain identical correlations. The subscripts are reversed above and below the diagonal. This is unnecessary but convenient in the present example. The missing diagonal entries would be self-correlations or test-retest reliabilities (r_{aa}, r_{bb}, etc.)

TABLE 4. Correlation Matrix and Tetrad Derivation

Matrix					Equations	Extremes = Means and Transposition = Tetrad
Test	A	B	C	D ...	1) $\dfrac{r_{ab}}{r_{ad}} = \dfrac{r_{cb}}{r_{cd}}$	$r_{ab}\, r_{cd} = r_{ad}\, r_{cb}$
A		r_{ba}	r_{ca}	r_{da}		$r_{ab}\, r_{cd} - r_{ad}\, r_{cd} = t_{abcd}$
B	r_{ab}		r_{cb}	r_{db}	2) $\dfrac{r_{ab}}{r_{ac}} = \dfrac{r_{db}}{r_{dc}}$	$r_{ab}\, r_{dc} = r_{ac}\, r_{db}$
						$r_{ab}\, r_{dc} - r_{ac}\, r_{db} = t_{abdc}$
C	r_{ac}	r_{bc}		r_{dc}	3) $\dfrac{r_{ac}}{r_{ad}} = \dfrac{r_{bc}}{r_{bd}}$	$r_{ac}\, r_{bd} = r_{ad}\, r_{bc}$
						$r_{ac}\, r_{bd} - r_{ad}\, r_{bc} = t_{acbd}$
D	r_{ad}	r_{bd}	r_{cd}			
...						

You can derive the tetrads shown in Table 4 by first copying the correlation matrix three times. Then striking out row A, column B, row C, and column D on one copy leaves four correlations arranged as shown in Equation 1. Multiplying extremes and means and then transposing gives tetrad$_{abcd}$. The subscripts identify the order in which the tests were stricken alternately in a row and a column. Striking out row A, column B, row D, and column C on the second copy gives Equation 2 and tetrad $_{abdc}$. Striking out row A, column C, row B, and column D on the third copy gives Equation 3 and tetrad $_{acbd}$. Each equation involves 4 of the 6 correlations (or of 12 counting duplicates). The subscripts show that all four tests are involved in each equation and each test is involved twice, either as the first subscript in the numerator and denominator of each ratio, or as the second subscript in the numerator or denominator of both ratios. Having the same test represented in the numerator and denominator tends to cancel any specific factor in one test on each side of the equation. Having one test represented in both numerators and another test in both denominators tends to balance any specific factor in the other two tests across the equation. Each tetrad should approximate zero if the four correlations depend primarily on a common factor. The three tetrads should approximate zero if the four tests have a general (g) factor.

We obtained three tetrads from 6 correlations (or 12 counting duplicates). This seemed to reduce the information we needed to deal with. But using four tests gives $_4C_4 = 4!/4!0! = 1$ combination, so we got three tetrads from one combination of four tests. Having 10 tests would give $_{10}C_4 = 10!/4!6! = 210$ combinations and 630 tetrads from 45 correlations. Using 20 tests would give 14,535 tetrads from 190 correlations. The tetrad difference method compounds the problem of analyzing test covariability. The cancelling and balancing to remove test-specific factors also prevented finding common factors among subgroups of tests. However, Spearman and his students analyzed correlation matrices assiduously to determine whether the tetrad differences met the criterion of proportionality or approximated zero within the limits of sampling error. The results partially supported the two-factor theory. But having too many tetrads too large left it highly questionable.

Thomson (30) generated artificial "test scores" by letting the sum of two or three dice throws represent part of a "subject's score" common to several tests. The remainder of the "score" was a separate throw of two or more dice specific for each "test." Groups of scores thus had a "common factor" but no g factor was common to all tests. The intercorrelations formed a hierarchy and the tetrad differences met Spearman's criterion of proportionality (approximated zero) as well as actual test data had. Appearing to justify the two-factor theory with no g factor present made "general intelligence" seem an illusion. Thomson (31) later proposed a "sampling theory" which viewed groups of tests as tending to intercorrelate highly when they measured various common factors, but lowly when they measured different common factors or specifics. Thomson (32) in 1935 again advocated his sampling theory, but concentrated on using Spearman's methods to disprove the two-factor theory, and failed to develop any mathematical basis for determining which groups of tests measured which factors in common.

Multiple Factors

Thurstone (33) proposed in 1931 an ingenious and novel method for extracting any number of common factors from an intercorrelation matrix. His "method of principal axes" partitioned the covariance among tests into portions common to two or more tests and portions representing test-specific and error variance. He originally viewed these principal axes (mutually perpendicular reference axes, or later, "centroids") as directly interpretable psychologically. He later viewed them as merely a convenient orthogonal framework for deriving the "factorial matrix" (table of mutually independent coordinates for each test, or "factor loadings"). Interpretation required rotating the factorial matrix (analytical framework) so the axes fitted the subgroups of similar tests and thus represented the various common factors. Thurstone summarized in 1935 the early theoretical and mathematical developments that evolved from studying mental ability in *The Vectors of Mind* (34). His completely revised second edition, *Multiple Factor Analysis* (35), appeared in 1947. Both are highly complex but well written. Both prefaces summarize the evolution of multifactor analysis interestingly and nontechnically.

A factor analysis starts with perhaps 40 tests administered to 100 subjects, or 4,000 scores. As retesting for reliability coefficients would require 4,000 more scores, this is generally avoided. Computing all possible intercorrelations gives $n(n-1)/2 = (40)(39)/2 = 780$ correlations for the half-matrix less the major diagonal. Assuming that six factors are sufficient, and skipping over their extraction temporarily, the six factors for 40 tests give 240 factor loadings for subsequent analysis. Factor analysis systematically reduces the essential information one needs—in contrast to generating 549,240 tetrads from 40 tests. The ideas underlying factor analysis are relatively simple if you understand the geometry of hyperspace, sampling theory, and matrix algebra. This is a large order.

We consider space three-dimensional and have little trouble visualizing three dimensions, although our vision is two-dimensional (uniplanar). Three mutually perpendicular, orthogonal, or independent dimensions seem sufficient until someone asks, "Why not more?" We can consider a three-dimensional structure moving, so time becomes a fourth, independent dimension. The geometry of hyperspace concerns spatial relations with more than three dimensions. The question is not whether more than three dimensions exist, but how to treat things (or correlations between tests) in terms of more than three dimensions, assuming that more are possible. The answer is to locate things (or tests) on one dimension first in such a way that any remaining (residual) distances or amounts on the other dimensions are balanced (sum to zero). Then this dimension is moved out of the space and locations relative to a second independent dimension are determined as in the first step. The second dimension is moved out of the space and the process is repeated until the residuals approximate zero. This locates the tests on n independent dimensions. You might visualize this as 40 star-tests in a portion of the Milky Way. The star-tests are held together by their common variances at relative distances proportional to their correlations. We see them on a plane but we "know" some are farther away than others and that they are moving. Two tests form a line. Three tests form a triangle. A fourth test might require a third-dimensional distance to locate it. And more tests might require more dimensions.

The multitude and diversity of human ability and behavior involve experiential, genetic, perceptual, and physical components and presumably emanate from independent, elemental factors. Myriad tests sample these underlying factors. Because no test measures a single factor completely or discretely, test scores represent compounds of factors. Tests covary or correlate to the extent that they sample common factors. Two tests must sample the same factor to have common variance. Each test has some specific variance or measures something independently from any other test in the battery, since their "combinations of specified conditions" differ. Subjects vary within themselves and this introduces some random fluctuation in their scores from test to test (error variance).

Factor analysis views the variance of test A (s_a^2) as composed of some proportion of variance (k^2) attributable to sampling some independent underlying factors in common with other tests in the battery (k_1^2 to k_n^2), some test specific variance (a_s^2) and some error variance (a_e^2). With the common, specific, and error components defined, we can represent the variance of test A as:

$$s_a^2 = k_1^2 + k_2^2 + \ldots + k_n^2 + a_s^2 + a_e^2 = 1.00 = \text{all the variance of A.}$$

The proportional parts for the various tests in a battery differ, of course, depending on how much of each factor each test samples. The collective, common-factor variance of a test is called its *communality*, and $h_a^2 = k_1^2 + \ldots + k_n^2$. The specific ($a_s^2$) and error ($a_e^2$) variances could be separated if the test reliability (r_{aa}) was available, since $a_s^2 = r_{aa} - h_a^2$, and $a_e^2 = 1 - r_{aa}$. Guilford (14:477) and McCloy (17:435) present the same basic formula for factor analysis with different symbols. But the main idea is that the variance of a test consists of common-with-other tests, specific, and error variances. Factor analysis partitions these variances by means of matrix algebra.

Partitioning Test Variances

We start with an intercorrelation matrix, such as that in Table 4, which lacks the self-correlations or test reliabilities r_{aa}, r_{bb}, etc. The reliability of a test should be at least as high as its correlation with any other test. So we assume in the centroid method that the highest correlation in a row (and column) is the best approximation of the test reliability and insert this in the diagonal as r_{aa}, r_{bb}, etc.—always with a positive sign. Then the correlations for each test, or in each column, are summed separately to get the $\Sigma r_a.$, $\Sigma r_b.$, etc. The period in $\Sigma r_a.$ means "summed over all." Then that column sums are summed to get the total sum of correlations (Σr_t). The square root is extracted ($\sqrt{\Sigma r_t}$). Dividing each column sum by the square root of the total sum of correlations ($\Sigma r_a./\sqrt{\Sigma r_t}$, $r_b./\sqrt{\Sigma r_t}$, etc.) gives the *first factor loadings* (k_1) for each test (k_{1a}, k_{1b}, etc.). The first factor loadings locate each test relative to the other tests along an imaginary axis, the first centroid. Each factor loading is squared and this represents the proportion of the variance of each test that is accounted for by this factor loading.

A second matrix is prepared containing the products of the first factor loadings. The squared factor loadings (k_{1a}^2, k_{1b}^2, etc.) are entered in the major diagonal at their respective row-column intersections. Then each test factor loading is multiplied by every other test factor loading.

The $k_{1a}k_{1b}$ is entered in the *two* cells corresponding to r_{ab}; the $k_{1a}k_{1c}$ entry corresponds to r_{ac}, etc. The matrix algebra operation consists of subtracting each factor loading product from its corresponding correlation *cell by cell* $(r_{aa} - k_{1a}{}^2, r_{ab} - k_{1a}k_{1b}, r_{ac} - k_{1a}k_{1b}$, etc.). The differences are entered in a third matrix as the *first factor residuals*. These residuals represent the proportion of the variance of each test remaining after extracting the portion attributable to the first factor loading. The columns of residuals for each test are summed separately. They should sum to zero, which indicates that the residuals are balanced about the centroid. Any residual greater than about .005 indicates a computational error which must be located and corrected. When the residual matrix is error-free, the residuals in the major diagonal are removed and the largest residual in each row (and column) is substituted. The sign of the substituted residual is made positive and remains positive in the next operation.

The third basic operation involves moving the imaginary reference axis (centroid) out of the intercorrelation "test space." This seems semi-miraculous but it depends on two relatively simple ideas. The mean ($\bar{X}$) is computed from an actual or arbitrary zero used in obtaining raw scores. We shift the reference point to the mean when we compute variance (s^2) and the standard deviation (s). We use s as a standard unit and deviation scores ($x = X - \bar{X}$) in computing standard scores ($z = x/s$). Then we may set the mean equal to 50 and convert the z scores back to raw score units. Moving the reference point and changing the units does *not* alter the relative positions of the original scores. Moving the centroid out of the test space does not alter the relative position (factor loadings) of the tests, nor does it alter the residuals. The second idea in moving the centroid relates to an idea in correlation. The proportion of related variance (r^2) depends on the absolute magnitude of r and *not* its sign. The sign depends on which end of each test axis we chose to consider "up" in computing r. The sign can be reversed by inverting (reflecting) *one* test axis (not both). Now visualize our "star-test Milky Way" with a horizontal reference axis (centroid) running through it. The tests are located at relative distances along this axis by their factor loadings. But they are dispersed above and below this centroid in such a way that what is left (the + and − residuals) sum to zero. We can move the centroid downward out of the space without changing the relative location of the tests (their factor loadings). If + is up and − is down, moving the centroid downward eliminates the negative signs when we get the centroid out of the test space. The systematic movement of the centroid out of the test space by eliminating negative signs is called *reflection*.

Correlation matrices frequently contain negative correlations when two tests measure the same thing oppositely. We can make any separate negative correlation positive by inverting (reflecting) one test axis, but in a matrix we would have to reverse the sign of every other correlation in the row (and column), so we must proceed systematically. Guilford (14: 482–86) and McCloy (17:447–49) give detailed instructions for *reflection*. The operation involves only the signs of the correlations or residuals. You count the number of negative signs in each row; the number in the corresponding column is the same. Then you reverse all of the signs in the row and column with the largest number of negative signs. You start with the row (and column) having the largest absolute sum if several have the same number. Reversing the signs puts that test axis "right end up" temporarily. This reduces the total number of negative signs in the matrix, but it also increases the number of negative signs for those tests that previously had positive signs. You count the number of negative signs again for each test or in each row and column, and you reflect the test or reverse the signs in the row and column for the test with the largest number or largest absolute sum. You repeat this process until all negative signs disappear from the matrix (or a minimal number remain). Since the same test may require reflection more than once, you must record which tests and how many times each is reflected. Then the factor loadings of tests reflected once or an odd number of times are given negative signs. All factor loadings were treated as positive in generating the products of factor loadings, but subsequent reflection makes some negative. This does not alter the communality, which depends on squared factor loadings.

Extracting further factor loadings (k_2, k_3, etc.) involves simply repeating the operations used in obtaining the first: computing the loadings, extracting the residuals, and reflection, which also determines the signs of the loadings. The factor loadings of the separate tests fluctuate as progressively more common variance is accounted for by groups of tests. The absolute sum of the residuals also decreases progressively as more common variance is extracted. The mathematical operations in factor analysis may still seem semimysterious, but their purpose is to extract factor loadings (k's) representing common factors underlying groups of tests. Extracting as many apparently "common" factors as you had tests initially is obvious nonsense, since some of these must be "test specific." Random errors presumably correlate zero, but some apparent factors may be correlated errors. When to stop extracting factor loadings is a moot question. But when appreciable loadings for individual tests appear, the analysis has gone beyond "common" factors and is extracting test-specifics. You had better back up. The imaginary, independent axes (centroids) provide factor loadings which locate tests, but they are otherwise meaningless and do not represent the common factors underlying the test battery. However, the mathematical operations have systematically reduced the information we have to deal with.

Extracting Meaning

Factor analysis reduces the covariance among tests to an equal number of factor loadings for each test. These factor loadings locate each test relative to n imaginary axes (centroids) and thus also relative to each other. One way of looking at the results is in terms of the communalities of the tests (the h^2's) which represent the proportion of the variance of each test accounted for by the common factors in the test battery. Since 1.00 equals "all," having an h^2 approximate 1.00 indicates that practically all of the variance of that test was accounted for by factors in common with other tests. But h^2's far below 1.00 indicate considerable test specific (a_s^2) or error (a_e^2) variance.

Looking at the results involves graphing all pairs of factor loadings. Systematically graphing the pairs requires preparing $n(n-1)/2$ graphs with vertical and horizontal (centroid) axes and unit circles with a radius = 1.00 representing "all" the variance of any test. Label the pairs of axes I and II, I and III, etc. for the pairs of centroids. Then plot all tests according to their paired factor loadings starting with k_{1a} and k_{2a} as distances on axes I and II to locate test point a relative to centroids I and II. Then plot k_{1b} and k_{2b} to locate test point b, etc. Label each test point with its test letter (a, b, etc.) as you plot. Then look at the graphs. Good tests, careful measurements, and appreciable common factors result in having some test points near the unit circle. Poor tests, dirty measurements, and low communality result in having all test points near the center of the unit circle like full-choke, bird-shot test patterns—the result of "bird-shot" testing. Tests do not generally concentrate along the centroids, but this is immaterial. Tests move right ($+$) or left ($-$) along one axis according to one factor loading and up ($+$) or down ($-$) according to a second loading. The paired loadings move tests closer to the unit circle as their factor loadings account for more of their variance. You then look for what Thurstone called "simple structure"—groups of test points or tests tending to cluster along mutually perpendicular (independent) axes *other than* the centroids. Analyses with good structure have some tests near the unit circle (high communality) and all tests close to, but not necessarily exactly on, these "other axes."

The second step in extracting meaning (*rotation*) involves rotating the centroid axes clockwise until they provide the best apparent fit to the test clusters. Rotation also requires adjusting the factor loadings. Each pair of factor loadings represents two sides (a and b) of a right triangle and the hypotenuse (c) represents the contribution of these loadings to the communality of the test. The Pythagorean theorem ($a^2 + b^2 = c^2$) defines the relation of the sides. We can let $k_{2a} = a = .66$ and $k_{1a} = b = .45$, then $a^2 + b^2 = .2025 + .4356 = .6381 = c^2$, which represents a major part of the communality and must remain constant. We can rotate the axes so test A coincides with the rotated axis II (now II'). Then the previous side opposite (*a*) coincides with side *c*, and the previous side adjacent (*b*) becomes zero. Thus $a^2 = c^2 = .6381$, and $b^2 = .00$. The rotated factor loading of test A on II' (k_{2a}') becomes the square root of .6381, or approximately .80, while k_{1a}' becomes .00, since locating test A *on* II' leaves no factor loading on I'. Rotation thus changed the factor loadings from .66 and .45 to .80 and .00 without changing the communality, or the test variance previously accounted for by the factor loadings. Formulae for computing the rotated factor loadings may be found in Thurstone (35), Guilford (14), and McCloy (17). Plotting the factor loadings and inspecting the factor structure is still desirable, but guessing the most desirable rotation and using the angle in adjusting the factor loadings is no longer necessary. Kaiser (15) developed "varimax," which gives the rotated factor loadings with the best least-squares fit. This maximizes the factor loadings of tests on the axes they fit best and also minimizes their squared deviations on the other axes, that is, fits the tests optimally to their respective axes. The rotated factor loadings indicate how well each test measures each factor. Higher loadings are better.

The final step in extracting meaning involves logical analysis of the tests aligned along each rotated axis. The test with the highest loading measures this factor most accurately. Tests with negative loadings measure the factor in reverse. You ask yourself the double question, "What common quality (factor) are the tests with positive loadings measuring collectively and the tests with negative loadings measuring in reverse?" Your answer becomes the name of the factor. Authors, like parents, assign their brain children different names. Thus author labelling often results in different labels for seemingly similar abilities or qualities underlying human behavior and productivity, along with some same-label-but-different-components situations.

Factor analysis has many elegant ramifications. The rotated, orthogonal factor loadings represent independent vectors (distances on perpendicular axes). Vectors are additive algebraically so the "partialled out" components can be combined, as in multiple correlation. Oblique (nonperpendicular) rotation of an axis is possible, but oblique factors and factor loadings are interdependent, so tests of one factor still measure another factor in part. However, human abilities and qualities may not be reducible to independent underlying factors, as an orthogonal analysis assumes.

McCloy summarized the capabilities and limitations of factor analysis (17:440–45) and his comments are still essentially valid. Factor analysis can clarify the relations in a battery of tests, but it cannot cleanse dirty tests or correct sloppy measurements. Qualities or abilities not measured by at least two tests cannot appear as *common* factors, since specific variance (a_s^2) goes into $1 - h^2$ along with error variance (a_e^2). High communalities (h^2 above .8 or .9) signify good tests and reliable measurements, although low communalities may result from high test specificity (if you stop prior to the single-test "factors") simply because no other test in the battery measured this factor. Good analyses frequently result from moderate correlations (.6 to .4) when these are combined with correlations approximating zero. Factor analysis can be a very useful research tool except that extracting what one failed to include is impossible; testing all human factors in one test battery is virtually impossible, and bigger test batteries involve more error variance because humans are inherently erratic and adaptable and therefore they change between tests and as a result of being tested. Factor analysis clarifies interrelationships among tests and shows the relative effectiveness of similar tests. Many factor analyses have contributed materially to the interpretation of human data. Others with oddly labelled factors and some dirty data have also compounded confusion.

REFERENCES

1. Andrews, T. G. An introduction to psychological methodology. In *Methods of Psychology*. New York: John Wiley & Sons, 1948. 716 pp.
2. Boneau, C. A. The effect of violations of assumptions underlying the *t* test. *Psychological Bulletin* 57: 49–64, 1960.
3. Box, G. E. P. Non-normality and tests of variance. *Biometrika* 40: 318–335, 1953.
4. _____. Some theorems on quadratic forms applied in the study of analysis of variance problems. I. Effects of inequality of variance in the one-way classification. *Annals of Mathematical Statistics* 25: 290–302, 1954.
5. _____. Some theorems on quadratic forms applied in the study of analysis of variance problems. II. Effects of inequality of variance and of correlation between errors in the two-way classification. *Annals of Mathematical Statistics* 25: 484–488, 1954.
6. Bravais, A. Analyse mathématique sur les probabilités des erreurs de situation d'un point. *Ácademie des Sciences, Mémoires Présentés par Divers Savants*, IIe Série, 9: 255, 1846.
7. Duncan, D. B. Multiple range and multiple *F* tests. *Biometrics* 11: 1–42, March 1955.
8. _____. Multiple range tests for correlated and heteroscedastic means. *Biometrics* 13: 164–176, June 1957.
9. Edwards, Allen L. *Experimental Design in Psychological Research*. New York: Holt, Rinehart & Winston, 1960 (3d ed., 1968).
10. _____. *Statistical Methods*. 2d ed. New York: Holt, Rinehart & Winston, 1967 (3d ed., 1969).
11. Fisher, Ronald A. On the interpretation of χ^2 from contingency tables, and the calculation of P. *Journal of the Royal Statistical Society* 85: 597–612, 1922.
12. _____. *Statistical Methods for Research Workers*. 3d ed. London: Oliver & Boyd, 1930 (4th ed., New York: Hafner Publishing Co., 1970).

13. Galton, Francis. *Memories of My Life*. London: Methuen & Co., 1908. Reprint. New York: AMS Press, n.d.
14. Guilford, Jay P. *Psychometric Methods*. New York: McGraw-Hill Book Co., 1936 (2d ed., 1954).
15. Kaiser, H. F. The varimax criterion for analytic rotation in factor analysis. *Psychometrika* 23: 187–200, 1958.
16. Kuels, M. The use of the "studentized range" in connection with an analysis of variance. *Euphytica* 1: 112–122, 1952.
17. McCloy, C. H. The factor analysis as a research technique. In *Research Methods Applied to Health, Physical Education, and Recreation*. Washington, D.C.: American Association for Health, Physical Education, and Recreation, 1949. (Out of print)
18. Newman, D. The distribution of the range in samples from a normal population, expressed in terms of an independent estimate of standard deviation. *Biometrika* 31: 20–30, 1939.
19. Pearson, K. Regression, heredity, and panmixia. *Philosophical Transactions of the Royal Society* (of London), Series A, 187: 253–318, 1896.
20. _____. On the criterion that a given system of deviations from the probable in the case of a correlated system of variables is such that it can be reasonably assumed to have arisen from random sampling. (The London, Edinburgh, and Dublin) *Philosophical Magazine* (and Journal of Science), Series 5, 50: 157–175, 1900.
21. _____. I. Mathematical contributions to the theory of evolution. VII. On the correlation of characters not quantitatively measurable. *Philosophical Transactions of the Royal Society* (of London), Series A, 195: 1–47, 1901.
22. Peters, Charles C. and van Voorhis, Walter R. *Statistical Methods and Their Mathematical Bases*. New York: McGraw-Hill Book Co., 1940. Reprint. Westport, Conn.: Greenwood Press, n.d.
23. Scheffé, H. A method for judging all contrasts in the analysis of variance. *Biometrika* 40: 87–104, 1953.
24. Siegel, Sidney. *Nonparametric Statistics for the Behavioral Sciences*. New York: McGraw-Hill Book Co., 1956.
25. Spearman, C. "General intelligence," objectively determined and measured. *American Journal of Psychology* 15: 201–292, 1904.
26. _____. The theory of two factors. *Psychological Review* 21: 101–115, 1914.
27. Stevens, Stanley S. Mathematics, measurement, and psychophysics. In *Handbook of Experimental Psychology*. New York: John Wiley & Sons, 1951.
28. Student [Gosset, William Sealy]. The probable error of a mean. *Biometrika* 6: 1–25, March 1908.
29. _____. New tables for testing the significance of observations. *Metron* 5: 105–120, 1925.
30. Thomson, Godfrey H. A hierarchy without a general factor. *British Journal of Psychology* 8: 271–281, Sept. 1916.
31. _____. A sampling theory of ability. In *The Essentials of Mental Measurement*, 2d ed., edited by William Brown and Godfrey H. Thomson. Cambridge: The University Press, 1921.
32. _____. On complete families of correlation coefficients, and their tendency to zero tetrad differences. *British Journal of Psychology* 26: 63–92, 1935.
33. Thurstone, Louis L. Multiple factor analysis. *Psychological Review* 38: 406–427, Sept. 1931.

34. ———. *The Vectors of Mind*. Chicago: University of Chicago Press, 1935. 266 pp.
35. ———. *Multiple Factor Analysis*. Chicago: University of Chicago Press, 1947.
36. Tukey, J. W. Comparing individual means in the analysis of variance. *Biometrics* 5: 99–114, June 1949.
37. Winer, B. J. *Statistical Principles in Experimental Design*. New York: McGraw-Hill Book Co., 1962 (2d ed., 1971).

PART IV

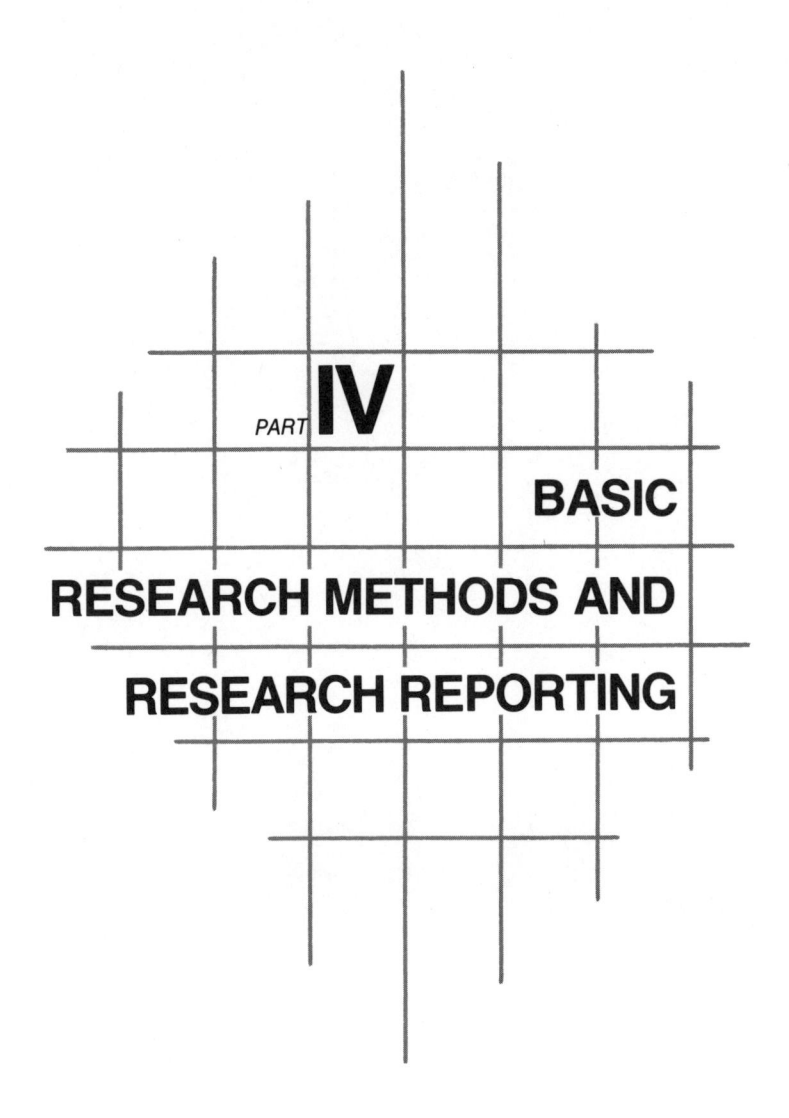

BASIC RESEARCH METHODS AND RESEARCH REPORTING

CHAPTER 10 EXPERIMENTAL RESEARCH

Robert N. Singer
Florida State University
Tallahassee, Florida

NATURE OF EXPERIMENTAL RESEARCH

THERE ARE MANY WAYS in which we obtain information about the world in which we live. Questions are raised and may be answered through logic, belief, appeal to authority, and experimentation. Much of our knowledge is determined from a combination of these sources, but in any given circumstance a focus on one method may be more desirable. Although common sense alone is appropriate at times in providing information and in directing behavior, action based on facts, yet tempered with reason, is most often favored.

One way to obtain facts is through controlled, systematically planned observations of one's environment. Science depends on this procedure. But science also operates on three basic premises, namely: (*a*) everything in nature occurs in some specific amount or to some specific degree and is measurable, (*b*) effects have causes, and (*c*) any authority may be questioned. With research, we examine and reexamine man and nature. And indeed, "the objective of *research* . . . is to use observation as a basis for answering questions of interest " (6:1). The nature of research is such as to present ways of studying problems in areas of interest as well as to provide tentative answers.

Scientific research resembles other forms of research when controlled and systematic observation is directed at differentiating, describing, and categorizing various things and events. The work of scientists involves these matters, but they are not specifically scientific techniques. Analysis and synthesis are not confined to science. A wide variety of research employs "scientific techniques" without being scientific. In scientific research, experimentation is crucial.

The Experiment

Experimentation involves formulating and testing hypotheses. We begin with a hunch. These hunches provide direction for our thoughts on problems, and an experiment allows us, in a formal setting, to see if they are confirmed. A planned attack is made on a particular problem and the research experiment is characterized by the fact that changes are induced in natural events and results are carefully observed, recorded, and analyzed. This is the earmark of experimental research as contrasted with descriptive research; there must be some manipulation or change in at least one variable under study.

Historically speaking, concepts and implications of experimentation have been diverse and misunderstood. At one time people expected miraculous answers from experiments but were, instead, disappointed and disillusioned. It is now understood that experiments do not provide once-and-for-all answers. Facts are not necessarily permanent, and numerous experiments, constantly refined in technique, provide tentative solutions to problems.

This is especially true with experiments dealing with human behavior. Going from the classical experiment in the physical sciences to experimental design in the social sciences is primarily a matter of inherent differences in the specimens tested to determine causal effects. The degree of control in and sophistication of an experiment in physics or chemistry is potentially far greater than for human behavior experiments as exemplified in psychology, sociology, physiology, and physical education.

A metal rod of specified composition and conformation can be subjected to a progressive stress (deforming force) and the strain (deformation) can be measured. The strain/stress ratio for metals tends to be linear, within limits, and this defines its modulus of elasticity. A second metal rod of the same composition and conformation will exhibit a practically identical modulus of elasticity. Testing numerous rods of the same composition and conformation rapidly becomes a waste of time. Metal rods of different composition and conformation exhibit different moduli of elasticity and differences in the way they become fatigued and fracture. But the response characteristics of identical metal rods tend to be highly consistent, so the result (effect or strain) of a specified stress (cause) can be accurately predicted. The stress/strain relation is sufficiently consistent to permit predicting backward from the observed effect (strain, deformation, or fracture) to the probable cause (stress) very accurately. "Backward prediction" can be used to determine the probable cause of airplane crashes from the effects.

Living tissues and organs of the same kind tend to respond or function similarly within and across species. Common structural and organic characteristics determine species and these extend over subspecies, although subspecies have other distinguishable differences. Individual specimens within species and subspecies have marked structural and organic similarity, so physiological responses across individuals within species and subspecies have marked similarity. Thus individual specimens tend to be typical or representative of their genetic group in terms of physiological responses. Man is a warm-blooded, mammalian vertebrate with temperature control, young-suckling, and skeletal characteristics basically similar to other warm-blooded mammalian vertebrates, and hence has markedly similar physiological responses. One human specimen tends to be typical of other human specimens physiologically. Organic functional changes can be determined experimentally by varying the stress (cause) and measuring the strain (effect). Predicting effects from causes is generally possible and determining causes from effects is also possible to some extent.

Studying animal (including human) behavior experimentally presents methodological problems different from those in the physical and biological sciences. Carnivores must hunt and kill to survive. This may seem instinctive but actually depends on parental training. Animals with adequate food and without this training live amicably with other animals that would normally be their foes or victims. Perceiving another animal as friend, foe, or victim depends on training and experience. The response of individual animals to the same stimulus situation may differ widely. Most animals depend on rather restricted combinations of environmental conditions for survival. Animals and birds stake out territorial claims and fight to defend them. Animals can either adapt, migrate, or die if their habitat becomes unsuitable. Animals limited to stereotyped responses cannot adapt. Man is the most adaptive animal, with rats a close second. Man can survive in almost any habitat, can survive on a wide variety of foods, and can also adapt nature to his needs and desires, often to the detriment of other animals. Rats cannot adapt nature to their needs, but beavers can. Humans are the most complex, individually different, and inconsistent animals behaviorially. Two humans subjected to the same stimulus situation (cause) may give vastly different responses. They may approach, avoid, or squat, depending on whether they view the situation as interesting or desirable, undesirable or dangerous, or simply uninteresting and inconsequential.

Sorting out cause and effect relations in humans is a highly complex procedure (see discussion of "cause," p. 30). No individual responds in the same way as all men, so we must use a representative sample. This raises sampling problems concerning how to select representative subjects and what larger group they represent. How they respond on the average (the dependent variable) indicates the effect of the experimental treatment (the independent variable). They may respond to ambient and irrelevant stimuli that happen to occur while they are being tested, so controlling or equating extraneous variables is a problem. Their responses may differ in kind, vary in amount, or simply be inconsistent. Mean differences show the effect of treatments, but means can differ by chance so you need some way of separating what seems chance (sampling error) and what seems other than chance (a real effect). Sampling, controlling irrelevant variables, and separating the apparently chance from the apparently real are the major methodological problems in experimentally determining cause and effect relations in human behavior—the problems of experimental design.

Limitations understood, the experimental method, in any discipline, probably best exemplifies the principles of scientific method. And for a workable definition of the word "experiment," let us accept Edwards' (6:9) statement that "when certain variables can be controlled or manipulated directly in a research problem by the investigator the research procedure is often described as an experiment." An experiment in scientific terms is the way of determining cause and effect relations quantitatively.

Correlation is a way of determining quantitatively the degree of relationship or covariance between two or more tests on the same group of subjects. (See pp. 215–219.) Height and weight covary appreciably in humans but neither can be systematically varied to produce a corresponding change in the other. Correlation requires data from a group but it is not a "group experimental method," since nothing is administered as a cause to produce an effect.

This chapter will focus specifically on what used to be called "group experimental methods," presently referred to as experimental design. Psychologists and others interested primarily in determining cause and effect relations in human and animal behavior adapted the experimental method to their material and problems by substituting a group for an individual specimen. This generated methodological problems of selecting a representative sample, controlling extraneous variables, collecting appropriate data, and then separating incidental chance changes from those that seemed other than chance. The methodological problems of designing effective experiments in this context become a major preoccupation; thus the label, experimental design.

It must be pointed out that experimentation need occur not only in the laboratory. *Laboratory research* and *field research* (in the classroom, swimming pool, and gymnasium) can and should be employed to investigate problems. Laboratory research permits more controlled operations but usually under artificial conditions. On the other hand, field research is more practical and realistic, but is undertaken in situations that are difficult to control. The results of each type of experimentation must complement each other to promote the application of research findings.

The typical physical educator, who is usually recognized as a practitioner, may see little value in laboratory studies. However, the advantages of the laboratory experiment, as Candland (4:7) reports, are—

1. The findings may be generalized to problems other than those posed by the original question.

2. It is less likely to produce erroneous or inexact results than an experiment conducted under nonlaboratory conditions.

Clearly, the well-controlled laboratory study can tease out more specific relations between variables. These relations can then be used to assist one's understanding of complex practical problems. However, before one can undertake a laboratory or field study, certain qualities are required of the experimenter.

Qualifications of the Experimenter

It bears repeating that, first of all, the experimenter needs a spirit of curiosity, or *inquiry*. A search for the truth, a dissatisfaction with the present state of knowledge, a desire to resolve an issue in a scientifically acceptable manner are all involved. Second, *background* information is necessary before an experiment can be seriously considered. Experience, reading, and communication contribute to the investigator's level of understanding of the problem, enabling him to raise legitimate questions, conceive of reasonable hypotheses, and formulate adequate experimental designs.

Since statistics and experiments often go hand-in-hand, an understanding of *mathematics* is most helpful. Statistics, as will be seen throughout this chapter, aid in various steps from the initial to the terminal stages of the experiment. Finally, good old-fashioned *common sense* is needed at all points throughout the experiment. The investigator must make numerous decisions as he proceeds, not all of which can be determined by formal guidelines. The evaluation of suggested procedures, the analysis of the particular experimental conditions, and the competency to handle unpredictable and unexpected occurrences all require common sense. Through these and other personal qualities, the experimenter can proceed to examine theories and statements, formulate workable hypotheses for a particular problem, and finally, execute the investigation.

PRINCIPLES OF EXPERIMENTAL RESEARCH

A number of essential features of the design of any experiment should concern the investigator. They help to promote more effective ways of securing information (data). Better designs are dependent on the qualifications of the researcher, background information about the problem, the understanding and application of design principles, and a knowledge of modern experimental statistics.

In order to test hypotheses, observations of behavior or performance must be made and data collected. The design of the experiment will systematically integrate the recording of observations, the operations to be undertaken, and the statistical analysis of the accumulated data. The ultimate goal of any experimenter is to obtain relevant data in the most practical manner, as far as time, cost, and general scope of the study are concerned. And, naturally, in any design the attempt is made to specify conditions, minimize procedural errors, and arrive at meaningful conclusions. Therefore, the design can be viewed as the *plan* for executing the experiment.

Understanding the Problem

Before attempting the design of any study, the experimenter should be thoroughly familiar with all aspects of the problem. This would imply an awareness of related research procedures and findings, an understanding of equipment that might be used, and as much background information as possible. Logical hypotheses cannot be generated and designs formulated unless the problem is clearly understood and defined.

Hypotheses

After the experimenter has identified the problem, he sets forth hypotheses (see pp. 33–34, 51–52) related to the observations he expects to collect. These hypotheses act as guidelines. They direct the experimenter in his thoughts and actions and provide tentative feelings regarding the outcome of the experiment. They are based on completed related research, authoritative opinions or theory, and the investigator's reasoning.

For example, if one group of subjects receives a reward—a form of motivation to improve performance—while another group of subjects does not, we may make a *specific prediction* of a performance difference in favor of the rewarded group. Formally speaking, this hypothesis of a difference in performance between groups is called a *directional hypothesis*. Prior research is, in general, in agreement as to the effectiveness of reward as a means of bettering performances. However, if each group were to receive a specific type of reward, we might speculate that there would be little or *no difference* between the groups in their resultant performances. The hypothesis of no difference between groups except chance is formally referred to as the *null hypothesis*. It indicates that no difference in observation is expected as a result of the experimental operations (manipulations) employed.

In most cases, we are not sure of any differential treatment outcomes between groups; hence, the null hypothesis is often postulated. Tests of significance result in the rejection or failure to reject the null hypothesis. Since decisions are based on a rejection or a failure to reject the null hypothesis, the hypothesis should be put in a testable form, e.g.: $U_1 = U_2$. In the hypothetical study alluded to in the previous paragraph, U_1 could represent the reward group and U_2 the nonreward group. Another illustration of the null hypothesis is the statement that two given samples are drawn from the identical population. A directional hypothesis indicating the expected outcome may be the null hypothesis we test.

Selection of Variables

When defining and delimiting the experiment (see pp. 49–54), one must specify the variables of concern while attempting to minimize the influence of extraneous variables. *Variables* for any given experiment refer to the alterable aspects that the experimenter attempts to identify, control, and manipulate. He decides what is important to hold constant, what to measure, and what to ignore.

Independent Variables

Everything in the immediate vicinity of the experimental situation constitutes stimuli. Those stimuli of interest to the investigator to control, manipulate, and compare are called *independent variables*. Treatments are operations which result in the manipulation of the stimulus conditions that experimental groups of subjects will experience. In a sense, then, these determined variables of concern are *fixed* by the experimenter to insure a given event. Specified conditions are deliberately varied and observations recorded. These experimental conditions or treatments may differ *qualitatively* (in kind) or vary *quantitatively* (in degree). Examples in research of independent variables would include a comparison of (a) teaching methods, (b) levels of motivation, (c) types of motivation, and (d) strength-developing techniques.

Dependent Variables

Just as it is necessary to specify operations that result in the manipulation of variables, it is also a necessity to indicate operations for recording results of possible changes in behavior. Variables resulting from these operations and which reflect performance, or behavior, are called *dependent variables*. Thus, in the classic sense, stimulation is the independent variable while the response constitutes the dependent variable. It is the variable the experimenter observes as a result of the manipulation of experimental conditions. In a learning experiment, the number of trials designated to learn a skill is the independent variable, while the dependent variable is the score recorded in each trial.

Individual Considerations

Sometimes variables are classified as *organismic*; that is, there is reference to measurements and observations made on the subjects such as height, weight, skinfold, reaction time, and the like. These measurements are calculated directly and are not the result of experimental manipulation. They are often used singularly or in combination as a means of placing subjects into matched groups (a technique to be discussed later in this chapter).

Irrelevant Matter (Extraneous Variables)

In experiments such as those in the natural sciences, it is relatively easy to control variables which are not of interest to the investigator but which may nevertheless confound the results of the study. In less well-controlled behavioral studies, contrarily, more variables usually interact which may affect the experiment. Nontreatment variables, or those that the experimenter would rather disregard, are *extraneous variables*. In any experiment, *all* variables that might possibly affect the observations and results should be identified. Not only must the independent variables be appropriately designated, but the so-called "irrelevant matter" should be randomized or systematically applied in such a way that it has an equal chance of affecting the outcome of all treatment groups. Other discussion in this chapter will elaborate on this point.

Selection of Subjects

The experimenter must now face the important decision of subject selection. The nature of the subjects, the method used in their selection, and their placement into treatment groups will greatly determine the validity of the experimental results and the inferences that might be drawn from these findings. It is essential that careful planning and consideration go into the designation of subjects.

The group of subjects with which the investigator works is a *sample* of a larger body of potential subjects (see pp. 145–153). The theoretical universe of subjects with characteristics similar to those in which the experimenter is interested represents a *population*. Obviously, if one were interested in comparing practice conditions and their effects on the acquisition of archery skill by freshman college women students, it would be totally impractical to use *all* freshman college women students throughout the country as subjects. However, from this population of potential subjects, a sample may be drawn. Different techniques of sampling for subject selection are found in the literature, some more practical than others, some theoretically better than others.

If inferences or generalizations are to be made to given populations, *subject representativeness* becomes an important aspect of sampling. The sample must also be large enough for reliable results, yet small enough to be practical to test. Tversky and Kahneman (17) warn against popular but erroneous suppositions about the laws of chance, especially for small samples. As they point out, the law of *large* numbers guarantees that large samples will be highly representative of their population. Only in some cases will small samples tend to be as highly representative. Typical means of subject selection are (*a*) random sampling, (*b*) stratified random sampling, (*c*) available intact groups, and (*d*) volunteers.

Random and Stratified Sampling

These techniques were treated fully in Chapter 8 (pp. 146–150). Mathematical models for inferential statistics are based on random sampling to eliminate any systematic bias. This makes random sampling a basic assumption in making inferences concerning the effects of treatments on the population. Selecting random samples from relatively large populations is theoretically desirable for representativeness but does not assure that the subjects will be either available or cooperative. Obtaining complete data from such samples is virtually impossible and missing data make the sample no longer truly random so inferences are doubtful. One way around the experimenter's perennial dilemma is to *assign* subjects *randomly*, and preferably in equal numbers, to the various treatments. This meets the basic "random sampling" assumption of an equal opportunity among subjects to receive any treatment. Random assignment is possible, necessary for using inferential statistics, and essentially equivalent to random sampling. The mathematician who made the model defined his "population" as the numbered beans in his bowl, not *all* beans of the same kind numbered consecutively. Then he sampled (selected them) by chance. You can also stratify or categorize subjects on one basis and then treat them in some way to determine whether they respond like random samples from a homogeneous population or the treatments had a differential effect.

Intact Groups or "Cluster Samples"

The *availability* of subjects is one of the prime factors in the acquisition of subjects. Thus, it is quite understandable (although often not forgivable!) why many experiments include subjects who were chosen for the *convenience* of the investigator. "Captive audiences" are ready-made subjects. It is no wonder, then, that Meyers (12:13) writes of the college sophomore and the rat as representing the most frequently-used subjects! Both are readily available for testing purposes. In fact, in many universities serving as a subject is a requirement for psychology majors.

Intact groups can serve convenient purposes in the experimental study. It is suggested, however, that with data collected under such conditions, conclusions be applied only to the groups and conditions of the study. Random sampling permits generalizations beyond the scope of the experiment, and the arbitrary selection of average or specific subjects is not as ideal as if the subjects were chosen randomly. Kerlinger warns, "When working with samples that have not been selected at random, generalization to the characteristics or relations between characteristics in the population is, strictly speaking, not possible" (9:60).

Nevertheless, it is possible that an arbitrarily selected group of subjects or a group composed of volunteers would have a number of characteristics typical of the population from which they came. Thus making inferences from data collected under such circumstances is not totally dangerous. The nonrandom sample must be described in detail if inferences are to be drawn to and relations seen with individuals outside of the study. The cluster sample is discussed further on pp. 150–151.

Volunteers

When the investigator asks for volunteers to participate in his study, he is not working with a representative sample. The experiment is biased because of this method of selection. Research indicates that volunteer subjects tend to reveal personality traits different from those of nonvolunteers. Since the random sampling technique has not been invoked, the precautions and steps suggested for intact groups are recommended with the use of volunteers. This does not mean that volunteers, as subjects, are frowned upon. Instead, advantages and limitations of this sampling technique should be recognized. The difficulty in obtaining subjects for most experiments encourages the widespread use of volunteers. The obvious advantage is their willingness to participate in the study. Appropriate statistical designs and limited data inferences should also be recognized. Intact groups and volunteers should be assigned randomly to treatments.

Control

Since an experiment is viewed as *controlled inquiry*, one of the basic principles of experimental design is effective control of all relevant aspects of the investigation. The experimenter can *vary* things as he sees fit in order to fulfill his objectives. Much responsibility for correct decisions and adequate control of experimental events rests on his shoulders. In the usual experiment undertaken in physical education, events are not merely observed in their natural setting; rather, subjects are viewed in contrived circumstances. If experimental results are to be accepted with confidence, control is needed from the moment of subject sampling to the ultimate statistical analysis of the data.

Subject Selection

Questions to be answered in this area are (*a*) What type of subjects are of interest? (*b*) How shall they be sampled? (*c*) How many subjects are needed? (*d*) How shall they be placed in groups?

Subject Manipulation

The investigator must decide on how the subjects are placed into groups and how many groups are to be formed. The placement can be random, arbitrary (specific intact groups), or based on the characteristics of these subjects by which they are matched when assigned to groups. The number of groups will depend on the nature and extent of the observations of interest. Furthermore, subjects are manipulated when the investigator states how, where, and when they are to be tested, and under what preexperimental and experimental conditions.

Experimental Materials

The variable(s) of interest can often be measured several ways. The investigator must decide which apparatus, equipment, instruments, and conditions are to be used. The nature of these materials and their specific usage within the context of the experiment are also of concern. Independent variables are controlled or manipulated in the experiment, and the extent of this control is the investigator's responsibility. When the experimental conditions are specified, they are considered fixed.

Environmental Variables

Extraneous variables are ever-present in any study, and they may be handled in essentially one of two ways. According to Kurtz (10), errors in measurement due to extraneous variables can vary (*a*) *randomly* or (*b*) *systematically* (see pp. 164–168). To review, factors that cannot be held constant from subject to subject but are allowed to vary in a chance fashion are said to be *random sources of error.* Systematic sources of *error* are experimenter-induced, and occur when, for example, subjects in one group are tested at one time of day, and subjects from another group are tested at another time.

Anything that might influence the dependent variable should be either (*a*) chance distributed, or (*b*) held constant from subject to subject and group to group. In the latter case irrelevant variables are uniformly applied to all subjects. Treatments should be as similar as possible with respect to factors *other* than the one(s) of concern to provide assurance that differences in treatment values were due to the experimental treatments alone.

Data Collection and Analysis

Means of collecting and analyzing information are sometimes dictated by the design of the experiment but more often tend to reflect the decisions of the investigator. (See Chapter 8 on data collection.) Therefore, by merely designating the tests and statistical tools to be employed, he demonstrates control in the study. The particular type of statistical analysis might very well yield results and permit interpretations dissimilar to the outcomes of other statistical models. In the final step of the experimental procedure, it is imperative that the experimenter has an understanding of inferences that results from statistical decision making.

Validity

Validity as a principle of experimental design has various implications. (For additional discussion of validity, see pp. 37-38, 81, 106-107. For Ray (13), it concerns the level of significance chosen by the investigator and the true probability of a Type I error occurring (to be discussed later). He suggests that randomization guarantees validity.

Campbell and Stanley (3) go into far greater detail, however, in their interpretation and considerations of aspects of validity. According to these writers, both *internal* and *external validity* problems must be reconciled. Internal validity signifies whether experimental treatments *really* made a difference (if one is statistically revealed), while external validity refers to those generalizations (what and to whom) that can be made as a result of the study. With regard to internal validity, Campbell and Stanley discuss a number of factors that might have a bearing, e.g., (*a*) the method of subject selection, (*b*) passage of time between tests and the influence of maturation, (*c*) the effects of one test on another test, (d) the consistency of the instrumentation, and (e) experimental mortality (the loss of subjects from the study). Experimental validity, in its broadest interpretation, will depend on a host of procedural and statistical operations.

Reproducibility

An experiment that has been well designed and clearly reported is more apt to be duplicated with similar results. It is obvious that several replications of an experiment are essential if certain relations of variables are to be verified. As the term is used in this connection, the function of reproducibility is to enable any researcher to repeat an experiment, to observe similar conditions, and determine the similarity of results between these experiments. An experiment that cannot be reproduced has little or no inferential value but may produce findings of practical value. When controls are precise and procedures are acceptable (in both studies), a second experiment serves as a valid check on the results of the first experiment. No matter how much confidence one has in his original data, replication of results certainly enhances their reasonableness. But we must not deceive ourselves by having unduly high expectations about the reproducibility of significant findings, and Tversky and Kahneman (17) explain why. They also discount the widespread belief that replication samples can be smaller than original samples. On the contrary, they argue for the replication sample to be larger if the once-obtained significant finding is to have a high probability of being verified.

Biases

It is probably impossible to expect that biases will not enter into various stages of the experiment. These biases could arise from a number of sources. Although they may not be completely avoided, they should at least be recognized and minimized.

Subject Bias

Individuals may differ in their reaction to an experimental situation. Intra-individual differences may also be observed if testing occurs on a number of occasions. Experiment-induced reactions include (a) expectations, (b) motivation, and (c) needs. One subject may not care about the study in which he participates nor about his performance, another may be extremely motivated. A subject may feel he should do better under a certain treatment condition, worse under another, and his preconceived notions could result in treatment differences because of psychological factors and personal bias rather than the treatments themselves. Naturally, these distinctions between individuals also hold true for the same individual when he is tested repeatedly.

Experimenter Bias

Unwittingly, the investigator may influence experimental outcomes through his own prejudices. He may hope or expect to find something and therefore encourage results leading in this direction. For example, treatment A and treatment B are administered to two different groups of subjects. If the experimenter hopes that treatment A will be more effective than B, he may knowingly or unknowingly provide directions and situations which will benefit the A Group. In reality, he should treat all subjects and groups the same except for the imposed treatment conditions.

There are so many ways in which intentional or unintentional experimental errors may arise as a result of the investigator's characteristics that an entire book is devoted to the problem, Rosenthal (14). The subject interacts with the experimenter to such an extent that consideration must be given to their relationship in matters of race, religion, sex, age, anxiety, and the like. It has been found that if the experimenter has a high need for approval, subjects score better on their tests. How the investigator looks, acts, and behaves may affect the subjects' responses. Rosenthal (14:61) concludes that generally ". . . subjects tend to respond in the way they feel to be most proper in the light of the investigator's attributes." The experimenter may inadvertently play a greater role in affecting subjects' behavior than he realizes.

Instrument Bias

Not all experiments employ apparatus and equipment. Those instruments in use, however, should be constantly checked and calibrated. Minor discrepancies in measurement because of the instrument itself may result in biased findings. For instance, if three different hand dynamometers are used by three different groups of subjects, each should be compared against an accurate strength gauge and against the others to ensure their validity. Timing apparatuses, as well as any other pieces of equipment used for measurement purposes, are possible sources of bias. They need to be continually checked.

STATISTICS

Statistics involve mathematical ways of dealing with problems. From the simple to the most complex, statistical models help to lend greater credence to that which we would like to consider as facts. As was pointed out earlier, a prime objective of research is to determine facts, and statistics in experiments play an important role in reaching this objective. An entire chapter is devoted to a full-scale discussion of statistical methods (Chapter 9), but it is necessary to mention several important applications to experimental research.

Use of Statistics in Experiments

Stated most simply, statistics in any experiment serve in the *collection* and *interpretation* of data. They aid in the solution of problems. The interrelationship of statistics with the design of a study has been best explained by Fisher, one of the earliest and leading contributors to aspects of experimental design: "Statistical procedure and experimental design are only two different aspects of the same whole, and that whole is the logical requirement of the complete process of adding to natural knowledge by experimentation" (7:3).

It has already been emphasized how statistical probability procedures may be used for the purposes of sampling subjects and assigning them to groups. With regard to interpretation of recorded observations, statistics reduce large quantities of data to workable figures. Statistical tools offer an efficient and effective means of analyzing and therefore interpreting data. Without interpretation, observations are meaningless.

When two treatments are compared, we want to know if there is a *real* difference between them. Utilizing statistical operations, a probability statement about the significance of a difference can be made. Not only are conclusions drawn for a particular sample in a given study, but inferences may be made about the probability of such results occurring in an entire population that is exposed to similar conditions. Thus statistics, as a part of the experimental design, help the investigator to select and designate subjects and conditions, collect data, reduce data, analyze and interpret data, and make conclusions and inferences about the data.

Level of Significance

Various tests of significance may be applied to data in order to make inferences. These mathematical models and their appropriate uses have been described elsewhere in this book (Chapter 9). The particular test of significance used to compare treatment differences is typically based on the null hypothesis; i.e., that there will be no differences found in the comparisons. Not only must the investigator select the statistical test, he also must decide on the *level of significance* with which he wishes to work.

The level of significance is associated with the outcome of an experiment, for it concerns the decision as to whether to reject or fail to reject the null hypothesis. In the words of Ray (13:23), the choice of level "... fixes the number of chance outcomes he [the investigator] is willing to interpret mistakenly as real effects." The level of significance represents the risk he wishes to take in rejecting the null hypothesis when it is true.

Sometimes the terms *level of significance* and *level of confidence* are used incorrectly, in an interchangeable manner (16). The first actually is incorporated in hypothesis testing; the latter in estimating parameter values. A confidence interval estimates with a certain predetermined degree of assuredness where a particular obtained value lies. Therefore, we can use the .95 level of confidence, for example, to determine the probability that a population mean will be surrounded by 95% of all such calculated intervals using the same sample size. With the level of significance, the concern is with the probability of rejecting the null hypothesis when it is true and the probability of failing to reject it when it is false. Often the .05 level is utilized in making tests of significance. With the significance level set at .05, the confidence level is .95. These levels are complementary to each other but there is a difference in the information provided by each.

Probability

Probability statements underlie the interpretation of the selected levels of significance. A student reading an experimental research article invariably comes across such statements as "the .05 level of significance was used," or "the .01 level served as the rejection value." These two significance levels are those most often found in the research, although they need not be the only ones which the investigator may choose.

By selecting a level such as the .05, the researcher indicates that there are but five chances in 100 that a difference this large could occur by chance alone. If the difference between comparisons is significant, say at the .05 level, the null hypothesis is rejected and this difference is viewed as *real*, or *true*, rather than chance. When a nonsignificant value is obtained (perhaps the .06 level or greater), the null hypothesis is retained and any observed difference in the experimental results is said to be due to chance.

Errors

A great difficulty encountered by researchers is the choice of a significance (alpha) level. It was previously mentioned that the .05 or the .01 level of significance is generally employed. The researcher, however, is not restricted to these probability values. Instead of proceeding in an arbitrary fashion, consideration of the nature of the study and the implications of its results should determine the level.

If the results of an experiment can lead to tremendous medical advancement, perhaps a more lenient significance level will be selected, e.g., $p = .10$. Further experimentation in the area would be encouraged rather than discouraged. Perhaps all that is needed is a slight refinement in the medical procedures for a breakthrough to occur. Then again, if the results will make the difference between the wide-scale adoption and use of a drug, the most strict rejection value, such as $p = .01$ or .001, is necessary. In typical behavioral experiments, the findings will not be of such importance. We might, therefore, think it wise not to be too severe in the selection of a significance level. On the other side of the argument, control of variables is often difficult to obtain to the desired degree in such experiments (as opposed to chemistry and physics research) and one might want to employ a value such as the .01 in order to compensate for such shortcomings. Perhaps those two viewpoints are the leading cause for a more middle of the road approach and the usual selection of the .05 level in physical education research rather than, say, the .01 or .10 levels. In any event, the investigator weighs the nature of his study and its possible effects on those who would be concerned with and apply these findings and then decides on the size of the significance level *before* he collects the data.

One of two types of errors may result from the size of the rejection value selected: Type I, an error of the first kind; or Type II, an error of the second kind. A *Type I error* occurs when the null hypothesis is rejected when it should have been retained. A *Type II error* refers to failure to reject the null hypothesis when it should have been rejected. The probabilities of Type I and Type II errors are determined by the researcher, the first by his choice of significance level and the second by his willingness to make a Type II error. Type I and Type II errors do not always vary inversely. Alpha (probability of Type I errors) and beta (probability of Type II errors) should ideally be set prior to experimentation, and, in fact, with the appropriate formula, can be used to determine the minimum sample size required in testing or a treatment effect (5). In any case, alpha and beta should be as close to 0 as possible.

Associated with not making a Type II error is the *power* of a test. If the directional hypothesis is true and the null hypothesis is rejected when it should be, reference is made to power. With a lowering of the level of significance, a reduction in errors, more precision in data collection, and large samples, power may be increased. Practical applications of Type I and Type II errors and a call for a greater consideration of the implications of the Type II error are made by Roundy (15).

Variance

The results of most experiments are affected by the treatments employed and the experimental errors as expressed by individual variability in performance. *Error*, in a statistical sense, is often expressed as *variance*. Treatment and error variances, as measures of the variability of group and individual scores, are compared in the form of a ratio in statistical models applicable for testing group mean differences. When a large ratio exists (treatment variance over error variance), confidence is increased that treatment differences are not due to chance but instead are real.

When groups are compared on some criterion measure, the difference between them is expressed as between-group, treatment, or interindividual variance. It is thus important that groups be randomly sampled, or matched and therefore similar on possibly confounding experimental variables. In this way, large between-group variances can be primarily associated with the treatments employed. It is expected that people will vary when we measure them on a particular variable. The question is whether this variation can be confidently associated with treatment effects.

The individual scores around a group mean are called within-group, intra-individual, or error variance. Scores that fluctuate randomly and are unaccountable constitute error variance. The experimenter attempts to minimize these fluctuations and maximize treatment differences in order to determine whether true differences between groups do exist. According to Brown and Ghiselli (1), error sources are related to performance differences between individuals as well as within groups. In the first case, people will vary in performance when measured on a particular variable. It is therefore important to motivate all subjects to the limit of their output. In the second case, the same person tested repeatedly will demonstrate a fluctuating performance because of changing interval and situational variables. These should be as consistent as possible.

Differences between groups of subjects reflect both within-group (sampling) error and treatment effects. This total variance can be statistically partitioned in order to reveal the relative contributions of each source of variance. And in the last analysis, the ratio of one to the other yields a figure which can be interpreted for group comparisons at a specified significance level.

Data Analysis and Interpretation

The statistics used are only as good (meaningful) as the design of the study. There is some tendency on the part of researchers to overemphasize the role of statistics while paying little heed to the many details that arise in any experiment which may affect and alter true results. Appropriate statistical models complement well-designed experiments.

Various techniques for data analysis and their interpretation are detailed in books such as the one by Winer (18). In the next section of this chapter, different types of designs, from univariate to multivariate dimensions, will be discussed. Although appropriate statistical models will not always be related to each design, the reader should realize that statistical techniques have been developed and specified for each design. The researcher is obligated to the intelligent use and interpretation of statistics. Let us now turn to possible designs.

TYPES OF DESIGNS

The intent of the investigator will determine the design he employs in the investigation. Naturally, more simple purposes lend themselves to simple designs; more complex purposes lead to intricate designs. Factorial and functional experiments have been distinguished. A factorial experiment is considered to be one in which the goal is to determine if differences exist, and typically a control group is compared to a treatment group. The effects of presenting and removing the experimental variable are compared. An examination of the degree differences that might exist as a result of various treatments is the essence of the functional experiment. Several independent values are compared or the independent variable is varied to determine relative effects.

Functional designs extend factorial designs by using three, or preferably more, successive levels of a treatment. This permits separating curvilinear from rectilinear relations by trend analysis. Various authors sometimes report a treatment as either aiding, impairing, or not producing a significant change in performance. These conflicting reports almost invariably result from factorial designs when the underlying relation is curvilinear and how much "some" represents is indefinite. Factorial designs are quicker and simpler, but they also lead to conflicting results and dirty inferences when "some" happens to be not enough or an overdose worse than "none." Functional designs require more data but determining how a treatment functions in human operations is safer and sounder. (See also Chapter 9.)

Comparing a treatment with no treatment to determine whether or not this treatment alters human performance significantly indicates, or fails to indicate, whether this treatment is a factor in human operations. Experimental designs involving two levels of a treatment, some versus none, and posing an either-or proposition have been called factorial.

The primary question is whether the ingredient is a factor in human operations. Information feedback in terms of right or wrong answers, praise or reproof, and any other experiment involving two levels of a treatment is factorial. You might have males and females, given the number right or wrong, and praised or reproved in a 2 × 2 × 2 factorial design. Any design involving a dichotomy or using one or more dichotomized treatments is factorial regardless of the number of factors. Multifactor factorial designs are possible.

Comparing the effect of three or more levels of the same treatment determines how the successive increments function in human operations. Smaller increments give better approximations of the functional relation, but three levels equally spaced are minimal. The primary question is *how* the ingredient functions in human operations. Functional designs with more than one factor, or multifactor functional designs, are possible. Studies involving distribution of practice, durations or intensities of exercise, or different amounts of an incentive are functional designs if three or more levels are used.

Today, many experimenters also classify studies as being *single factor* or *factorial* experiments. In a single-factor experiment, a comparison is made of two or more treatments on one criterion. An example would be the effect of verbal instruction versus no instruction on the acquisition of a motor skill. Or it might be a comparison of such techniques as praise, disregard, and reproof on the learning of a task. "Factorial experiments permit the experimenter to evaluate the combined effect of two or more experimental variables when used simultaneously" (18:140). There are at a minimum two factors and two levels (values) of each factor employed in such an experiment. We might be interested in the factors (*a*) teaching method and (*b*) sex of child. In our study, each factor would, for the sake of simplicity, have two levels: (*a*) teaching method = (a_1) praise and (a_2) reproof, and (*b*) sex = (b_1) boys and (b_2) girls. The effects of each factor singly and the interaction of both factors on performance could be identified.

Because it is typical to have a number of factors operating in real life situations, many investigators are attempting to determine such interactions in their experiments. With the use of multivariate statistics, many variables can be studied in one experiment as they act independently or in combination. The classical concept of the single variable, i.e., control of all variables save one, has been rejected by many experimenters. Sophisticated statistical methods now exist that can handle multifactor experiments, and most problems require more complex investigation. Although it is still true that the investigator might attempt to regulate all variables and manipulate one, there are many avenues open to him when he designs his experiment.

Experiments are concerned with causation. In the so-called "true" experiment, some sort of control is demonstrated by the investigator as he manipulates variables. For example, subjects might be randomly assigned to two groups. One receives leg exercises while the other does not, and all other variables are at least theoretically controlled. If a significant difference between the groups in favor of the exercised group on a posttest jumping test is noted, we infer that the specified exercises *caused* the group differences in jumping performance.

In most studies, causation is implied from the results of a comparative experiment. However, because of the possible variables that might interact and thus influence final outcomes despite efforts made to minimize them, cause and effect statements are always made with reservations. It is only when the same results are obtained in a number of studies that antecedent conditions and consequences can be specified. Let us examine some of the more commonly used designs, from the simple to the complex. These examples by no means exhaust all the possible designs available to the researcher.

Single Variable: One-Group and Two-Group Designs

In the less complicated experiment, the presence or absence of one variable and the resultant effect is the object of concern. In order to determine the effect of this variable, one group can be tested twice—once under the treatment, once without it—and performances compared. Or, two groups (an experimental group and a control group) may be formed, with performances measured and compared. The experimental group is a group subjected to some sort of experimental treatment or manipulation. The control group receives no treatment; it is used as a comparison against the experimental group in order to determine the effects of the treatment. If we were interested in the effect of sleep deprivation on reaction time, data could be obtained in the following ways:

	Reaction Time Test I	Reaction Time Test II
Single-Group Design: (same group tested under both conditions)	with sleep	without sleep
Two-Group Design: (each group tested under one (condition)	with sleep	without sleep

Changes within each group, or difference scores from Test I to Test II, could be compared between each group.

In the single-group design, the subjects act as their own controls. In the two-group design, the subjects randomly form the groups or are equated on one or more criterion variables and then placed into groups. One of the weaknesses in the single-group design is the ordering of treatments and the effects of this order. How should the group be tested first? With sleep or without sleep? The mere experience of being tested under one condition may alter performance on the second test. With two groups, the main concern is the equality of the groups on all variables of potential influence on the experimental results. The accurate equating of groups is so important that the next section will deal expressly with this problem.

Ray (13) is in favor of the two-group design in preference to repeated measures on one group. Campbell and Stanley (3) point out inadequacies in the internal validity of both designs and recommend the following modification: two equivalent groups of subjects, randomly selected, both of whom (control and treatment) are pretested and posttested. These writers then suggest (*a*) the computation and comparison of "gain" scores, (*b*) randomized blocking on pretest scores, or (*c*) covariance analysis, using pretest scores as the covariate. These techniques will be discussed shortly.

Matched (Level, Parallel) Groups

If the matched groups design is used, whether the need is for two, three, or more groups, internal validity of the experiment is best met through the accuracy of the matching technique. It is fallacious reasoning to assume that groups matched on mean scores on some criterion test will be truly equal. Variability of the scores is not taken into consideration here, and there are other and better ways to form matched groups.

One acceptable method is to place subjects randomly into respective groups. Although this procedure does not ensure group equality, on a probability basis, the groups should be evenly matched (assuming the samples are large enough). Another procedure, called *leveling*, involves matching the subjects in the groups on some measure or measures. In many cases, the subjects are equated on the dependent variable of concern. In the jumping experiment (p. 259), with one group operating as a control and the other as the treatment group, both groups could be pretested on a jumping test. Subjects would be paired-off by initial jumping ability and randomly placed into groups.

In other cases, it would defeat the purpose of the experiment to pretest on the dependent variable. Another variable or variables thought to be related could be tested instead and subjects would be paired on the basis of obtained scores. For instance, height, weight, and intelligence, individually or collectively, might serve as criterion scores. Accurate matching decreases the possibility of a Type II error. As a result, there is a better chance for true significance differences to be shown. The objective of the paired-groups techniques is homogeneity of the subjects, and it is important to realize that differences in matched groups become smaller as the number of subjects is increased. All is not lost if by design or accident the groups are *not* parallel, since analysis of covariance takes into consideration the initial dissimilarity between groups and adjusts posttest scores accordingly.

Repeated (Correlated) Measures

When two or more treatments are administered to the same subjects, it is appropriately called a repeated measures design. Some experimental statisticians also refer to this design as treatments-by-subjects. An example would be the investigation of 100-yd running time following four conditions of preparation: (*a*) calisthenics, (*b*) hot showers, (*c*) mental practice, and (*d*) no preparation. The same subjects are tested under each situation and group means are compared for any significant differences.

A good feature of the repeated measures design is the lesser number of subjects essential to obtain the necessary information, compared to other designs. For instance, 25 subjects could serve under this design, whereas 100 might be needed if different groups of subjects (four groups, 25 subjects per group) were formed for each treatment. Since subject acquisition is always a problem, this design warrants consideration where subjects are scarce. If the subjects are acquired in acceptable fashion, there will be less error than when matched groups are compared. Appropriate statistics will minimize the error (denominator) term in repeated measures designs.

The order or sequence of treatments must also be taken into consideration. The "treatment effect" will be discussed further under "rotational designs." Furthermore, subjects tested over a long period of time or on too many measures may yield data that are confounded by extraneous variables.

Randomized Design

A randomized design implies that all subjects are tested only once in the experiment, or at least only one score will be used to represent each subject. Subjects are randomly placed in the number of groups needed (not over four or five are recommended) and appropriate statistical analysis is made on the data. If subjects are randomly assigned to groups, there is no need for a pretest, as there is with the matched groups or leveling design. Groups are randomly assigned to treatments, as well as subjects to groups.

Randomized Blocks

If subjects are paired off into groups on the basis of some pretest score, the randomized block design can be utilized. Experimental units (matched subjects) are grouped into blocks. In psychologically-oriented statistics, a unit refers to a subject. A block indicates a group of subjects matched on some measure and therefore relatively homogeneous. Edwards (6:155–156) states that on occasion the randomized blocks design is favored over the randomized design (e.g., widespread individual differences on the dependent variable and treatment effects are apt to be slight). Because blocks are formed on the basis of some criterion measure, a proportionally smaller error term is yielded than when groups are completely randomly selected. The basis for the statistical treatment lies in determining differences between the scores within each block. In the t test, differences between each pair of scores in every block are calculated; in the analysis of variance, the mean difference score is determined from the mean score for each block.

The randomized blocks technique could be used in the following way. Suppose we wished to compare the effectiveness of verbal encouragement versus verbal criticism on motor performance. Fifty pairs of subjects might be matched on the basis of pretest performance. Fifty blocks are thus formed, with either the criticism or verbal encouragement treatment randomly assigned to each pair within a block.

Rotational Design

Subjects can serve as their own control by having all subjects receive all treatments. Practice, fatigue, experience with the test, and other possible effects of previous treatments on subsequent treatments produce serial order effects. That is, they can produce nondesirable effects in testing. These are inescapable, but they can be balanced or equated. Balancing requires that all subjects receive all treatments, that equal numbers of subjects receive each treatment during successive test periods (or days), and that each treatment precedes and follows every other treatment an equal number of times. Having the total number of subjects a multiple of the number of treatments provides equal subgroups. Assignment to subgroups may be randomized, but who gets which treatment is irrelevant, so random assignment is unnecessary. Let us consider three Latin squares involving four treatments:

Simple	Random	Balanced
A B C D	B D C A	A B D C
B C D A	A B C D	B C A D
C D A B	A C B D	C D B A
D A B C	B A D C	D A C B

The simple Latin square was formed by assigning the treatments in order to the first subgroup (row) for the successive test periods (columns) and then assigning the next treatment successively to subsequent subgroups going down the columns. Equal numbers receive each treatment during each period, so that is balanced. But the orders A–B, B–C, and C–D each occur three times, and B–A, C–B, and D–C never occur, so any effects of A on B, etc., would accumulate and bias the results.

The random Latin square was generated by starting in a randomly designated column of the random number table reproduced on page 147. We let A= 1, etc., skip all numbers over 4, and skip any duplicates of previously chosen numbers from 1 to 4 for each subgroup. Only the second column (test period) contains all treatments once. The only balanced pair is C–A and A–C. One balanced column and one balanced pair leaves too much imbalance. Starting elsewhere in the table might generate a balanced Latin square purely by chance, but finding one would be a tedious operation.

The balanced Latin square has all treatments tested in different subgroups during each period (like the simple one) and also has every treatment precede and follow every other treatment only once. The key to balancing is a formula devised by Williams in 1949 and presented in Edwards (6:193). The formula, with numbers representing the treatments, up to $n =$ the last (4 in this case), is:

$$1, 2, n, 3, n-1, 4, n-2, 5, n-3, \ldots$$

Converting the numbers to letters makes the test order for the first subgroup ABDC. The test order for the subsequent subgroups is obtained by moving to the next letter in going down each column and returning to A when we reach the nth number (as in the simple rotation). Balancing the Latin square is simple with the formula, except that we must have an even number of treatments to balance it in one rotation. The formula can be used to generate one (unbalanced) rotation for an odd number of treatments but we must then replicate that rotation with each row reversed for a balanced design, so the number of subgroups must be twice the number of treatments. The only difference between the simple and balanced Latin squares is in assigning treatments to the first subgroup. Thus transposing the third and fourth columns in the simple design should produce a balanced design—and it does.

We can test for serial order effects with an analysis of variance for "periods" based on summing over all treatments in each column. The resulting F should be nonsignificant. Testing for treatment effects requires collecting the data for *each* treatment in separate columns. The total sum of squares can be partitioned into between-treatments, between-subjects, and a residual sum of squares. The variance for treatment means is common to all subjects. The variance for subjects (across all treatments) is of no experimental interest (people obviously differ), but removing this treats the subjects as their own control. The residual variance (error mean square) represents any random variation of subjects or atypical interaction with particular treatments.

Adjusting with Covariance

Often intact groups are selected for experimental purposes. Because of this method of selection, it is entirely possible that the groups will differ on some pretest measuring the variable of concern or on some other variable that might contribute to treatment differences and therefore confound the results of the study. It is also possible that even after the process of random placement of subjects, the groups so formed are not homogeneous at the start of the experiment.

Partial correlation, multiple correlation, and factor analysis analyze covariance or represent methods for "covariance analysis." Analysis *of* covariance is a traditional misnomer, since the process does not actually analyze covariance. Analysis with covariance. is a more appropriate label for what is really an analysis of variance adjusted with covariance (see pp. 207–210). The pre- and posttreatment (or pre- and postest) sums of squares are partitioned (separated) according to the sources of variance by separate analyses of variance. Then the corresponding portions of the variance between pre- and posttest data are used to adjust the posttreatment variances as though the treatment groups were equated (had equal means) initially. This is analysis of variance with covariance added to remove any initial bias (inequality of means), which necessarily confounds the analysis of posttreatment variance. The uncorrected analysis of posttreatment variance reflects the treatment effects plus any initial inequality among groups resulting from sampling error. Random sampling (or assignment of subjects to treatments) presumably assures that the means of the treatment groups vary within the limits of sampling error initially. But these random differences among sample means introduce some initial bias. Analysis with covariance removes this bias.

Initial differences between groups are removed and thus provide a more precise analysis. Analysis with covariance involves replication (more than one score per subject). The posttreatment means (sometimes called "criterion means") can be adjusted before or after analysis with covariance. Sliding them up or down the common regression line to the grand mean of the pretest treats them as though the groups were equated initially, or as though the covariate was held constant. Adjusting the means is a separate operation. The source of the inequality of pretreatment means in intact groups or randomly selected groups can be removed if there is a pretest and if analysis with covariance is used. Analysis with covariance removes the bias from the partitioned variance. It can be used with confidence if the subjects have been randomly assigned to groups and with caution if intact groups are used.

In recent years, the analysis of covariance has come under some attack with regard to the conditions and assumptions necessary for its appropriate application. Lord (11) provides an example of a situation in which this statistical model does not provide the appropriate adjustment to compensate for preexisting differences between groups. Other problems have been examined (8) and recommendations made for appropriate designs, e.g., that the covariate be unaffected by the treatment.

Factorial Designs

Factorial designs, it was explained earlier (pp. 224–228), deal with the study of the effects of two or more variables and the interaction between them. These designs permit a number of generalizations from the analyzed data and can replace several separate experiments in which each factor is studied singly. The designs explained thus far, with the exception of the single variable one, can be used in a factorial experiment.

From the relatively simple 2 × 2 design (two factors with two levels for each factor or variable) to the more complex, e.g., a 4 × 6 × 3 design, the investigator can expect to meet the particular objectives of his experiment. There exist so many potential designs that Winer (18), Edwards (6), Bruning and Kintz (2), and other writers devote a good portion of their respective books to illustrating examples of factorial experiments. Most factorial designs contain two or three factors, although theoretically it is possible to employ in one experiment as many factors and levels of each factor as one desires. In this chapter, it will be possible to represent but a few such designs. It is important to keep in mind, though, that the number of factors and factor levels found in any experiment is determined by the investigator upon considering the inferences he wishes to make.

In the 2 × 2 factorial design example offered in the beginning of this section of the chapter, the factors teaching method and sex of child were of interest. The levels of the teaching method factor were praise

(a_1) and reproof (a_2), while those of the sex of the child factor were boys (b_1) and girls (b_2). In this study, information would be yielded on the main effects: a comparison of boys and girls in performance following the combined effects of the teaching methods, and the comparison of teaching methods on boys and girls combined, as well as the interaction of the factors: a comparison of the two groups of subjects across the two teaching methods.

A three-factor design could be employed in the following situation. Perhaps the investigator is concerned with such variables as anxiety level (A), age (B), and learning trials (C). Two groups of subjects are formed, one high in anxiety (a_1) and the other low in anxiety (a_2), as determined by scores on a test purporting to measure anxiety. Three different age classifications comprise each anxiety group, say ages 10 to 12 (b_1), 13 to 15 (b_2), and 16 to 18 (b_3). The learning task might consist of five blocks of trials (c_1, c_2, c_3, c_4, and c_5) in which group differences on each trial are of interest. This is a $2 \times 3 \times 5$ factorial experiment. Three main effects (A, B, and C) as well as four interactions (AB, AC, BC, and ABC) are determined.

The main effects would indicate the following: Factor A provides information on differences in performance due to anxiety; Factor B refers to the effect of age on performance; and Factor C covers trial-to-trial differences in performance. Interaction indicates the way these factors operate in conjunction with each other to affect performance output. In the AB interaction, differences in performance due to anxiety level are reflected by the age of the group. The AC interaction concerns rate of change differences during the learning trials for the high and low anxious groups. A significant $A \times B \times C$ interaction would indicate that high and low anxious subjects learn at different rates at different ages. We might expect improvement over trials, with increasing age, and perhaps with low anxiety. Finding significant two-way interactions or a three-way interaction would provide additional important information.

Factorial designs are becoming increasingly popular, especially in behavioral research. Computers now perform the computations quickly. Techniques in sampling, the formation of groups and designation of treatments, the application of appropriate statistical models, as well as the pitfalls and loopholes in various experimental designs, should be understood by the experimenter.

APPLICATION OF RESULTS

The purpose of any experiment is to be able to predict future outcomes from the results when similar situations occur. Conclusions drawn from an experiment hold practical value if they can be applied in an immediate situation. Experimental findings also form the bases for theories and principles. These theories in turn generate ideas for further investigation and the circular process continues. At the so-called ground-floor level, however, the data collected in a study permit the drawing of inferences through processes of deduction and induction.

Deducing (L., *deduco*, to lead down) and inducing (L., *induco*, to lead in) are both ways of reaching conclusions (for further discussion, see pp. 26–28). Deduction in logic means "reasoning from stated premises to the formally valid conclusion; also, reasoning from the general to the specific." Induction in logic means "the process of inferring or aiming at the general from observation of the particular"—or reasoning from the specific to the general. Assumption and hypothesis are defined in the dictionary so that in one sense they are synonymous, which is confusing. They can be differentiated by considering an *assumption* a belief or premise (stated or unstated) and a *hypothesis* as a proposition or a testable proposition which must be stated specifically in order to be testable or *proven*, where *to prove* means *to test*.

Deduction

Deduction is used in philosophy (or may be used) to test the validity of premises. Experimenters proceed deductively in arranging hypotheses to test and inductively in reaching conclusions and generalizations. Experimentation proceeds in a logical manner. Hypotheses, based on theories or previous research, are formulated by scientists through the process of deductive logic. Accordingly, these hypotheses are tested experimentally. The theories or previous research findings provide premises which, if valid, should answer the specific question, solve the specific problem, or support the hypothetical outcome.

Induction

The prime purpose of experimentation is to be able to generalize or infer with data obtained from a sample to the population which this sample represents. This is called the process of induction. It is seldom that we are concerned only with the characteristics or behavior of a particular group of subjects. Rather, we like to make inferences from the particular situation in which experimentation is done with a predefined sample to the large group of people from which the sample arises.

Take, for example, a study concerning college varsity swimmers and the effect of a designated meal on swim performance. If we find that the time at which this meal precedes the swim test does not result in significant differences in performance, the natural urge is to generalize these effects across *all* college varsity swimmers. Generalizing to all college varsity swimmers competing at the distance tested in the study would be fairly sound, but failing to limit the generalization to the distance tested would be a gross and unwarranted overgeneralization. For instance, channel swimmers ingest food and water while swimming. Although there are great dangers in induction, most interest in experimentation appears to be of this nature because proceeding from specific data from a sample to conclusions and generalizations concerning the population necessarily depends on inductive inferences. It remains virtually impossible to collect data on entire populations. The inferential method permits conclusions about populations to be drawn from samples. Incomplete data yield information sufficient to enable us to make probability inferences concerning the nature of large groups of people.

Indeed, not every conceivable situation concerning the problem of food ingestion effects on swimming performance can be measured. A number of investigations would be needed in order to handle adequately all aspects of the topic. Some of the more basic considerations would be the nature of the meal, its relation in time to swim performance, the nature of the swim test, the number of subjects and groups to be used, and the nature and experiences of the subjects. Time of day of testing, condition of subjects, personal feelings, health and status the day of testing, temperature of the water, testing devices, and the like, point up other problems. There are many more. If it were intended that every combination of possible interacting effects of these variables should be measured, we can readily see how impossible a task it becomes. Therefore, with but a few studies on the topic and incomplete information, broad generalizations are made about the relation of food ingestion to swimming performance.

Any aspect of the preswim meal problem could be experimented with. Conclusions would be derived inductively in an intelligent way within the framework of the limitations of the testing procedures and the sample used in the study. On the basis of these and other data, additional hypotheses would be deductively conceived for further testing.

REFERENCES

1. Brown, Clarence W. and Ghiselli, Edwin. *Scientific Method in Psychology*. New York: McGraw-Hill Book Co., 1955.
2. Bruning, James L. and Kintz, B. L. *Computational Handbook of Statistics*. New York: Scott, Foresman & Co., 1968. 269 pp.
3. Campbell, D. and Stanley, Julian C. Experimental and quasi-experimental designs for research on teaching. In *Handbook of Research on Teaching*, edited by N. L. Gage. Chicago: Rand McNally & Co., 1963.

4. Candland, Douglas K. *Psychology: The Experimental Approach*. New York: McGraw-Hill Book Co., 1968.
5. Cohen, J. *Statistical Power Analysis For the Behavioral Sciences*. New York: Academic Press, 1969.
6. Edwards, Allen L. *Experimental Design in Psychological Research*. 3d ed. New York: Holt, Rinehart & Winston, 1968.
7. Fisher, Ronald A. and Prance, Ghiuean T. *The Design of Experiments*. London: Oliver & Boyd, 1937 (8th ed., New York: Hafner Publishing Co., 1972).
8. Harris, David R.; Bisbee, Charles T.; and Evans, Selby H. Further comments —Misuse of analysis of covariance. *Psychological Bulletin* 75: 220–222, 1971.
9. Kerlinger, Frederick N. *Foundations of Behavioral Research*. New York: Holt, Rinehart & Winston, 1964.
10. Kurtz, Kenneth H. *Foundations of Psychological Research*. Boston: Allyn & Bacon, 1965. 402 pp.
11. Lord, Frederic M. Statistical adjustments when comparing preexisting groups. *Psychological Bulletin* 72: 336–337, 1969.
12. Myers, Jerome L. *Fundamentals of Experimental Design*. Boston: Allyn & Bacon, 1966.
13. Ray, William S. *Introduction to Experimental Design*. New York: Macmillan Co., 1960. 254 pp.
14. Rosenthal, Robert. *Experimenter Effects in Behavioral Research*. New York: Appleton-Century-Crofts, 1966.
15. Roundy, Elmo S. Notes on problems associated with accepting the null hypothesis. *Research Quarterly* 39: 831–832, Oct. 1968.
16. Stallings, William M. and Singhal, Sushila. Confidence level and significance level: Semantic confusion or logical fallacy. *Journal of Experimental Education* 37: 57–59, Summer 1969.
17. Tversky, Amos and Kahneman, D. Belief in the law of small numbers. *Psychological Bulletin* 76: 105–110, 1971.
18. Winer, B. J. *Statistical Principles in Experimental Design*. New York: McGraw-Hill Book Co., 1962 (2d ed., 1971).

SELECTED READINGS

Anderson, Barry F. *The Psychology Experiment: An Introduction to the Scientific Method*. 2d ed. Belmont, Calif.: Wadsworth Publishing Co., 1970.

Bakan, D. The test of significance in psychological research. *Psychological Bulletin* 66: 423–437, 1966.

Boring, E. The nature and history of experimental control. *American Journal of Psychology* 67: 573–589, 1954.

Campbell, D. Factors relevant to the validity of experiments in social settings. *Psychological Bulletin* 54: 297–312, 1957.

Cattell, Raymond B. The principles of experimental design and analysis in relation to theory building. In *Handbook of Multivariate Experimental Psychology*. Chicago: Rand McNally & Co., 1966.

Cochran, W. G. and Cox, G. M. *Experimental Designs*. 2d ed. New York: John Wiley & Sons, 1957.

Davies, Owen L., ed. *The Design and Analysis of Industrial Experiments*. 2d rev. ed. New York: Hafner Publishing Co., 1967.

Hyman, Ray. *The Nature of Psychological Inquiry*. Englewood Cliffs, N. J.: Prentice-Hall, 1964.

Kirk, Roger E. *Experimental Design: Procedures For the Behavioral Sciences*. Belmont, Calif.: Brooks/Cole Publishing Co., 1968.

Lyons, Joseph. *A Primer of Experimental Psychology*. New York: Harper & Row, 1965.

McGuigan, F. J. *Experimental Psychology: A Methodological Approach*. 2d ed. Englewood Cliffs, N.J.: Prentice-Hall, 1968.

Orne, Martin T. On the social psychology of the psychological experiment: With particular reference to demand characteristics and their implications. *American Psychologist* 17: 776–783, 1962.

Plutchik, Robert. *Foundations of Experimental Research*. New York: Harper & Row, 1968.

Sarason, I. G. and Harmatz, M. G. Interrelationships among subjects, experimenter, and situational variables. *Journal of Abnormal Social Psychology* 67: 87–91, 1963.

Tate, Merle W. *Statistics in Education and Psychology*. New York: Macmillan Co., 1965.

Townsend, John C. *Introduction to Experimental Methods*. New York: McGraw-Hill Book Co., 1953.

Travers, Robert M. *An Introduction to Educational Research*. 3d ed. New York: Macmillan Co., 1969.

Underwood, Benton J. *Experimental Psychology*. New York: Appleton-Century-Crofts, 1966.

Van Dalen, Deobold B. *Understanding Educational Research*. 2d ed. New York: McGraw-Hill Book Co., 1966.

Webb, Eugene J. et al. *Unobtrusive Measures: Nonreactive Research in the Social Sciences*. Chicago: Rand McNally & Co., 1966.

Zimny, George H. *Method in Experimental Psychology*. New York: Ronald Press Co., 1961.

CHAPTER 11 DESCRIPTIVE RESEARCH

Anna S. Espenschade
Retired, University of California
Berkeley, California

G. Lawrence Rarick
University of California
Berkeley, California

DESCRIPTIVE RESEARCH IS ESSENTIALLY a fact-finding procedure with an interpretation of how the facts relate to the problem under investigation. It must be kept in mind that descriptive research must go beyond mere data gathering. Unless the facts are marshalled in such a way that they bear meaningfully on the reasearch problem, the fact-finding operation is of little value.

For descriptive research to be meaningful, the investigator must not only decide on what data to collect, but also how to classify and analyze these to meet the purposes of the study. Since descriptive research by its nature is well suited for attacking problems on a broad front, it is often used as the initial research procedure in opening up a new area of investigation where there is insufficient knowledge for experimental work to be profitable. Thus, many investigators employ descriptive research in order to establish hypotheses which can be tested under controlled experimental conditions.

While descriptive research follows the general procedures characteristic of all other research methods, it does utilize a variety of techniques. It should be kept in mind that certain techniques which are highly important in descriptive research, such as sampling and statistical procedures, are not discussed in detail here because they are considered elsewhere in this book (Chapters 8 and 9). It is the purpose of the present chapter to consider those descriptive methods which are peculiarly well suited to research in physical education. These include status studies, opinion polls, normative studies, comparative studies, causal-comparative studies, case studies, and developmental studies.

STATUS STUDIES

Investigations of this type are commonly called surveys. The basic purpose of the survey is to determine conditions as they presently exist. Surveys may range in scope from nationwide to regional or local, or they may be confined to single units, as one school or even one class. In all cases, the procedure follows logical steps: the purpose or problem must be clearly stated, the data needed to solve the problem and means of obtaining it determined, and the appropriate method of analyzing the data selected. Further, populations or samples to be studied must be available and the individuals involved must be cooperative. The investigator must have the resources to carry out the study and to report the findings.

Many curricular studies in health, physical education, and recreation have used surveys as a first step (26). The recent status survey conducted by the School Health Education Study (31) is an excellent example of this type of investigation. The survey was preceded by a review of research relating to instruction. On the basis of this review and the knowledge and experience of the principal investigator and consultants, the questions which the survey was to answer were formulated. Several decisions were made in regard to sampling. For example, it was decided that a smaller sample studied in depth would be of greater value for the purposes of this investigation than a more extensive sample where follow-ups would not be possible. The actual selection of the sample was turned over to a professional sampling organization.

In all large surveys today, the data will be computer-analyzed, so it is essential that an appropriate design be selected. Before any decisions are made concerning procedures, consultations with programmers should be held.

The method of data collection must be carefully considered. Surveys such as that in school health education, referred to above, can be done through correspondence with administrators involved. When results are perceived as valuable for participating schools and if the information requested is either available or can be collected through existing channels, cooperation is readily obtained. A stipulation in school surveys that the published report will not identify individual class, school, or teacher involved usually results in almost 100% response.

Frequently, the questionnaire approach does not meet the necessary conditions, a poor response is obtained, and the results cannot be generalized beyond the sample included. Wherever possible, data should be collected through personal contact. Whether the investigator employs tests, evaluation schedules, or interview forms, the information obtained will be more accurate and complete if collected in person. More than one individual can participate in this process, of course, provided all are trained in the procedures. Standardized tests may be given by qualified examiners, but ratings or items involving judgment must be done by experienced judges to be of value.

It should be clear from this discussion that a status survey involves considerable expenditure of time and money. The first question which the investigator should ask is, "Is this study worthwhile?" Since the results will present a picture of conditions as they are at the moment, can the survey be completed and the data analyzed in time to be of value? Will the study be useful for comparative purposes or provide a basis for future research? If it is evident that the study will make an important contribution, the next questions should ascertain whether or not the principal investigator is qualified to conduct the investigation, if expert consultants can be found, if time and money are adequate. Unless all of these questions can be answered satisfactorily, it is unwise to undertake the survey.

OPINION POLLS

The rise of a scientific approach to opinion polling has been rapid in recent years and some attention should be given to this, although it may not qualify as research. In politics, manufacturing, and businesses of various sorts where huge investments of time or money are involved, it is important to ascertain the probable reactions of people before embarking on various projects. Computer analysis of voting trends, buying habits, TV-viewing, and other behaviors of various segments of the population have led to sampling procedures which predict very closely outcomes in these fields.

In health, physical education, and recreation, opinion polls are frequently conducted to obtain some information regarding reactions of students, parents, or participants in programs, facilities, instruction, or other areas. These surveys, in common with the polls discussed above, have a momentary importance or value in relation to the sample studied but the findings permit little generalization. For example, attitudes of one group of students toward physical education, even though a fairly well constructed scale is used, can only represent reactions of the group measured. Too many local conditions which are known to affect results, such as staff, facilities, rules and regulations, even climate, are not comparable from place to place and so invalidate comparisons (4).

DOCUMENTARY RESEARCH

One type of status study that may be done by correspondence or in person involves the use of published materials or documents as the source of information. College or university catalogs, for example, may be examined to study course offerings, major curricula, or graduation requirements. Legislation regarding education, public health, or recreation can be obtained. This type of investigation is similar to historical study but differs in that the documents examined are of relatively recent date. Here, as in all research, the steps to be taken and questions to be asked are the same as those already outlined under status studies. In addition, there may be some question concerning the completeness and even the accuracy of the source material available.

NORMATIVE STUDIES

Information collected for the purpose of establishing norms usually involves new or revised measuring instruments. A standardized test by definition is one with norms established for a specific population. Thus a test of performace or achievement that has been developed by appropriate steps and tried out in a limited area may be standardized for wide usage by testing an appropriate sample. The AAHPER fitness test national norms were developed in this way. A sample of boys and girls, grades 5–12, was selected (25) and the subjects were tested by trained examiners (15).

Results on the actual performance of a "normal" population provide a standard of comparison for evaluating performances of other individuals and groups and so many serve as a basis for many investigations. Standardized achievement tests in school subjects, for example, can determine the status of any class and are indispensable in studying deviant or handicapped subjects (24).

Established norms, like the data from all status studies, represent conditions or performances at a given moment in time and so must be updated at intervals.

COMPARATIVE STUDIES

Studies somewhat more complex than the simple status study may use the same descriptive procedures. The difference lies in the design of the study and in the analysis of results. As we have suggested, a common form of comparative study is one involving comparison of groups to established norms. The last decade has seen many studies in physical education which used the norms of the AAHPER fitness test as a basis of comparison. Others have used the Kraus-Weber Test, although both sampling and statistical techniques of the latter have been questioned.

It is not necessary to use norms as the standard of comparison in studies of this type. Two classes in the same school can be compared, for example (5). It is also possible to study age, sex, or race differences in this way (19).

The question asked in the comparative study is, "Does one group differ significantly from another in certain measures or characteristics?" The selection of appropriate statistical procedures is extremely important.

CAUSAL-COMPARATIVE STUDIES

When comparative studies are designed, the investigator may wish to study not only possible differences, but causes of differences. Because it is often impossible actually to experiment with human beings or to institute rigid controls needed for such investigations, many attempts to investigate cause and effect relationships use descriptive methods.

A design which has been of value in educational research is illustrated in a study which examined the effectiveness of programmed materials in teaching school health (28). Two groups of subjects were given an initial test and equated on the basis of results. A period of instruction followed in which different methods were used with the different groups. Results on a final test were compared. Since past experience, native ability, motivation, health, and a host of other factors are operative and cannot be controlled, even in a well-planned investigation, conclusions from such studies must be examined with care and should be accepted as tentative until further evidence is accumulated.

INTERRELATIONSHIP STUDIES

When two or more sets of data are collected on the same individuals, correlations can be computed. Although correlation gives only degree of relationship, it may appear logical to the investigator that a cause-effect relationship exists. Hypotheses may be stated relating body build to physical performances, for example, and investigated by surveying a selected population. Since relationships in many studies of this type in physical education are too low to permit prediction, the emphasis has changed to an examination of whether or not any significant relationship between variables does in fact exist (3,9,20,30).

Analysis by computer has introduced more sophisticated statistics and made possible more complex studies. Multiple correlation, factor analysis, and certain types of variance analyses may be used to investigate interrelationships. The investigator in this area must be well-informed both in regard to experimental design and data analysis before embarking upon such a study.

THE CASE STUDY

The case study is used to provide detailed information about an individual, institution, or situation. It is concerned primarily with determining the unique characteristics of the exceptional, rather than the attributes which are typical of many. The case approach has perhaps enjoyed the most widespread use in medicine, law, and clinical psychology, for in each of these fields the practitioner deals with problems of a highly individualized nature. In schools, the case method has been effectively used in the individual study and guidance of children with reading difficulties, speech problems, or psychological-emotional disturbances. However, few research studies using the case method have been reported in physical education literature, although it is a technique which coaches routinely employ in the critical analysis of the performance of their athletic teams.

Although the case study is most frequently used in the solution of individual problems, an accumulation of data from several similar cases frequently furnishes important data for comparative studies and for examining factors intimately associated with specific problems. For example, many advances in the field of medicine have come from careful study of case records of practicing physicians.

The case method has also been used effectively to study in detail the unusually successful or unsuccessful person, as a means of identifying the traits which characterize him. While the presence or absence of the observed traits does not necessarily establish a causal relationship, identification of these characteristics does give the research worker something definite upon which to build. In the behavioral sciences, where identification and isolation of basic factors in behavior problems is extremely difficult, the case method has been used effectively. In fact, in many fields of human inquiry where precise methods are not available for establishing cause and effect relationships, the case approach has provided sufficient evidence for establishing well-defined hypotheses concerning the interaction of associated variables. The case method, therefore, is an effective approach in resolving a particular difficulty and frequently provides valuable data for formulating tentative generalizations concerning individuals or groups of marked similarity in some important respects.

The problem of delinquency is particularly well suited to the case approach, and as a result many case reports on delinquents are available. One of the early, classical studies in delinquency is the report by Healy and Bronner (12) of a single case referred to the Judge Baker Foundation in Boston. The report includes a complete record of the personal, social, and environmental background of the child. A broader approach to the study of delinquency is illustrated by Harvey (11), who examined records of a large number of socially maladjusted American and Mexican boys in an attempt to gain insight into the physical, psychological, and social factors associated with delinquent youth. In a study more closely oriented to physical education, Sheldon (27) utilized the case approach in studying the physique of delinquent youth. On the basis of data collected from some 200 cases, Sheldon supports the belief that delinquency has definite biological roots.

Case studies in which the individuals were selected because of their unusual capacities or talents frequently furnish valuable information on the factors associated with these abilities. For example, Cureton (6) has provided a considerable body of individual data on 58 male athletes of national championship and Olympic caliber. This study gives information on the physical attributes, performance abilities, and organic efficiency of these men and provides some insight into the role these variables play in top-quality performance. To illustrate further, Dill et al. (7), in presenting the athletic and medical case histories of 16 former champion runners, have effectively combined elements of the longitudinal method with the case approach in providing data on changes in physiological functions of these men some 20 years after their competitive years. The wide individual difference in the physiological responses of the men later in life reflected their varied patterns of living, indicating clearly the need of longitudinal and case data in assessing the long range effects of strenuous physical activity on man. Rarick and McKee (22) have presented case data on 20 children, 10 of whom were high achievers and 10 of whom were low achievers on a battery of motor tests. The findings provided information on the differences in the early play experiences of the children in the two groups.

The case approach is also an effective method for studying communities, schools, organizations, and the various institutions of our society. An excellent illustration of a comprehensive study of community life and the impact of social institutions upon the lives of adolescents is the work of Hollingshead (13). This study which provides data on some 735 adolescents growing up in a midwestern community, points out the important role which family status in the social structure of the community plays in determining such factors as the social behavior of the adolescent in relation to the school, the church, recreation, his peers, and his family.

Usual Steps in Conduct of Case Study

Determining Value

The investigator makes certain that the person, institution, or situation is sufficiently different to warrant detailed investigation. If an investigation of this type is to be of value, it should be directed toward the solution of a real difficulty or provide some insight into the organization of factors associated with some unusual phenomenon.

Obtaining Relevant Data

The investigator first obtains all data believed to be relevant to the problem. Where the problem pertains to a person or persons, the following sources of information may be used.

1. A complete *medical examination* may be necessary. However, the nature of the problem under investigation determines the type of health data which are needed. Frequently, special tests of vision, hearing, or nutritional status may provide valuable information on the problem.

2. *Standardized tests* upon which norms have been developed are valuable in making estimates of the "normality" of the case under observation.

3. The *interview* provides a valuable source of personal data and is included as a basic research method in many case studies.

4. Data covering *observations of behavior* may include recorded observations of play or social behavior, or provide subjective judgment of physical performance.

5. It is often necessary to develop *special purpose devices* to measure particular traits or abilities. To investigate certain kinds of behavior, it may be desirable to use instruments to record certain aspects of the behavioral phenomenon. For example, Hubbard (14) used mechanical and electrical recording instruments in studying the difference between trained and untrained runners. Zimmerman (34) employed cinematographical analysis in studying the characteristics of skilled and unskilled performance in the standing broad jump.

6. Often *historical data* covering an earlier period of time is needed in order to interpret present status. This information may be obtained from permanent record files, documents (local or governmental), periodical sources, or personal interviews. Cumulative school records are a reasonably sound source of data for case studies. Care must be taken that all sources of a historical nature have been checked for accuracy. (See chapter on historical method, pp. 289–304.)

The investigator must also be sure that all data-collecting devices have been validated and checked for reliability. Finally, a critical review needs to be made of all data, both present and past, to ensure authenticity and accuracy of all relevant information.

Analyzing the Data

An understanding of the interaction of the variables at work in the situation under investigation can come about only after the data have been logically classified and subjected to appropriate methods of analysis.

The logical organization and grouping of like data ordinarily present no problem. However, the limited number of cases and the nonrandomized character of the sample place restrictions on the statistical methods appropriate for these kinds of data. This does not reduce the effectiveness of the analysis, since the vast array of data on each case provides the opportunity to search for patterns of factors or events related to the phenomenon under investigation. In fact, the limited number of cases typical of the case study is well suited to a pattern analysis. This approach is particularly fruitful in gaining insight into the relative effect which different variables have on the present status of the case. Furthermore, intelligent use of data collected on the case at an earlier time may provide valuable clues in interpreting the findings. For example, Wetzel (33), in his discussion of growth failure in children, illustrates through case studies the need for interpreting present status in the light of the past. The analysis of case data utilizes all relevant information, past and present, which may help to explain the circumstances as they exist at the moment.

Making the Recommendations

Frequently, case studies are conducted to throw light on a concrete problem or difficulty with the view to making recommendations for change or treatment. In such instances, the experiences gained in the successful treatment of identical or highly similar cases are useful in making recommendations for the future course of action. Care should be taken that an accurate record is kept of all procedures used in the treatment program.

On the other hand, the case approach may not involve treatment but may be used as a means of identifying the characteristics of persons who have demonstrated unusual ability in some line of endeavor. Obviously, in instances such as these, the concern is directed toward learning more about the clustering of traits under the given conditions and to the possible interaction among the variables which may have produced the desirable condition.

Appraising Effectiveness

The final step in the case study is the appraisal of the effectiveness of the recommended change. This may be accomplished by testing procedures, observational techniques, or various special purpose devices. Ordinarily, the effectiveness of the instituted change cannot be evaluated adequately immediately after the program has been discontinued but must be judged in terms of its more lasting effects.

Values and Limitations

Caution must always be exercised in making generalizations about a single case. Statistically, an N of 1 provides little or no ground for scientific prediction, even though the case has been exhaustively studied. However, with many replications, the case approach becomes a powerful device for providing important information about personal and social phenomena which may be used to advance human knowledge in terms of basic understandings as well as of future courses of action.

DEVELOPMENTAL STUDIES

Developmental studies are designed to advance knowledge of the growth and development of children. It is worthy of note that many current child rearing and educational practices have evolved from the findings of developmental studies. Studies of this kind employ either the longitudinal or the cross-sectional approach. The former makes repeated observations on the same individuals at predetermined time intervals, often over a period of many years. Cross-sectional studies, on the other hand, make observations on different individuals of varying chronological ages or different levels of maturity.

The Cross-Sectional Method

The chief advantage of the cross-sectional method lies in its economy. The investigator, by selecting samples of children of the ages in which he is interested, can collect the data in a relatively short period of time—an important consideration for many research workers, particularly the graduate student. Furthermore, the cross-sectional method eliminates the problem of loss of subjects or the need to locate subjects who have moved out of the area, a difficulty often encountered in longitudinal studies.

It should be recognized, however, that there are definite weaknesses in cross-sectional studies, particularly where the primary intent is to draw inferences regarding growth and development. Growth curves based on data from independent samples of children, independent by age or maturity level, may not portray adequately the course of development. In fact, cross-sectional studies when used to describe developmental change frequently distort the picture. For example, when mean values of standing height are plotted by chronological age from cross-sectional data the adolescent growth spurt is not realistically portrayed and in no sense reflects the dramatic increase in height which is characteristic of the individual or of groups of individuals maturing at the same rate. Those who use the cross-sectional method must recognize that different groups of subjects at different ages are not necessarily comparable, and, therefore, caution must be exercised in using cross-sectional data in describing developmental trends.

The Longitudinal Method

Much of the early information on the growth and development of children was based on cross-sectional data accumulated on large numbers of individuals. Its became apparent, however, that growth patterns of individual children were often substantially different from the growth curves plotted from normative data. Recognition of the marked individual differences in rates of growth and in the timing of developmental changes raised serious questions concerning the value and use of growth curves obtained from cross-sectional data, a shortcoming which is circumvented in the longitudinal method.

The longitudinal method offers many advantages in studying developmental phenomena. The plotting of individual growth curves provides a means of comparing rates of development of different growth variables for a particular individual and also permits interindividual comparisons. Furthermore, means and standard deviations can be computed at any point in time, as in the cross-sectional method. Determinations can also be made of growth increments for the individual and for groups. And finally, the interrelationships among specific growth factors which are operating over time can be determined, since all data are from the same children. Thus, the longitudinal method provides a much sounder basis for drawing inferences concerning the nature of development than occurs when data are collected on different children at different stages of development.

Kodlin and Thompson (17) point out that the longitudinal approach is the only procedure appropriate for accurately describing the growth phenomenon. Growth implies change and change can be assessed only by repeated measurements on the same individual. Furthermore, repeated measurements on the same individuals make it possible to determine the correlation between measurements at different age levels, the basis upon which mathematical predictions of growth can be made. To illustrate, data from a recent longitudinal study (23) in which measures of physical growth and motor performance were secured annually on the same group of children throughout childhood and again at 17 years of age showed that the superior performers on tests of strength and motor performance at age 7 were not necessarily the superior performers at age 17. Predicting the course of development cannot come from the cross-sectional approach.

Other studies in physical education and allied fields have successfully employed the longitudinal method. As a part of the California Adolescent Growth Study, Espenschade (8) and Jones (16) have provided valuable data on motor performance changes and strength development of a group of adolescent boys and girls. The work of Gesell (10) and Shirley (29) on the early motor behavior of infants demonstrated the value of the genetic method in observing sequential behavior patterns during early development. In the above studies care was taken that the measuring devices utilized were suitable for recording accurately the phenomena under observation at each point in the developmental sequence.

One of the unique contributions of the longitudinal method lies in its potential for accurately predicting the development of individual children. For example, when growth curves are plotted for children of the same chronological age who differ markedly in their rates of sexual maturation, the trend for growth in body size and physical performance is distinctly different for the early and late maturers. Therefore, knowledge of the physical maturity status of the child, as well as information on other related factors, increases the power of predicting future developmental trends for individual children. This is borne out by the work of Bayley (1), in which growth curves, based on measurements of height and weight, have been established for a group of some 300 children on whom repeated measurements were taken from birth to 18 years of age. The grouping of data on children similar in physical maturity, from which growth curves were plotted, provided a much more accurate prediction of individual growth than could be obtained by growth curves established from cross-sectional data.

In the conduct of a longitudinal study, the following procedures are usually carried out.

Initial Planning

The investigator makes certain that the problem is suitable for employing the longitudinal method. This means that the hypotheses under examination can be most effectively explored by data secured on the same subjects or the same institution at regular intervals over a long period of time. In physical education, longitudinal studies offer a rich opportunity to study the role which such factors as physique, maturity, and strength play in the acquisition of motor skills as children advance toward maturity.

Careful planning is perhaps more important in longitudinal studies than in other kinds of investigations, since several years of continuous work are necessary. This means careful planning not only in regard to the basic design of the study, but also in establishing the project schedule and in handling and processing the data. In the planning and conduct of the investigation, agreement should be reached on the exact points in time when the measurements are to be taken. For example Meredith (18) operates on a rigid time schedule of securing data within three days of each child's birthday. There should be assurance that all measures are valid and reliable and that all testers are trained to ensure objectivity and accuracy of measurement. If possible the same testers should be used throughout the study.

Collection and Recording of Data

The data-collecting devices for longitudinal studies are similar to those described in the case study section. However, great care needs to be taken in the selection of tests and measuring devices, since the recording of developmental change requires highly accurate tools of measurement. This is particularly important when the time intervals between measurements are short and the amount of growth small.

The data collected in a longitudinal investigation assume large proportions, and hence a systematic method is needed for recording and filing all data. It is recommended that a folder be kept on each child and that all test scores be recorded on permanent blanks and immediately filed in the child's folder. It is particularly important in a longitudinal study that the exact date of every observation be recorded.

Periodically, outside checks should be made on the characteristics of the study group by running controlled observations on other samples of children. This may tell the investigator something of the influence which dropouts may have had on the characteristics of the study group.

Treatment of Longitudinal Data

One of the major difficulties in these studies is the problem of processing and treating serial records. The plotting of individual growth curves for specific growth variables is one approach that has been used in individualizing the treatment of developmental data. Obviously, this approach has its limitations, especially if one attempts to plot on a single graph data for several subjects recorded in different units.

Several methods are available for transforming raw data expressed in different units into equivalent values so that the data can be readily plotted. Olson (21), in his longitudinal study of children, converted each child's scores on each variable into an age unit based on norms for each variable. The use of this technique is open to question since there is little likelihood that the age variables have the same standard deviations, and hence the computed "ages" are not necessarily comparable. Conversion of raw scores into standard scores provides a more satisfactory means of establishing each child's relative position in the group for each growth variable. This is not only effective for plotting individual and group curves, but is also useful in developing a profile of traits for individuals at various points in development. Standard scores have been used effectively in handling growth data by Jones (16), Bayley (2), and Sontag (32).

A method of treating data which gives insight into the relative velocity and timing of growth is to convert raw scores into percentages of terminal status. Jones (16) used this approach in examining sex differences in growth of different strength variables during adolescence. Patterns of growth of different variables for both individuals and groups are frequently analyzed in terms of increments based on percentage rate of growth. The problem of analyzing longitudinal data can be resolved in part by the use of correlation methods, so that the relationship among variables over points of time can be determined, as well as interrelationships among variables at specific points in the growth cycle.

Interpretation of Findings

Although longitudinal data do provide valuable information on changes occurring in an individual over well-defined time intervals, the factors causing these changes may not be easy to identify. Caution must be exercised in drawing unwarranted conclusions, for the association of variables over a period of time does not necessarily establish a causal relationship.

In conducting longitudinal studies, care must also be taken that inferences are drawn only for the age levels fully encompassed by the study. As Meredith (18) has pointed out, generalizations have been made on growth which have been based on extrapolation backward as well as forward, rather than within the boundaries of the study. Likewise, there is danger that the age limits set up by the study may result in a segmental approach to the study of development and in the use of truncated trends in the analysis of individual or group trends; that is, curves classified as linear might well have exhibited an acceleration phase had the study been conducted over a longer time span. As in other methods of research, inferences drawn from longitudinal data should be confined to the sample studied or to the population from which the sample was drawn.

Difficulties

The extended period of time required to conduct a longitudinal study tends to discourage many research workers. This is particularly true of the graduate student who finds the pressures of time and finances a real problem in graduate study. However, in institutions where longitudinal growth studies are underway, students have made valuable contributions through their affiliations with on-going projects in studying the relationships and interactions among growth variables at designated points in the developmental phenomenon.

The maintenance of an intact group of subjects for the duration of the project is a major problem. By selecting subjects who are likely to be permanently located, the researcher can reduce this problem but he also increases the likelihood of establishing a biased sample. In spite of the risk of dropouts, it is usually better to use an unbiased sample from which inferences can be legitimately drawn. Cooperation of parents, school personnel, and the children themselves must be enlisted and maintained, if the project is to prove successful. Where the same performance tests are repeated periodically, care needs to be taken that identical conditions and testing procedures prevail. At times, differential factors of motivation, hour of testing, or season of testing may distort the data.

Need in Physical Education

Many important questions in physical education will remain unanswered until carefully conducted studies have been made on the same group of individuals over long periods of time. The long-term effects of exercise upon humans have not yet been adequately explored, although there is a tendency to draw inferences from mortality tables based largely on normative data. Little is known concerning the age and maturity levels at which skills can be most economically learned. Answers to these important questions will depend upon combined experimental-longitudinal studies. Although the longitudinal approach presents many difficulties and problems, it perhaps offers the most fruitful approach for obtaining answers to some of the most significant questions which confront physical education today.

REFERENCES

1. Bayley, Nancy. Growth curves of height and weight by age for boys and girls, scaled according to physical maturity. *Journal of Pediatrics* 48: 187–194, 1956.
2. _____. Individual patterns of development. *Child Development* 27: 45–74, 1956.
3. Burdeshaw, Dorothy. Acquisition of elementary swimming skills by Negro and white college women. *Research Quarterly* 39: 872–879, Dec. 1968.
4. Campbell, Donald E. Wear attitude inventory applied to junior high school boys. *Research Quarterly* 39: 888–893, Dec. 1968.
5. Conger, Patricia R. and Wessel, Janet A. Physical performance and body form as related to physical activity of college women. *Research Quarterly* 39: 908–914, Dec. 1968.
6. Cureton, Thomas K., Jr. *Physical Fitness of Champion Athletes.* Urbana, Ill.: University of Illinois Press, 1951. 458 pp.

7. Dill, D. B.; Robinson, S.; and Ross, J. C. A longitudinal study of 16 champion runners. *Journal of Sports Medicine and Physical Fitness* 7: 4–27, 1967.
8. Espenschade, Anna. *Motor Performance in Adolescence*. Millwood, N.Y.: Kraus Reprint Co., 1940. 126 pp.
9. Fieldman, Harold. Relative contribution of the back and hamstring muscles in the performance of the toe-touch test after selected extensibility exercises. *Research Quarterly* 39: 518–523, Oct. 1968.
10. Gesell, Arnold and Ames, L. B. The ontogenetic organization of prone behavior in human infancy. *Journal of Genetic Psychology* 56: 247–263, 1940.
11. Harvey, Louise F. The delinquent Mexican boy. *Journal of Educational Research* 42: 573–585, April 1949.
12. Healy, William A. and Bronner, Augusta F., eds. *The Judge Baker Foundation Case Studies*. Series 1, case study no. 1. Boston, Mass: Judge Baker Guidance Center, 1922, 42 pp.
13. Hollingshead, A. *Elmtown's Youth*. New York: John Wiley & Sons, 1949. 480 pp.
14. Hubbard, Alfred W. An experimental analysis of running and of certain fundamental differences between trained and untrained runners. *Research Quarterly* 10: 28–38, Oct. 1939.
15. Hunsicker, Paul A. and Reiff, Guy G. *A Survey and Comparison of Youth Fitness 1958–1965*. Cooperative Research Project no. 2418. Washington, D.C.: Department of Health, Education and Welfare, 1965.
16. Jones, Harold E. *Motor Performance and Growth*. Berkeley, Calif.: University of California Press, 1949. 181 pp.
17. Kodlin, Dankwara and Thompson, D. J. An appraisal of the longitudinal approach to studies of growth and development. *Monograph Society Research in Child Development* 33; no. 1: 67, 1958.
18. Meredith, Howard V. Longitudinal anthropometric data in the study of individual growth. *Annals of the New York Academy of Sciences* 63: 510–527, 1955.
19. Morgan, Robert F. The adult growth examination: Preliminary comparisons of physical aging in adults by sex and race. *Perceptual and Motor Skills* 27: 595–599, 1968.
20. Newman, Earl N. Personality traits of faster and slower competitive swimmers. *Research Quarterly* 39: 1049–1053, Dec. 1968.
21. Olson, Willard C. and Hughes, Byron O. The concept of organismic age. *Journal of Educational Research* 35: 525–527, March 1942.
22. Rarick, G. Lawrence and McKee, Robert. A study of twenty third-grade children exhibiting extreme levels of achievement on tests of motor proficiency. *Research Quarterly* 20: 142–152, May 1949.
23. Rarick, G. Lawrence and Small, F. L. Stability of growth in strength and motor performance from childhood to adolescence. *Human Biology* 39: 295–306, 1967.
24. Rarick, G. Lawrence; Widdop, James H.; and Broadhead, Geoffrey D. *Motor Performance and Physical Fitness of Educable Mentally Retarded Children*. Madison, Wis.: Department of Physical Education, University of Wisconsin, 1967.
25. Reiff, Guy; Kish, Leslie; and Harter, Jean. Selecting a probability sample of school children in the coterminous United States. *Research Quarterly* 39: 409–414, May 1968.

26. Scott, M. Gladys, ed. *Research Methods in Health, Physical Education and Recreation.* 2d ed. (Chapter 12 Research and the curriculum). Washington, D.C.: American Association for Health, Physical Education and Recreation, 1959.
27. Sheldon, William H.; Hart, Emil M.; and McDermott, Eugene. *Varieties of Delinquent Youth.* New York: Harper & Brothers, 1949. 899 pp. Reprint (2 vols.). New York: Hafner Publishing Co., 1970.
28. Shevlin, Julius B. Effectiveness of programmed materials in teaching a secondary school health education unit. *Research Quarterly* 39: 704–707, Oct. 1968.
29. Shirley, Mary M. *The First Two Years: A Study of Twenty-Five Babies.* 3 vols. Vol. 1. *Postural and Locomotor Development.* Minneapolis: University of Minnesota Press, 1931. Reprint. Westport, Conn.: Greenwood Press, n.d.
30. Singer, Robert N. Interrelationship of physical, perceptual-motor, and academic achievement variables in elementary school children. *Perceptual and Motor Skills* 27: 1323–1332, 1968.
31. Sliepcevich, Elena M. *School Health Education: A Summary Report.* Washington, D.C.: School Health Education Study, 1964. (Out of print)
32. Sontag, L. W. and Reynolds, E. L. The Fels Composite Sheet, I. A practical method for analyzing growth progress. *Journal of Pediatrics* 26: 327–335, 1945.
33. Wetzel, Norman C. *The Treatment of Growth Failure in Children.* Cleveland: Newspaper Enterprises Association Service, 1948. 102 pp.
34. Zimmerman, Helen M. Characteristic likenesses and differences between skilled and non-skilled performance of standing broad jump. *Research Quarterly* 27: 352–362, Oct. 1956.

CHAPTER 12

THE HISTORICAL METHOD

D. B. Van Dalen
University of California
Berkeley, California

HISTORIANS COLLECT FACTS that are relevant to a problem considered to be significant, verify and classify these facts in accordance with specific standards, and interpret and present them in an orderly narrative that will stand the test of critical examination. The tools and techniques that have been developed by historians for ascertaining the meaning and reliability of past facts can be used by anyone in daily life or in any discipline. Even if an investigator is not engaged in a historical study, he may employ the critical standards established by historians to help him evaluate the previous studies relating to his problem. For this reason, every researcher should be familiar with this method of investigation.

PURPOSE AND SCOPE OF HISTORY

The purpose and scope of historical writing have changed down through the ages. Most of the early historians preserved folk tales and created epic poems to entertain or inspire the reader. Their objectives were literary rather than scientific in nature. A few ancient Greek scholars, however, envisioned history somewhat as a science—a search for truth. Thucydides, who wrote his historical accounts in the fifth century B.C., aspired to be more than an imaginative storyteller. His objective was to present an accurate account of the past in order to aid "in the interpretation of the future." Thucydides based his writing on his own observations or the reports of eyewitnesses whom he subjected to detailed tests of reliability. But most historians did not employ these procedures; many of them wrote history to glorify the state or church or to promote or defend a particular cause rather than to arrive at objective truth. However, some historians were more disciplined than others by the rigorous critical standards of research, and this practice became more commonplace after intensive debates concerning the historical method took place about the turn of the present century.

Is history a science? Modern historians agree that within limits the historical method is scientific, for an investigator can establish many facts about the past in as critical and objective a manner as in experimental research. Some scholars are convinced that history is a science or will become a science; other scholars believe that history is concerned with a different and more complex kind of subject matter than science, and, therefore, requires a different method and interpretation.

Historians have to cope with many handicaps that physical scientists have overcome or do not encounter. Physical scientists place the same meaning on the same technical terms and symbols. Historians do not have a precise technical vocabulary. They have an enormous amount of work to do in establishing consistent definitions of historical terms so as to minimize variations in the use of words and symbols used by different scholars. Unlike a physical scientist, a historian cannot observe personally the past events in which he is interested. He cannot set up a laboratory experiment in which he controls a, b, c, d and adds or removes x to measure the effect of its presence. In many instances, he cannot locate or isolate pertinent past facts, and the facts he does obtain are based on the observations of other people. Consequently, the knowledge the historian produces is never a total account of past actuality, but rather an incompleted jigsaw puzzle of the surviving "bits and pieces" of credible records concerning a unique event.

The scientist's ultimate objective is to establish broad generalizations, laws, or theories that 1) explain many unrelated, individual events and conditions, and 2) have precise predictive power. Some historians contend that constructing laws by generalizing about similarities between past events is entirely outside the province of historical research. They hold that history is concerned with uniqueness and individuality; thus an investigator should confine himself to describing and interpreting a past happening without employing any all-embracing theory of causality or an explanation that applies only to that particular historical sequence. They hold that the role of history is to particularize and the role of sociology is to generalize about recurrent events.

Other historians believe that it is their responsibility to generalize about the similarities found in past events, but it is not within their power to predict future events. Some scholars who are influential today believe that by making historical comparisons and studying historical trends they may suggest in some instances various possible outcomes "one or more of which may be anticipated with a high degree of probability" (5:139). The possibility that historians may someday draw conclusions about causes and make predictions that are as decisive as those in the physical sciences intrigues modern scholars, but many believe that they will have to settle for a more modest role. All agree that many handicaps will have to be overcome in making history more scientific, and the initial attempts will be crude and unsophisticated.

PROCEDURES IN HISTORICAL RESEARCH

Several procedures are involved in the historical method of research: selecting the problem, collecting and classifying source materials, criticizing source materials, formulating hypotheses to explain events or conditions, interpreting the data, and reporting the findings. These procedures will be considered separately and successively in the following discussion, but a researcher may pursue them in various orders and may shift back and forth between the steps as he proceeds.

Selecting the Problem

With a little probing, a student can find a number of worthwhile problems in our field to investigate, for little work has been done in the past. As Thomas Woody points out, "Institutions, movements, men and women, associated with the development of play and physical education, are awaiting an historic interview" (6:186). A historian can investigate individuals, institutions, organizations, laws, sports, games, dances, textbooks, teacher preparation, equipment, facilities, prevailing ideas, and other phenomena that relate to our field during a specific period of time in a given culture—ancient or modern—or in a subculture determined by nationality, color, religion, sex, age, work, or social class. He may confine his study to one era and one sequence of events, in a local, national, or regional setting, or he may compare events in different eras, societies, or civilizations.

A student may locate a problem by immersing himself in the literature and previous research in our field. The selected readings at the close of this chapter list some studies. The *Research Quarterly* publishes studies in our field. *Completed Research in Health, Physical Education, and Recreation* includes a list of relevant articles published in a wide range of periodicals and a bibliography of theses and dissertations, many of them with abstracts. Unpublished dissertations and theses can be located in the *Health, Physical Education and Recreation Microcard Bulletin*,

Volume 1, October 1949 through 1965 and *Volume II* (annual supplements), Microcard Publications, University of Oregon. *Revue Analytique D'Education Physique et Sports* presents abstracts of articles in our field in English and French.

A student can also locate problems and discover concepts, theories, and methods that may help him interpret historical data if he becomes familiar with the literature and research in related fields such as history, sociology, social psychology, anthropology, art history, archaeology, and the classics. He may, for example, employ a sociological or psychological method to analyze his data, or examine the archaeological, artistic or literary evidence of a given culture that relates to sports and interpret its meaning and effect on that society.

Some of the journals in the field of history are: *History of Education Quarterly, American Historical Review, Catholic Historical Review, Civil War History, Comparative Studies in Society and History, Hispanic American Historical Review, Historical Abstracts, Historical Journal, History and Theory, Journal of Negro History, Journal of Southern History, Journal of World History, Mississippi Valley Historical Review,* and *Pacific Historical Review.* To locate journals in other fields see *The Standard Periodical Directory,* 1967, which lists United States and Canadian periodicals and has semi-annual supplements.

Collecting and Classifying Source Materials

A historian locates and examines records and remains of human activity that testify about past events and from these remnants selects evidence that is relevant to his problem. In the beginning, secondary source materials may be employed but the ultimate objective is to locate primary sources.

Primary and Secondary Source Materials

Because the historian cannot observe personally the events that he is investigating, he endeavors to obtain the best evidence available from *primary sources*: 1) the reports and records of able eye and ear witnesses to past events, and 2) the actual remains of items used in the past that can be examined directly. The importance of possessing these sources to gain some understanding of the past cannot be overemphasized. Without them a historian is helpless—"Without them history would be only an empty tale, signifying nothing" (6:185).

A competent historian obtains evidence from the closest witness to the past event or condition. A newspaper account of what transpired at a meeting of an Olympic Committee would not satisfy him if he could obtain the official minutes of the meeting. A translation of the speeches given at an international meeting would not satisfy him if he could obtain copies of the original speeches. Whenever possible, he would visit the remains of a Roman bath or a South American ball court rather than study pictures.

A historian makes every effort to locate firsthand evidence about the past, but sometimes he must employ *secondary sources*; that is, information provided by a person who did not directly observe an event. This information, which appears in encyclopedias, newspapers, periodicals, and other references, is based on second- or even on fourth- or fifthhand information. Secondary sources are never as satisfactory or trustworthy as primary sources, but they do serve useful purposes. Secondary sources may be used as initial exploratory tools. An investigator may use them to obtain an overview of a problem area, to become acquainted with the work of other investigators in that area, to locate possible problems, working hypotheses, and important primary sources, and to accumulate background information for his problem.

Records

Most of the primary source materials a historian employs are records that have been preserved with the conscious intent of transmitting information. Among the diverse types of records that are available are:

1. *Official Records*—Federal, state, or local legislative, judicial, or executive documents such as constitutions, laws, charters, court proceedings and decisions, tax lists, and vital statistics; church records; and health, physical education, or recreation records of federal and state departments, special commissions, professional organizations, school boards, or administrative authorities, such as minutes of meetings, committee reports, administrative orders or directives, catalogs, surveys, annual reports, budgets, courses of study, class schedules, salary lists, honors and awards, attendance records, health records, accident reports, and sports records.

2. *Personal Records*—Diaries, autobiographies, letters, wills, deeds, contracts, lecture notes, original drafts of speeches, articles, and books.

3. *Oral Traditions*—Myths, folk tales, family stories, dances, games, superstitions, ceremonies, reminiscences by eyewitnesses to events, and recordings.

4. *Pictorial Records*—Photographs, movies, drawings, paintings, microfilms, sculpture, and coins.

5. *Published Materials*—Newspaper, pamphlet, and periodical articles; literary and philosophical works that convey information about health, physical education, or recreation.

Remains or Relics

The second type of primary source material is objects or materials handed down from the past without the specific intent of imparting information. Remains sometimes reveal the actual practices and conditions in the past better than official records. A law may be found, for example, stating that certain recreational, military, or health practices were forbidden in a given society, but the skeletons and the remains of sports or dance equipment or activity areas at scattered sites may reveal that this law was not observed. Various types of remains are available, for example:

1. *Physical remains*—Buildings, facilities, grounds, furniture, equipment, costumes, implements, awards, and skeletal remains.

2. *Printed materials*—Textbooks, blank diplomas, record blanks, contracts, certificates, attendance forms, report cards, and newspaper advertisements.

3. *Handwritten materials*—Pupil manuscripts, drawings, and exercises.

Because relics and remains are evidence that the researcher can weigh, measure, and examine personally, they are more trustworthy as sources than records.

Location of Source Materials

In his initial search for a problem, an investigator may find helpful leads in the card catalog, periodical indices, bibliographies, historical reviews, dissertations, and research journals. But his ultimate objective is to locate primary source materials. Some individuals, universities, and organizations have collected such records and remains and have preserved them in historical depositories. Some institutions have extensive collections of a particular kind; other institutions have fragmentary collections from different areas. Some collections have been cataloged, but many of them are unorganized. Because of changes in leadership or space and funding problems, these collections are moved from time to time.

In 1934–35, the American Association for Health, Physical Education, and Recreation created a Committee for Permanent Historical Records and Exhibits. Since the 1950s, a concerted effort has been made by historians in the field to add to the Association's archives, which are in Washington, D.C.

Several universities and special centers have also collected papers, memorabilia, or records that relate to phenomena in our field. Mabel Lee has compiled a list of 24 such repositories and has identified the nature of their collections (4:6). In addition, the following repositories and source materials are available: New York Public Library—A.G. Mills, Chairman of the Spaulding Baseball Commission; Stanford University—Jesse F. Williams; University of California, Berkeley—Winifred Van Hagen, Anna Espenschade, the American Academy of Physical Education; University of Pittsburgh—the Dr. John Neitz collections of old health textbooks; Yale University Library—Walter Camp; and the University of Illinois, archives of the Illinois Association for Health, Physical Education, and Recreation and archives of the National College Physical Education Association for Men.

The Library of Congress, the New York Public Library, and some other libraries have excellent collections of books, photographs, and primary source materials that relate to phenomena in our field. Some state and local historical museums and societies, sports bodies, nationality groups, voluntary organizations, church organizations, labor groups, and sporting goods companies have preserved records and remains, such as newspapers, photographs, sports equipment and costumes, minutes of meetings, annual reports, correspondence, and programs of sports and dance events. Established collections of historical materials are also at the Basketball Hall of Fame in Springfield, Massachusetts, which houses the papers of James Naismith, the Baseball Hall of Fame at Cooperstown, New York, the Ski Museum at Oslo, Norway, and similar institutions.

A historian may unearth significant data by examining archaeological evidence, the classics, and art; by talking with "old timers" in the profession or sports world; exploring secondhand stores or bookshops and the attics, basements, or storage areas of homes, schools, and athletic facilities; visiting the sites of old schools, athletic facilities, or playing areas; examining the correspondence, lecture notes, or manuscripts of retired teachers and coaches; and studying federal, state, city, church, schoolboard, or institutional reports, records, laws, or regulations.

Criticizing Source Materials

An investigator is always suspicious of the authenticity and reliability of the raw data he collects, for "in historical studies doubt is the beginning of wisdom" (2:50). Because research based on untrustworthy sources is labor lost, a historian subjects his source materials to rigorous external and internal criticism.

External Criticism

External criticism is concerned with establishing the date, place, and authorship of the document and restoring it to its original form. Some documents do not bear a date, or they omit the name of the author, conceal his identity with a pseudonym, or present a man as the author who wrote little or none of the work. Professional organizations, government offices, and school administrators often issue reports that do not clearly identify the author. Three men may sign a report, but only one of them may have written it. An important man may have given a speech or have had a book published, but one of his subordinates may have written all or most of it. If a college or school board published a report about racial problems or unethical practices in sports, a historian may ask: Did one person or several persons contribute to the report, and if several people contributed, did anyone correct, alter, omit, suppress, or expand parts of their reports? If the wife, children, or friends of a professor donated his letters and papers to a historical depository, an investigator may ask: Did the donors omit items intentionally or alter any of the materials?

To establish authorship, trace anonymous and undated documents, ferret out forgeries, detect plagiarism, spot incorrectly identified items, or restore a document to its original form, a historian examines his source materials carefully and asks questions such as: Are the language, style, spelling, handwriting, and printing of the document typical of the author's other work and the period in which it was written? Did the author exhibit ignorance of things a man of his training and time should have known? Did he write about events, things, or places that a man of that period could not have known? Did anyone alter the manuscript by copying or translating it incorrectly, adding to it, or deleting passages? Is this an original draft of the author's work or a copy? If it is a copy, is it reproduced in the exact words of the original? If the manuscript is undated or the author unknown, are there any internal clues in the document that reveal when, where, why, or by whom the document was written?

An investigator will experience greater success in determining whether a document is what it appears or claims to be if he possesses an ample fund of varied historical and general knowledge, a good chronological sense, and an intelligent understanding of human behavior. To solve a problem, he may have to have a knowledge of numismatics, art, the classics, chemistry, paleography, cartography, psychology, anthropology, or ancient languages. A historian cannot have a knowledge of everything. He usually acquires special training in the fields that are most closely related to his problem and seeks the help of competent experts if he is not qualified to undertake some aspects of textual criticism.

Internal Criticism

After establishing the genuineness or validity of a document, a historian endeavors to ascertain the meaning and trustworthiness of the data within the document. In this process, which is called internal criticism, he asks the following questions: What did the author mean by each word and statement? Are the statements the author made credible?

Many words and social and scientific concepts in older documents do not have the same meaning today that they had in earlier times. Likewise, attitudes toward recreation, health, sports, exercise, bodily beauty, and sex vary in different cultures and eras. To interpret the meaning of an author's statement, a historian may have to ask several questions: What geographical, social, religious, political, economic, or professional environment did the author experience? What was the nature of the knowledge in the various disciplines of the time in which he was writing? What was the quality and nature of his relationships with members of his family, friends, and professional associates? If a historian can answer such questions and can determine why an author wrote a report, he can interpret its meaning more accurately. A wealth of background information helps an investigator determine whether an author was writing seriously, humorously, ironically, or symbolically and whether he was voicing his real convictions or mouthing conventional phrases or establishment views for public consumption. If a historian uses a translation of a document or does the work himself, he makes certain that the translation conveys the same meaning as the original.

To determine whether the author was willing or able to tell the truth, an investigator asks some of the following questions: Is the author accepted as a competent and reliable reporter by other authorities in this special field? Were his facilities, technical training, and location favorable for observing the conditions he reported? Did emotional stress or health conditions cause him to make faulty observations or an inaccurate report? Did he report on direct observations, hearsay, or borrowed source materials? Did he write the document at the time of observation or weeks or years later? Did he write from carefully prepared notes of observations or from memory? Did he have biases concerning any nation, race, religion, person, political party, social or economic group, professional body, teaching method, educational philosophy, or activity that influenced his writing? Did anyone finance his research work with the hope of securing a report favorable to a specific cause? Did the author write under any economic, political, religious, or social condition that might have caused him to ignore, misinterpret, or misrepresent certain facts? Was he motivated to write by malice, by a desire to justify his acts, or by a desire to win the approval of succeeding generations? Did the author distort or embellish the truth to achieve colorful literary effects? Did the author contradict himself? Do accounts by other independent, competent observers of different backgrounds agree with the report of the author?

Examples of Criticism

When an investigator engages in historical criticism, he encounters varied problems. To give some insight into typical tasks he performs, the following discussion presents a case of 1) determining authorship, 2) checking origin, 3) finding the correct spelling, and 4) correcting dates.

1. Determining authorship—A book on gymnastics that was used in some early American schools had the name of Salzmann on the title page. But scholars have since found that Johann C. F. Guts Muths, a teacher in Salzmann's school, was actually the author of the original book, *Gymnastik für die Jugend*, which was published in 1793 in Schnepfenthal, Germany. An English publisher translated Guts Muths' book in 1800 and placed Salzmann's name on the title page because that was the name appended to the advertisement in which the book was announced. The American edition of the book in 1802 repeated this error of authorship. A comparison of the various editions of the book reveals that the later editions were also altered and condensed.

2. Checking origin—Abner Doubleday is commonly credited with being the inventor of baseball. How he acquired this reputation and the historical criticism of the claim is an interesting story. As the popularity of baseball spread in this country after the Civil War, enthusiastic fans claimed the game was of American origin. Henry Chadwick, a British-born sportsman, challenged this theory, for he held that baseball was a direct descendant of the English game of rounders. In 1905, A. G. Spaulding, who supported the American theory, complained that he had been fed this "rounders pap" for 40 years and refused to swallow the story without substantial proof. He proposed to settle the argument in "some comprehensive and authoritative way, and for all time" (1:172) by establishing a commission of six men to investigate.

The public was invited to send in whatever information they had. The commission issued a report in 1907 based on the testimony submitted in a letter by Abner Graves, who wrote that his boyhood friend, Abner Doubleday, originated the game. Without any additional evidence to support Graves' story, the commission announced that Doubleday invented and named the game "base ball" in 1839 when he marked off a diamond-shaped field and diagrammed the location of players at Cooperstown, New York. This report remained unchallenged by most people for years and was copied in a number of textbooks, newspapers, and sports books.

Many years later, Robert Henderson subjected the report to historical criticism. He discovered that A. G. Mills, the chairman of the commission and a military friend of Doubleday, apparently based his findings on a letter written by Abner Graves, for no documents by any other person and no contemporary records were presented to support the Graves' story. Henderson pointed out that when Doubleday supposedly originated the game in Cooperstown, he was actually in West Point and did not return to Cooperstown on leave. After retiring from the army, Doubleday wrote many articles for publication but none about baseball. Moreover, when he died in 1893, his obituary notice did not mention that he invented the game.

A critical examination of the commission's report revealed many other weaknesses. The name "baseball" and some of the rules that Doubleday supposedly invented in 1839 had appeared in print before that time. Although it was claimed that Graves was present when Doubleday traced the first baseball diamond in the dirt, the original Graves' letter did not mention this fact. A later letter that appears to have been written by Graves disclosed that he did not know "where the first game was played according to Doubleday's plan." Moreover, a few books printed before 1839 discussed or illustrated a baseball diamond. Comparisons of the two Graves letters revealed some inconsistencies, which was not surprising, for the man wrote from memory almost seven decades after the event.

Henderson believes that certain personal factors may have caused members of the commission to accept the report. Because of the pressure of other duties, they probably did not check the facts thoroughly. Perhaps patriotic prejudices also influenced their decision. Some men were eager to prove that baseball was of American rather than British origin. The possibility that General Doubleday, a famous Civil War soldier, invented the great American pasttime must have appealed to them.

3. Correcting spelling—In recent textbooks, Barbara Hoepner noted a discrepancy in the spelling of the first name of the pioneer educator, Catharine Beecher. Some sources used the letter "a" as the second vowel, while others used the letter "e." Verifying the correct spelling was not an easy task. An examination of the title page in the books Miss Beecher had written revealed that the name was spelled "Catharine." But in a later section of one book which listed the "Catalogue of the Officers, Teachers, and Pupils of the Hartford Female Seminary, 1829," the principal is listed as "Miss Catherine E. Beecher." Since some doubt about the speeling still existed, the investigator decided to find out how Miss Beecher herself spelled her name. At the Yale Library she located three letters written by Miss Beecher to a friend. To her dismay, they were all signed "C. E. B." or "C. E. Beecher." But a further search let to the location of five letters written by Miss Beecher to her family; all were signed with the name "Catharine."

4. Correcting dates—In examining the listings of the American Association for Health, Physical Education, and Recreation presidents,

and the dates of their elections and terms of office, Mabel Lee thought she detected inaccuracies and discrepancies. From a study of the minutes of the official meetings from 1885 through 1932, she compiled an accurate list. Her research revealed that inaccurate listings based on published materials rather than original documents had been published since 1910 (3:29–31).

General Principles of Criticism

Investigators make many judgments when they subject source materials to historical criticism. Not all of the principles of criticism can be presented in this text, but the following suggestions made by Woody will serve as a general guide.

1. Do not read into earlier documents the conceptions of later times.

2. Do not judge an author ignorant of certain events, necessarily, because he fails to mention them (the argument *ex silentio*), or that they did not occur, for the same reason.

3. Underestimating a source is no less an error than overestimating it in the same degree, and there is not more virtue in placing an event too late than in dating it too early by the same number of years or centuries.

4. A single true source may establish the existence of an idea, but other direct, competent, independent witnesses are required to prove the reality of events or objective facts.

5. Identical errors prove the dependence of sources on each other, or a common source.

6. If witnesses contradict each other on a certain point, one or the other may be true, but both may be in error.

7. Direct, competent, independent witnesses who report the same central fact and also many peripheral matters in a casual way may be accepted for the points of their agreement.

8. Official testimony, oral or written, must be compared with unofficial testimony whenever possible, for neither one nor the other is alone sufficient.

9. A document may provide competent and dependable evidence on certain points, yet carry no weight in respect to others it mentions (6:190).

Students who plan to engage in historical studies can find more detailed discussion of the problems and principles involved in external and internal criticism in books by outstanding authorities in the field. (See selected readings at end of chapter.)

Formulating Hypotheses and Interpreting the Data

Historians do not aimlessly collect source materials, subject them to intensive criticism, and then present the mass of facts—names, events, places, and dates—to the public like "beads on a string." Unrelated bits of information do not advance knowledge appreciably. Even if scholars group their facts and arrange the groups in a logical order, they produce a narrative that is little more than a series of disconnected and unexplained events. Isolated facts lack meaning; they "never speak for themselves but only *to* someone who has a hypothesis which he wishes to test" (5:123-24). Consequently, research scholars go beyond the amassing of facts or the mere describing and classifying of them in accordance with their superficial properties. As discussed in earlier chapters (pp. 33-34 and 51-52), to produce works of value, researchers formulate tentative hypotheses that explain the occurrence of events and conditions. They seek the underlying patterns, hidden connections, or general principles that explain or describe the structural interrelations of the phenomena under study. Having established hypotheses, they search for data that will confirm or deny them.

The nature and significance of the hypothesis are discussed elsewhere in this text (pp. 33-34, 51-52, and 244-245) and in several texts listed in the selected readings. The following investigation by Henderson may give readers insight into the use of a hypothesis in historical research.

When Henderson became interested in the origin of ball games, he found some suggestions in the literature that they stemmed from ancient rituals but found no conclusive evidence that traced games from rites to pasttimes. He decided to test the hypothesis that "all modern games played with bat and ball descend from one common source: an ancient fertility rite observed by Priest-Kings in the Egypt of the Pyramids" (1:4). To test his hypothesis, he examined the religious rites and folk customs of ancient societies and traced the evolution of games played with a ball. Henderson reported finding evidence in rituals, customs, and tombs to support his hypothesis that the modern bat-and-ball games are vestigial remains of ancient rites.

In the early stages of research, graduate students usually do not have clearly defined hypotheses. After blocking out an area of study, they explore the literature in a rather general manner for some time. In analyzing their tentative problems, they discover that the data are vague or incomplete, that some elements do not appear to be related to other known elements or to fit into any particular order, or that there are no adequate interpretations for some phenomena. They are puzzled and disturbed. How can they complete the data, systematize the information, and give some interpretation that will explain the unknown factors? Now they stand on the threshold of research! If they can construct hypotheses (explanations) for the unknown phenomena and test them, they may push back the frontiers of knowledge. To build schemes of explanation that account for the factors they are trying to understand, they engage in a high order of conceptualization.

Hypotheses consist of elements expressed in an orderly system of relationships which seek to explain conditions or events that have not yet been verified by facts. Some elements or relationships in hypotheses are known facts, others are conceptual. The conceptual elements are products of research workers' imaginations. They leap beyond the known facts to give plausible explanations for unknown conditions. Hypotheses may provide the conceptual elements that complete the known data, conceptual relationships that systematize unordered elements, and conceptual meaning and interpretations that explain the unknown phenomena. Thus, hypotheses logically relate known facts to intelligent guesses about unknown conditions in an effort to extend and enlarge our knowledge. Through conceptualization, which makes it possible to introduce elements and relationships that are not directly observable, investigators can go beyond the known data and set up possible solutions to problems.

The explanations or hypotheses proposed by scholars lack proof at the time they construct them. It is their duty to formulate the conceptual and factual elements and relationships in the hypotheses in such a precise and objective manner that they can test the implications of the hypotheses. In the testing process, they reexamine old evidence and search for new that will either confirm or disprove the hypotheses.

Because historical phenomena may have a greater number of antecedent factors and a more complicated pattern of interaction among them than physical science phenomena, a historian usually presents a pluralistic rather than a monistic explanation. He does not speak of the one and only cause, but rather about the more important cause or causes. He presents a network of hypotheses to account for the multidimensional forces from which historical events spring. He may utilize the theories concerning games or borrow generalizations from sociology, economics, geography, anthropology, or psychology to interrogate the past, and he does not hesitate to devise his own hypotheses. But a competent historian always guards against employing hypotheses, classification schemes, or terms that are based on outdated concepts or scientific ideas.

A historian not only describes what happened, he also tries to detect relationships between events that explain why and how they happened in a particular order and what impact they had upon society. He searches for meaningful interrelationships among events in a person's life, among people, institutions, sports, and phenomena in his field and other fields. To help him detect significant relationships, he becomes familiar with the literature in his own field and with the current concepts, theories, and methods in the related disciplines. He also becomes familiar with the collective psychology and the concepts and ideas that dominated intellectual life at the time of his study. He examines the personal and interpersonal experiences and the writing and work of a man, or the nature of games and dances, or the structure processes and products of organizations and institutions. He endeavors to ascertain to what extent their nature, outlook, or actions were influenced by the existing environmental forces and, in turn, what effect they had on social, political, or economic life. He tries to determine to what extent various activities, institutions, or men's views were the same, how they differed, how they influenced one another, what the contribution of each was, and what their common contribution was.

A historian realizes that men and institutions are not static entities and strives to detect changes in them and the factors that contribute to these changes. He is concerned about failure and declines as well as success and progress and knows that unconscious motives, irrational impulses, and emotional factors, as well as reason and rationality, produce events. He is aware of the role of leadership and personality in social movements and knows that the conspicuousness and influence of a man are not necessarily correlative. The historian searches not only for evidence that A was influenced by B, but also for data that eliminate the possibility that X, Y, or Z may have influenced A or the extent to which they may have contributed to A's acts or nature.

Reporting the Findings

The network of hypotheses or the explanatory scheme the historian employs helps him determine not only what data are relevant and irrelevant to his study, but also provides him with a framework for stating the conclusions of the study in a meaningful way. Within the framework of the explanatory scheme, of course, he patterns his materials in some systematic order, such as chronological, geographical, topical, or a combination of them. In writing his report, the historian imaginatively projects his own consciousness into the past and strives to convey the "distance resonance" of a leader, institution, or era without embellishing his narrative with dramatic flourishes that distort the truth. His objective is to write a lucid, lively, logical account of what happened without violating the rigorous rules of critical scholarship.

REFERENCES
1. Henderson, Robert W. *Ball, Bat and Bishop: The Origin of Ball Games.* New York: Rockport Press, 1947. 220 pp.

2. Johnson, Allen. *The Historian and Historical Evidence.* Port Washington, N.Y.: Kennikat Press, 1926.
3. Lee, Mabel. AAHPER presidents through the years. *Journal of Health, Physical Education, Recreation* 39: 29–31, Jan. 1968.
4. _____. Archives of the profession. *Journal of Health, Physical Education, Recreation* 38: 6, Oct. 1967.
5. Social Science Research Council. *Theory and Practice in Historical Study: A Report of the Committee on Historiography.* Bulletin 54. New York: Social Science Research Council, 1946.
6. Woody, Thomas. Of history and its method. *Journal of Experimental Education* 15: 175–201, March 1947.

SELECTED READINGS

American Historical Association. *Guide to Historical Literature.* New York: Macmillan Co., 1961. 962 pp.

Bloch, Marc. *The Historian's Craft.* New York: Alfred A. Knopf, 1953. Reprint. New York: Random House, n.d.

Carr, Edward H. *What Is History?* New York: Alfred A. Knopf, 1961.

Collingwood, R. G. *The Idea of History.* Edited by T. M. Knox. New York: Oxford University Press, 1956.

Dray, William H. *Philosophy of History.* Englewood Cliffs, N.J.: Prentice-Hall, 1967.

Gardiner, Patrick. *The Nature of Historical Explanation.* London: Oxford University Press, 1968.

Garraghan, Gilbert. *A Guide to Historical Method.* New York: Fordham University Press, 1946. 482 pp.

Gottschalk, Louis. *Understanding History: A Primer of Historical Method.* 2d ed. New York: Alfred A. Knopf, 1969.

Higham, John; Krieger, Leonard; and Gilbert, Felix. *History.* Englewood Cliffs, N.J.: Prentice-Hall. 1965 402 pp.

Hockett, Homer C. *The Critical Method in Historical Research and Writing.* 3d ed. New York: Macmillan Co., 1955.

Hook, Sidney, ed. *Philosophy and History: A Symposium.* New York: New York University Press, 1963.

Löwith, Karl. *Meaning in History.* Chicago: University of Chicago Press, 1949.

Meyerhoff, Hans, ed. *The Philosophy of History In Our Time.* Garden City, N.Y.: Doubleday & Co., 1959.

Social Science Research Council. *Generalization in the Writing of History: A Report of the Committee on Historiography.* Edited by Louis Gottschalk. Chicago: University of Chicago Press, 1963. 255 pp.

_____. *The Social Sciences in Historical Study: A Report of the Committee on Historiography.* Bulletin 64. Edited by Thomas C. Cochran et al. New York: the Council, 1954. 181 pp.

Thucydides. *The History of the Peloponnesian War.* Translated by H. Dale. London: Bell Co., 1912.

Van Dalen, Deobold B. *Understanding Educational Research.* New York: McGraw-Hill Book Co., 1966. 525 pp.

Walsh, William H. *Philosophy of History: An Introduction.* New York: Harper & Row, 1960. 176 pp.

CHAPTER **13**   # THE PHILOSOPHIC METHOD OF RESEARCH

Richard B. Morland
Stetson University
DeLand, Florida

MANY PROFESSIONALS, AND WITH GOOD REASON, would question the inclusion of philosophy among the standard methods of educational research. Research must be scientific, they hold, and science is empirical, quantitative, and objective. Philosophy, on the other hand, is rationalistic, qualitative, and subjective. The contributions that philosophy can make to science by clarifying assumptions and assessing the relevancy of facts are recognized, but research involves more than precision in thought. Like salt, which adds savor to any dinner but hardly qualifies as a meal in itself, philosophy is relegated to an adjunctive role in the science of research.

QUESTION OF LEGITIMACY OF PHILOSOPHIC METHOD

Before attempting to set forth a method that could be called "philosophic,"[1] it is important to consider the arguments for excluding philosophy as one of the accepted methods of research.[2] Three reasons are advanced for the prevailing consensus among textbook writers for this stand. First, philosophy is built into all research. As Dunkel (8:26) points out, it is not

---

[1] There is no clear distinction in the literature between the usage of the two adjectives, "philosophic" and "philosophical." In this chapter, the former is used to denote a particular procedure or set of beliefs. The latter term is used in a broader sense to indicate general characteristics ascribable to philosophy, such as philosophical attitudes or considerations.

[2] In a survey of 29 texts dealing with educational research, only five of the authors treat the philosophic method.

possible to make research so scientific it is "philosophy-free." Every investigation begins with a "felt difficulty" or hypothesis. The researcher bases his study on implicit or explicit statements of assumptions and ends with conclusions that are logically supportable.

Because philosophy is woven into the fabric of whatever method is adopted, a statement to the effect that the elements of philosophy were used is gratuitous. An illustration drawn from athletics will clarify this relationship. If asked to describe his style of offense, the basketball coach would not say that he employs the "shooting" offense. Whether he instructs his team to bring the ball down the court with the speed of gazelles or tortoises, whether he has his players maneuver in set patterns or shoot at the first opportunity, his purpose is to score more baskets than his opponents. This fact is taken for granted, and to state it as a purpose is as unnecessary as saying that he will play by the rules of the game.

Similarly, the researcher is expected to use philosophical techniques throughout his investigation. His study commences with philosophical assumptions, uses procedures that are logically defensible, and concludes with findings that are deducible from the data he has analyzed. Even in statistical studies, the decision to use the .01 or .05 confidence interval is basically philosophical. Hence, nothing is gained by restating the obvious. The survey by Griffiths (9:34–41), in which he reports the 10 most significant findings in educational research in the decade 1956–66, conclusively demonstrates the role of philosophy in studies of all types.

A second reason is the belief that for any investigation to qualify as research, there must be controlled experimentation with data that can be quantified, classified, analyzed, and replicated. The raw materials of philosophy are the thoughts of men. Ideas, points of view, values, principles, implications, interrelationships, means, and ends are subjective. They do not lend themselves to quantitative analyses and controls. There is no way to isolate these components as dependent variables, much less to manipulate them. Philosophy as the focus of a research problem thus fails to qualify as genuine research. Kerlinger (14:20) is cited as representative of those who adhere to this view. He maintains, "Certain philosophic and theological questions, while perhaps important to the individuals who consider them, cannot be tested empirically and are thus of no interest to the scientist as a scientist."

The third objection deals with the manner in which philosophers have addressed themselves to the types of problems they find useful and significant. In the classical sense, philosophy is prescriptive. The philosopher who is oriented to traditional modes of thought is not content merely to describe phenomena or to examine the meaning of language. He is committed to "what ought to be." The force of his writings beckons the reader to see the validity of his position and the importance of its adoption.

Treatises of this sort may be of infinite worth, but they do not meet the basic requirements of objectivity and detachment. As Barr (3:1164) writes, "The 'goodness,' 'worth,' or 'value' of facts is not ordinarily thought as being within the province of scientific research." Because much of the writing in the field of philosophy deals with values, cognitive claims, interpretations of the human situation, and criticisms of normative behavior, subjective factors dominate. Classical philosophers make no assertions that the techniques they use in their analyses are "scientific." This has led to the belief that philosophy, aside from the contribution it makes to procedures, is too far removed from science to serve as a research method.

As sound as these reasons may be, the irony is that many of the dissertations being accepted for advanced degrees today apparently do not qualify as research if the thinking of those cited above is taken as the yardstick. An examination of *Dissertation Abstracts*, particularly the volumes pertaining to the social sciences and the humanities, will confirm this. How, then, are these "nonresearch" studies to be classified as to method? The answer is that in most cases no label or classification is considered necessary. The graduate student in the humanities, for example, is expected to be thoroughly grounded in his discipline and to know what scholarship means when he reaches the point of writing the dissertation. Courses in research methods, except in certain of the social sciences, are seldom found. The method that is usually employed by humanists is here referred to as the philosophic method, whether it is called "literary scholarship," (25:1–25) "analytical research," (22:35) "theoretical research," (23:492) or "critical research " (11:102).

PHILOSOPHIC METHOD DEFINED

If a question is asked about the effects of participating in a high school physical education class, it can be answered empirically. Data can be collected and conclusions drawn from an analysis of the findings. But suppose these questions are asked: What are the purposes of the physical education program? How should it be conducted? How can it be related effectively to other curriculum experiences? Should physical education be required of all students? To answer questions like these, one is thrust headlong into judging values and the worth of experiences. One way to obtain answers is to gather data by polling panels of experts, surveying samples of participants, or using other techniques that measure opinion. All of these procedures, however, are limited in that they merely quantify prevailing attitudes. If the researcher desires to go beyond the normative to develop constructs or models that may not even have been tried, he needs a method that does more than describe. The method is philosophic.

What is the philosophic research method? For the purposes of this essay, it is defined as follows: *In formal research, other than purely descriptive and historical studies, the philosophic method is the rigorous application of the principles and processes of logic, within carefully defined limits, to the analysis of nonempirical problems.*

The basic terms in this definition require explanation. *Formal research* is used to distinguish the systematic, intensive, and in-depth investigation from the type which is called casual or incidental research. Most articles appearing in the literature are representative of the latter. The author is philosophizing, i.e., endeavoring to prove a point or to provide a rationale for a position that he has already accepted as the most efficacious one. An example would be an article demonstrating the superiority of isometrics over other methods of conditioning or one where the author is making a case for school camping programs. While an article of this sort may be based on research findings, it cannot be considered formal research. In formal research, the investigator sets out to find answers to questions, not to advance preformed conclusions. He is not committed to any particular outcome. Instead, he is prepared to accept any conclusion, even one that may not be attractive to him. He states his problem in precise terms, investigates all aspects within the framework he has established, and sets forth his procedures in such a fashion that each step can be followed. These characteristics are seldom found in term papers, journal articles, and philosophical essays.

The rigorous application of the principles and processes of logic may appear to be tautological, for one could argue that nonrigorous logic does not exist. The adjective, *rigorous*, is inserted to give added emphasis to the fact that every step in the completed study must meet the test of logical consistency for the conclusions to stand. As John Stuart Mill (18:7) wrote over a century ago, "If one link of an argument breaks, the whole drops to the ground." Each link in any investigation, from the assumptions through the conclusions, must satisfy logical requirements for the work to be valid. The philosophic method is only as strong as the logic of its analysis.

Within carefully defined limits is the discriminating factor that sets off formal research from philosophizing. Some of the differences have already been mentioned. However, since the understanding of this concept is basic to the philosophic method, this term will later be discussed in greater detail.

Nonempirical problems constitute the subject matter of the philosophic method. As opposed to the type of problem that can be solved through quantification of data and experimental procedures, the philosophic method is employed when the researcher seeks to analyze qualitative components.

Other than purely descriptive and historical studies is the qualifying expression offered to emphasize the fact that not all studies which treat qualitative data can be classified as philosophic. The reason for excluding descriptive studies is self-evident, for philosophical analysis is not employed. The distinction between the historical and the philosophic is not as obvious. Both are analytic. Both deal with qualitative factors, and both depend on logic for the generalizations reached. The difference lies in the focus of the investigation and how the raw data are used.

The historian re-creates the past. He searches for clues to explain and interpret causes, influences, and interrelationships among past events. He strives for "conceptual perspicuity," as Muller (19:300) says, by "laying bare structual and functual connections." The philosopher may use historical materials, but his purpose is not the same. Collingwood (7:4) stresses the point that the historical factors must be treated as "mere preliminaries to the main question." The central question, if it is philosophical, cannot be answered by a portrayal of events or by an analysis of causal factors. While the philosopher has a healthy respect for the facts, his concern is not with the facts themselves but with the logical implications that can be demonstrated to flow from the facts. Of greater concern are the ideas that gave rise to the facts. The emphasis, therefore, is on "why" rather than on "when" or "how." The philosophic task is to bring into relief the meaning of ideas in order to gain the unified understanding that is necessary to bridge the gap between means and ends.

Along with these explanations and qualifications, the fact should be made clear that there is no single or universal philosophic method. The modes of inquiry set forth by various philosophers such as Descartes, Kant, Mill, and Dewey are commonly referred to as philosophical methods. The linguistic analysts, perhaps the dominant school of philosophy in America today, have expounded another type of philosophic method where the emphasis is placed on the meaning of language. Though relevant and timely, these interpretations are not covered in this exposition. The discussion which follows is limited to the application of philosophy as a research tool in the context of theses and dissertations. It is predicated on the assumption that ideas are researchable, and that there is a method through which this can be accomplished that meets the canons of research.

PHILOSOPHY AS RESEARCH TOOL FOR THESES AND DISSERTATIONS

Nature of Assumptions

Perhaps the greatest pitfall encountered by those undertaking theses and dissertations is the candidate's failure to think through his problem to the point that he is assured his study will rest on sound assumptions.[3] If the theoretical foundations are ambiguous or questionable, the investigation collapses at the outset. This applies to all studies, irrespective of the method of inquiry or the field of investigation.

What is an assumption? As noted in Chapter 2 (p. 31), *an assumption is a statement that is generally accepted as true without the necessity of investigation.* Another way of saying this is that the validity of the statement is readily apparent and accepted as self-evident by those knowledgeable of the circumstances or conditions to which the assumption is directed. Of course, there is seldom complete agreement on anything, and the possibility always exists that widely held assumptions are erroneous. Still, there has to be a starting point. If the researcher were unable to make certain assumptions about the values inherent in play, the development of human potentials, or that opportunities for learning should be maximized, he would have to start from scratch with each problem that dealt with these factors. Assumptions are reached deductively, based on facts, consensus, and well-accepted principles that are considered axiomatic.

What cannot be assumed? One does not assume a test to be valid or a sample to be representative if the parameter is known. These have to be established. A fact, however, is an established truth, e.g., that football is played in many high schools or that exercise increases organic efficiency. A fact needs no help to stand as a fact. What the researcher does assume is that necessary relationships exist among the facts, or that certain conditions obtain when the facts are organized or utilized in a particular manner. The assumption could not be made, for instance, that all girls who try out for the cheerleading squad are agile and svelte, but it would be in order to assume that they desire the recognition afforded by being a member of the squad and the opportunity to perform at athletic contests. To use other examples, one could assume that interscholastic athletics fosters competition among schools or that running is essential in the conditioning programs of baseball pitchers.

An analysis of the above examples will illustrate the difference between assumptions and facts. The expressions, "football is played," and, "exercise increases," are statements with an experiential base that is beyond challenge. To restate them as assumptions adds nothing to their meaning and tends to cast doubt on their validity. In the second set, however, the terms, "fosters competition" and, "is essential," are not

---

[3] To determine the quality of articles in educational research, a committee of the American Educational Research Association, headed by Edwin Wandt, evaluated a random sample of 125 articles published in 39 journals in 1962 (26: 1–6). Only 19% were rated by the panel of experts as "acceptable for publication without revision." Of the 25 criteria used in evaluating the articles, "assumptions are clearly stated" received the lowest mean-rating.

assertions of fact. They imply qualitative factors that usually, but not necessarily, follow. The type of emphasis placed on interscholastic athletics will determine if competition is fostered, and it is conceivable that baseball pitchers could stay in shape by following a different type of training program.

How does one arrive at assumptions? While in the process of selecting his topic, the researcher should ask himself, "What conditions or factors, singly or in combination, must I accept as true in order to proceed with the solution of my problem?" The answers resulting from a careful analysis of this question will provide the solid footing required for an acceptable research design.

The following examples, drawn from different types of studies, illustrate the manner in which assumptions are used in shaping a problem:

1. In postulating some basic assumptions implicit in motor performance, Metheny (17:489) stated that "motor performance ... can be either quantitatively or qualitatively described in such a way that degrees of difference between two or more samples of it can be detected."

2. Basic to Welch's (28) biography of Dr. Edward Hitchcock, whom he called the founder of physical education in the college curriculum, was the assumption that the educational component was not a major consideration in the limited programs of physical training that existed before the Civil War.

3. In his study to determine the attitudes of the early Christian Church Fathers toward physical activity, Ballou (2) had to assume that their beliefs reflected the dominant influences of Greco-Roman culture and that they must be assessed in this context.

4. Wilson's (30) study to assess the degree of proficiency in the performance of physical education skills by college women majoring in physical education was based on several assumptions. Among them was that the students had already attained some competency in the various sports or they would not have selected physical education as their major.

5. In her dissertation entitled, "The Phenomenology of Dance," Sheets (24) had to make certain assumptions about the existential qualities of movement—that there is meaning in motion which transcends the physiological and the kinesiological.

6. As part of his definitive study, Kenyon (13) compared the sociocultural characteristics of prospective teachers of physical education with those of prospective teachers of other subjects. Before proceeding with this investigation, the author had to assume that the attitudes toward common educational practices could differ among professional subgroups and that any given difference could be quantitatively assessed.

Each of the above statements is a substantive premise that provided one of the rationales for the ultimate design of the study. Even though articulating the assumption was important to each, what is more important was the process of critical reflection involved in arriving at the assumption. The failure of the student to come forward with tenable suppositions is an indication that he has not sharpened his perceptive and analytical skills to the degree required for scholarly research. To acquire that absolutely essential perspective, he must think his problem through to its theoretical foundations. The student who fails to follow such a procedure is headed for trouble.

Philosophic Research Method Applied to a Hypothetical Problem

An investigation built on the philosophic method must meet the criteria that govern all scientific research—it must proceed in accordance with the steps of the scientific method. The researcher must maximize objectivity and free himself of any bias in order to find the relationship as it actually exists, rather than as he hopes or feels it should exist.

Like other established methods, the design of the philosophic method will include these elements: 1) the problem clearly and succinctly stated, 2) the terms defined in the context of their usage in the study, 3) the scope of the study set forth within carefully defined limits, 4) the underlying assumptions delineated, 5) the hypothesis or hypotheses stated in propositional form, 6) the rationale and significance of the problem established, 7) the pertinent literature reviewed and its relationship to the proposed study demonstrated, and 8) the procedures outlined in such a manner that the collection of the data as well as the logic of the analysis can be followed easily from the sources of the evidence through the completion of the investigation.

The example presented below concentrates on the procedural aspects. Suppose the candidate is interested in the problem of interscholastic athletics in the junior high school. He starts with the question: "Are interscholastic athletics in the junior high schools educationally defensible?" From this he formulates the statement of his problem. One that would include qualifers such as, "the need for," or, "in defense of," interscholastic athletics in junior high schools would be unacceptable. By revealing his bias, the investigator has violated the canons of scientific research at the outset. His problem would be stated simply as an investigation of the arguments for and against interscholastic athletics for junior high schools. He will conclude, on the basis of the evidence he has collected and analyzed, whether the program is defensible.

The researcher would then advance a hypothesis to give specific direction to his investigation. Since an affirmative hypothesis is always preferred to a negative, he could hypothesize that interscholastic athletics for junior high school students are educationally beneficial. "Educationally beneficial" would be defined operationally so that a specific determination could be made, based on an analysis of the evidence, as to the justification of students participating in competitive sports sponsored by the school. The needs and interests of students in this age group, as well as the long-range and immediate effects on the school and community, would be major considerations.

One way of proceeding with the collection of data would be to divide the study into aspects of human growth and development as they relate to adolescents. These aspects could include the psychological, physiological, skill-learnings, and sociological factors. Since the study is grounded in the literature, criteria would be established for selecting the authorities in the fields of physical education, educational psychology, medicine, and human development whose writings would be examined. Their views as to the advantages and disadvantages of participation in competitive sports by this age group would be presented. Particular emphasis would be placed on empirical research conducted by the selected authors.

The researcher then would organize his data and critically analyze the evidence he has collected. Some points that he might cover would be to determine if research supported the physiological claims, if the sociological arguments were consistent, if the emphasis on winning tended to limit participation to only the few who are highly skilled, if there was evidence of exploitation, if the records of high school teams in districts that prohibited junior high school athletics compared favorably with their opponents who had "feeder" schools, if proper safety precautions were observed, if emotional pressures created undersirable effects, and if there were indications that extramural sports enhanced school spirit.

After weighing the pros and cons, the investigator would then return to the hypothesis he advanced at the outset of the study. In light of his definition of "educationally beneficial," he could affirm his hypothesis, accept it with certain qualifications, or reject it. He does not necessarily base his decision on the number of supporting views held by the authorities he was able to isolate. The fact that the majority believes a certain way is important, to be sure, but the researcher may be able to defend a counter position. The validity of his conclusion will rest on the thoroughness of his coverage, the perceptiveness he demonstrates in his analysis, and the logic of his exposition and final argument. As with other scientific research, whatever he postulates will be tentative, inasmuch as it will be within the framework he has established, and his findings will be subject to the scrutiny of other researchers who may challenge his sources, the way he handled his data, and reasoning process through which he reached his conclusion.

Suggested Problems for Research

A myth that needs to be shattered is that philosophical research has to deal with the subject matter of philosophy itself, i.e., it has to treat aspects of some "ism" or investigate ontological relationships. It is the method that is employed—the application of the philosophical tools of inquiry—that is the determining factor. A survey of the philosophical beliefs of leaders in recreation, for example, is not a philosophical study unless the beliefs are subjected to analysis and critical examination. On the other hand, a study of the value of different types of recreational experiences could qualify as philosophical research even though none of the terms common to philosophy is ever mentioned.

As Larson, Fields, and Gabrielsen (16:211) point out, the philosophic method can be applied to all types of problems in physical education, health, and recreation. This method is appropriate when it is desired to analyze ideas, relationships, principles, implications, the worth of experiences, or the value of particular activities. Ten major problems from which particular topics for research can be drawn are presented below.

Determining Aims and Objectives

Physical education and its related fields cannot afford to remain stagnant in this period of unprecedented social change. Are the objectives and content of present programs adequate to meet the needs of youth who are more aware, more outspoken, and more determined to have a voice in shaping their own destiny than any previous generation? What contributions should school programs and recreation make to an age where mankind is in danger of being strangled by conformity and where the forces of automation and mechanization are merging the individual into the mass? Educators at all levels are faced with the challenge to produce innovative and imaginative programs to combat dehumanization and to help the individual develop a set of values that he can live by. Because physical education involves the physical and emotional dimensions, it has a unique contribution to make to the development of the human personality. The various programs should be constantly reexamined to determine if the aims are current and if they are adequately preparing youth who will be living a considerable portion of their lives in the twenty-first century.

Health Education

The most pressing problems facing youth today are drugs, narcotics, and veneral disease. Is drug abuse the result of deep-seated psychological and sociological problems? What role should the school play in drug education? Should it be omitted entirely, taught in separate units, or infused throughout the curriculum? What are the arguments for and against each? If the stance is taken that drug education is the responsibility of the school, what are the alternative ways of teaching it? The same questions could be raised concerning sex education, especially in view of the campaigns to make illegal all instruction in elementary and junior high schools pertaining to this phase of human development. On what assumptions do these attacks rest? How valid are the arguments? What steps could be taken to obtain greater community support? Although the solutions to many of these problems in health education must await the findings of medical research, the questions of "should," "why," and "how" are philosophical ones.

Implications for Physical Education, Health, and Recreation in Recent Federal Legislation

Since 1964 the federal government has allocated billions of dollars to improve the plight of the disadvantaged and to strengthen programs of education from the preschool through the postdoctoral level. Studies are needed to point out untapped potentials and ways through which the profession can take maximum advantage of these resources. Funds are available to support creative and bold programs, especially in drug education and in programs that reach persons of all ages in the inner city. The philosophic task is to recognize the possibilities in the various titles and to propose viable programs that will contribute to the desired aims.

A Theory of Instruction

Jerome Bruner (5:31) asserts that, "the curriculum of a subject should be determined by the most fundamental understanding that can be achieved by the underlying principles that give structure to the subject." What are the underlying principles that give structure to professional courses in physical education, health, recreation, dance, and safety education? Are the courses structured in such a way that the student is able to integrate and internalize his knowledge to see the functional relationship with other courses in his major as well as those in cognate fields? Unless learning is synthesized and related operationally to other components in the total learning environment, it is unlikely to produce significant changes in human behavior. There is the need for serious, systematic inquiry into the principles that undergird the teaching of professional courses. Although methods of teaching the various sports skills have been popular subjects for investigation, few studies have dealt with the theory of the teaching-learning process in physical education. Fewer still have gone beyond the particular to formulate concepts applicable to broad fields.

The Body of Knowledge in Physical Education

Is there a discipline that can be called health and physical education? Franklin Henry (10) makes a convincing case for the affirmative. Many critics say, however, that other than the contributions made to the teaching of sports skills, everything physical education claims is borrowed from other fields. Huelster (12) and Zeigler (31) have initiated projects to isolate subject matter that is unique to physical education and related fields. The possibilities inherent in an undertaking of this scope generate many different problems that lend themselves to philosophical research and analysis.

The Language of Physical Education

Of all the disciplines, the contemporary emphasis in philosophy on the analysis of language has had the least impact on education. The broad field of physical education could benefit particularly from an analysis of the aims, definitions, and slogans that abound in the literature. What, for instance, do these statements, taken from popular texts, mean?

> As the child grows older and his backlog of experiences becomes greater, his store of knowledge, attitudes, skills, and understandings will be richer.

> The present critical world situation has brought intensified need for good programs of physical education which will help children and youth to achieve these goals: total fitness for the tasks to be performed; courage and morale; skills for protection and survival; skills and interests for off-the-job time; democratic beliefs and skills in human relationships; and moral and spiritual values.

Before these aims could be achieved, they would have to be translated into language that the practitioner could understand. The formulation of concise definitions, an analysis of popular slogans, and the clarification of contexts in which physical education is discussed are fields for research that are largely untouched.

Cross-Cultural Studies

There is the strong possibility that the last three decades of the twentieth century will witness the triumph of modern science over all of man's physical enemies, leaving only man himself as the principal adversary. The nations of the world, as Ward (27:vii) cogently points out, are so interdependent that "planet earth, on its journey through infinity, has acquired the intimacy, the fellowship, and the vulnerability of a spaceship." What role can physical education, recreation, health education, dance, and athletics play in furthering the international understanding that is so desperately needed? Understanding starts with a knowledge and appreciation of the value systems nations seek to inculcate in their youth. Although there is considerable interest among physical educators in international education, Nixon (20:121) reports that the field is largely untouched as the focus for rigorous research. The philosophic method is the one that would be employed in comparing and analyzing relevant data derived from the study of the mores, environmental influences, educational aims, and national aspirations of other cultures.

An Analysis of the Views of Leaders in the Field

The fact that physical education is accepted as a fundamental part of the curriculum in American schools and colleges is no accident. Its place was earned because leaders with vision recognized the educational potentials inherent in physical activity and developed programs to actualize these potentials. Biographies of most of these leaders have been written, but little research has centered on their philosophies. The bases for their beliefs—their theories of value, and the assumptions each had to make concerning human growth and development, the nature of the learning process, and the role of physical activity in education—have yet to be treated in depth. A comparative analysis of the views of two different leaders or a comparison of the views of a physical educator with a man or woman in the humanities or sciences are other fertile fields for research.

Curriculum Problems

Analytical research to evaluate the worth of curriculum experiences or procedures to achieve certain objectives are always timely. Each of the following questions yields researchable topics:

> Who shall be selected to teach health?
> What is the role of outdoor education in the curriculum?
> How should we determine policies in physical education?
> Should there be credit for physical education?
> How should students in physical education be evaluated?
> Can athletic tournaments be justified?
> Can we keep professionalism out of high school athletics?
> How should interscholastic athletics be financed?

These questions were selected from among the 75 pertinent administrative problems in need of answers that appeared in *Administrative Problems in Health, Physical Education and Recreation* (1) in 1953. How much attention has been directed in recent years toward the solution of problems of this type? According to Sanborn and Hartman (21), those in the above list that pertain to physical education are still issues today. Since every question is basically philosophical, philosophical analysis, rather than normative techniques, is required to come to grips with them. The fact that little of this has been done may be a clue to why they are largely unresolved.

The Affective Domain

Significant studies employing the philosophic research method have been made in recent years by Bloom and associates (4) in stating behavioral characteristics as educational objectives. The second volume (15) in this series sets forth in operational terms the specific responses that might be expected to accrue in the affective domain—those that pertain to attitudes, feelings, thoughts, and actions. Since no subject in the curriculum involves the student in emotional situations in quite the same manner as sport, a taxonomy of behavioral responses that might be expected under different conditions would effectively supplement Bloom's research. Each of the five values in the continuum—receiving, responding, valuing, organization, and characterization by a value complex—lends itself to several different substudies in all fields related to physical education. In addition to the affective, research is needed in the psychomotor domain—the third area in this comprehensive classification of educational goals. This is the domain of the physical educator. Although it would be a major undertaking, a collaborative project to complete the final part of the taxonomies would be a distinct contribution to the literature.

THE DIFFICULTIES INHERENT IN THE PHILOSOPHIC METHOD

Candidates with little feeling for quantitative analyses often are prone to leap to philosophy or to some other method of research that is nonempirical. Such a leap could prove to be fatal for the following reasons: First, it is much more difficult to limit the scope of the problem and to develop a suitable design than in other types of research where variables can be manipulated and the findings quantified.[4] Once the design is established in empirical studies, the researcher knows precisely what he must do to solve his problem. This type of built-in gyroscope is lacking in philosophical research. The student is apt to be bogged down at any point along the way because he is never sure where his readings will take him or if the ideas he might uncover will necessitate a reordering of his procedure.

Second, the philosophic method requires a broad general knowledge as well as an extensive background in the particular field of investigation.

---

[4] A point of more than passing interest here is that the time lapse for completing Ph.D. programs is 50% longer for candidates in the humanities than for those in the physical sciences. See Wilson (29: 22).

The student should have as a minimum the foundational courses in general philosophy and a sufficient number of advanced courses to acquaint him with philosophical analysis.

Third, there is the ever-present tendency to become infected with the "serendipity syndrome." The student who is stimulated and challenged by ideas is naturally curious. This trait, though highly desirable for any scholar, must be held in check. His curosity could lead him to become so engrossed with side issues and irrelevant matters that he will not make the progress necessary to complete the task at hand. This usually happens when poring over old books and journals where the preceding essay is too interesting to ignore. Strong self-discipline is required to resist the temptation to explore writings that have little bearing on the problem. Even though the practice of serendipity may result in the researcher stumbling on significant materials, he will have to revise his timetable for completion if he makes a habit of reading five articles when he sets out to abstract only one.

Fourth, the researcher will be beset with the frustration that comes to every scholar. The more he reads, the less he realizes he knows about his subject. If he proceeds under the assumption, however, that he will not be ready to write until he exhausts the literature, he could be ready for Medicare. The challenge is to chart a clear course between the Scylla of trying to read everything and the Charybdis of not reading in sufficient depth to do justice to the topic. It takes maturity and the ability to place values in perspective to avoid these two perils.

Yet, if one acquires the background, sets attainable goals, and disciplines himself to getting the job done, he will find the effort infinitely rewarding. He will never be bored because ideas generate new ideas. His imagination will be stretched, his analytical skills sharpened, and his knowledge broadened far beyond the ramifications of his original problem. He will also, in a small but significant way, make a contribution to his profession in a field where philosophical research is sorely needed.

REFERENCES

1. *Administrative Problems in Health Education, Physical Education and Recreation*, edited by a Joint Committee of the American Association for Health, Physical Education, and Recreation and the National Association of Secondary School Principals. Washington, D.C.: AAHPER, 1953. 136 pp. (Out of print).
2. Ballou, Ralph B. An analysis of the writings of selected church fathers to A.D. 394 to reveal attitudes regarding physical activity. Ph.D. dissertation, University of Oregon, 1965.
3. Barr, A. S. Research methods. In *Encyclopedia of Educational Research*, edited by Chester W. Harris, 3d ed., pp. 1160–1165. New York: Macmillan Co., 1960.
4. Bloom, Benjamin S., ed. *Taxonomy of Educational Objectives; the Classification of Educational Goals; Handbook I: Cognitive Domain*. New York: David McKay Co., 1956. 207 pp.

5. Bruner, Jerome S. *The Process of Education.* Cambridge: Harvard University Press, 1960.
6. Cahn, L. Joseph. The contributions of Plato to thought on physical education. Ed.D. dissertation, New York University, 1941.
7. Collingwood, Robin G. *An Essay on Philosophical Method.* London: Oxford University Press, 1933.
8. Dunkel, Harold B. Philosophical approach to research. *Phi Delta Kappan* 35: 25–28, Oct. 1953.
9. Griffiths, Daniel E. The ten most significant educational research findings in the past ten years. In *Dimensions of Physical Education*, edited by Charles A. Bucher and Myra Goldman. St. Louis: C. V. Mosby Co., 1969.
10. Henry, Franklin M. Physical education—An academic discipline. In *Proceedings of the 67th Annual Meeting of the National College Physical Education Association for Men*, pp. 6–9. NCPEAM, 1964.
11. Hillway, Tyrus. *Introduction to Research.* 2d ed. Boston: Houghton Mifflin Co., 1964.
12. Huelster, Laura J. The body of knowledge in physical education—Philosophical. *Physical Educator* 22: 6–8, March 1965.
13. Kenyon, Gerald S. Certain psychosocial and cultural characteristics unique to prospective teachers of physical education. *Research Quarterly* 36: 105–112, 1965.
14. Kerlinger, Fred N. *Foundations of Behavioral Research.* New York: Holt, Rinehart & Winston, 1964.
15. Krathwohl, David R.; Bloom, Benjamin S.; and Masia, B. B. *Taxonomy of Educational Objectives; the Classification of Educational Goals; Handbook II: Affective Domain.* New York: David McKay Co., 1964. 196 pp.
16. Larson, Leonard A.; Fields, M. R.; and Gabrielsen, M. A. *Problems in Health, Physical and Recreation Education.* New York: Prentice-Hall, 1953. 340 pp.
17. Metheny, Eleanor. Philosophical methods. In *Research Methods in Health, Physical Education, Recreation*, 2d ed., pp. 482–501. Washington, D.C.: American Association for Health, Physical Education, and Recreation, 1959.
18. Mill, John Stuart. *A System of Logic.* New York: Harper & Brothers, 1848. Reprint. Toronto: Univ. of Toronto Press, n.d.
19. Muller, Gert. History as a rigorous design. *History and Theory* 6: 299–312, 1967.
20. Nixon, John E. Comparative, international, and development studies in physical education. In *Proceedings of the 72nd Annual Meeting of the National College Physical Education Association for Men*, pp. 114–123. NCPEAM, 1969.
21. Sanborn, Marion Alice and Hartman, Betty G. *Issues in Physical Education.* Philadelphia: Lea & Febiger, 1964 (2d ed., 1970).
22. Sax, Gilbert. *Empirical Foundations of Educational Research.* Englewood Cliffs, N. J.: Prentice-Hall, 1967.
23. Selltiz, Claire et al. *Research Methods in Social Relations.* Rev. ed. New York: Holt, Rinehart & Winston, 1959.
24. Sheets, Maxine. The phenomenology of dance. Ph.D. dissertation, University of Wisconsin, 1963.
25. Thorpe, James. *Literary Scholarship: A Handbook for Advanced Students of English and American Literature.* Boston: Houghton Mifflin Co., 1964.
26. Wandt, Edwin. *A Cross-Section of Educational Research.* New York: David McKay Co., 1965.
27. Ward, Barbara. *Spaceship Earth.* New York: Columbia University Press, 1966.

28. Welch, J. Edmund. Edward Hitchcock, M. D., founder of physical education in the college curriculum. Ed.D. dissertation, George Peabody College for Teachers, 1962.
29. Wilson, Kenneth M. *Of Time and the Doctorate.* Atlanta: Southern Regional Education Board, 1965.
30. Wilson, Ruth M. *Assessing Competency in Physical Education Activities.* Springfield, Ill.: Charles C. Thomas, Publisher, 1966.
31. Zeigler, Earle F. The body of knowledge in physical education. Unpublished report of a project of the Western Conference Physical Education Directors. Urbana: University of Illinois, 1966.

SELECTED READINGS

Cobb, Louise S. Philosophical research methods. In *Research Methods Applied to Health, Physical Education, and Recreation,* pp. 136–147. Washington, D.C.: American Association for Health, Physical Education, and Recreation, 1949. (Out of print).

Cureton, Thomas K., Jr. The philosophical or group thinking method of research. *Research Quarterly* 11: 75–83, Oct. 1940.

Davis, Elwood Craig and Miller, Donna Mae. *The Philosophic Process in Physical Education.* 2d ed. Philadelphia: Lea & Febiger, 1967.

Zeigler, Earle F. *Philosophical Foundations for Physical, Health, and Recreation Education.* Englewood Cliffs, N. J.: Prentice-Hall, 1968.

———. *Problems in the History and Philosophy of Physical Education and Sport.* Englewood Cliffs, N. J.: Prentice-Hall, 1968.

CHAPTER 14
WRITING PROPOSALS, THESES, DISSERTATIONS, RESEARCH ARTICLES

Hope M. Smith
Purdue University
Lafayette, Indiana

NO MATTER HOW RELEVANT, important, or interesting is the research you have done, if the results of your investigation are not reported accurately and in detail you have completed only half of your work. Many a potentially fine researcher has fallen by the wayside because he has not been as meticulous in communicating his findings to others as he has been about building the rationale and design of his study.

Writing theses or dissertations is a highly demanding and technical job. There is no room for high-flown phrases. Each sentence and paragraph must be parsimonious but filled with meaningful information. Requirements for proposals for contemplated research and articles written for technical journals reporting completed investigations are just as stringent in their demands for a less than flowery literary style. This is not to say that one must use a "Jack and Jane" vocabulary, but it does mean that synonyms chosen for much-used words must be absolutely accurate or the reader may misconstrue what has been written.

Before writing your proposal, thesis, dissertation, or research article you should be supplied with: a standard dictionary (Webster's (5) is probably the best); a writer's manual such as Turabian's (4), Campbell's (1) or Hurt's (2); Roget's thesaurus (3); and a technical dictionary such as a medical dictionary if your topic deals with exercise physiology, a behavioral science dictionary if you are writing about motor learning or perceptual items, or a social science dictionary if if you are dealing with sports sociology or some other sociological phenomena related to human performance. Thus equipped, you will save much valuable time when writing and probably produce a more accurate and readable manuscript than you would without these sources.

With these suggestions in mind, let us discuss the peculiarities of each type of technical paper that has been mentioned. Since the research proposal is the forerunner of all types, it seems logical to start with its particular requirements.

RESEARCH PROPOSAL

The proposal is an extremely important document. It should serve as a solid base from which you begin to do your research. Some colleges and universities, or departments in these institutions, are not very demanding in regard to research proposals; the barest outline is acceptable and there is no insistence on a brief review of related literature. My personal preference, and I am sure there are many who agree, is that the proposal for a research project should be as all-encompassing as possible, just short of the actual collecting of data and reporting of results and conclusions.

Problem Statement

The key to an effective research proposal is a clear, concise problem statement for this determines the subproblems to be solved, the method for collecting data, and the statistical treatment to be used (where the study is experimental). If the research is to be normative, historical, or philosophical the same requirement holds true.

Many graduate students tend to become a bit impatient with their major advisors after the problem statement has been turned back for a rewrite for the fourth or fifth time. Impatience, however, does not speed up progress at this stage of the writing. Until you have communicated to others exactly what is the problem you wish to solve, there is no point in going further. A good practice in testing your statement for clarity is to ask someone who knows absolutely nothing about the topic you are going to investigate to read the problem statement and then tell you in his own words what it is that you are about to research. Very often this naive and unbiased interpretation will help you in writing precisely what you wish to communicate.

Subproblems

Some problems cannot be solved unless one has gathered prior information necessary to the solution of the primary question. In this case, one states subproblems that are substantive. Subproblems should not ask methodological or procedural questions such as, What skill test should be used to measure the throwing ability of sixth grade boys? Rather, a substantive question should be posed; for instance, What is the mean distance achieved by sixth grade boys in the performance of the overarm throw of a softball? If one is proposing to investigate the relationship between strength of selected muscle groups and overarm throwing ability of sixth grade boys, then prior information concerning throwing ability and strength levels must be obtained before the relationship can be established. Thus, two substantive subproblems could be stated in this instance, one dealing with strength and one dealing with the throwing ability of sixth grade boys. The method used to gather this information is described and justified below under "Methodology and Procedures."

Related Literature

Although in some instances proposals are required to contain very little, if any, review of related literature, it is this writer's opinion that the related literature section of a proposal should be well developed. There should be enough discussion of work relevant to the proposed investigation to demonstrate the rationale for the proposed study, enough to inform the reader of the proposal that the researcher-to-be is well acquainted with the important and significant work in his specific area of study.

Definitions, Basic Assumptions, and Hypotheses

Following a reasonable and clear discussion of related work, the writing of the definitions of terms, the assumptions undergirding the proposed research, and substantive hypotheses should pose no problem to the writer, although definitions are sometimes a bit difficult. One should avoid using the term being defined in its own definition, for instance:

> Strength: The total amount of strength exerted in the performance of three trials on the hand dynamometer.

A more definitive statement would be:

> Strength: The total number of pounds of pressure achieved by a subject in an all-out performance of three trials on the hand dynamometer, using the preferred hand for all three trials.

Clear definitions serve to put the writer and the reader on the same wavelength and help to avoid any misunderstanding or quibbling over terminology.

The statement of basic assumptions and hypotheses are discussed in detail in other sections of this book (pp. 31-34, 309-312), and the reader is directed to these discussions if he needs further clarification on the writing of these topics.

Methodology and Procedures

A crucial section of the research proposal is the one describing the method to be used in solving the problem and the procedures to be followed in collecting and processing the data. When a person spends many hours in intimate association with a research proposal, as he must if it is to be a viable plan, he often carries in his head many minute operations he intends to put into action. As the proposal is written those details, unfortunately, remain in his memory bank and are never put on paper. As a consequence, the reader of the proposal may raise many serious questions about the feasibility of the procedures. The writing of this section must leave nothing to chance. Each small detail must be described in full, for the methods description and the planned procedures act as the blueprint for the research to be done.

If one is to make any mistake in writing the procedures it is best to err on the side of over-description rather than extreme brevity. The descriptions in this section of the proposal should be clear and intelligible, even to someone who knows nothing about the problem to be solved. It is extremely difficult writing because it falls into the category of "how to" literature. Anyone who has attempted to construct a barbecue outfit from the components sent through the mail by following the accompanying instructions will have a fairly accurate idea of how a poorly written procedures section might affect the reader of a research proposal!

Treatment of Data

The proposal should contain a section that deals with suggestions for treating and analyzing the data after they are collected. In a projected experimental study the statistical design should be clearly commensurate with the hypotheses to be tested. When other types of research are proposed, it should be made clear that the data are to be analyzed in appropriate ways.

When statistical treatment is suggested, the level of significance that the researcher is willing to accept should be stated. In any case, it must be patently clear to the reader of a proposal that the researcher has thought through every step of the proposed study and that ex post facto findings have no part in any section of the proposed work.

THESES AND DISSERTATIONS

Well, your proposal was fine. With a few minor revisions suggested by your committee, you followed your proposed plan and your data have been collected and analyzed as you had projected. Now you are faced with another writing task that is most exacting and the second crucial step on the way to your advanced degree.

Format

Some departments or graduate schools have their own notions about the format one should follow when writing a thesis or dissertation. If this is the case in your institution, you should be aware of these requirements and follow them assiduously. In other situations there are minimal requirements for the format of the thesis or dissertation and you are pretty much on your own in the way in which you present your final materials.

In the latter case you should organize your materials in whatever way they will best communicate to readers. A general format usually includes an introduction, need for the study, related literature, delimitations, definitions, basic assumptions, hypotheses, methods and procedures, analysis of data and results, conclusions, discussion, and implications for further study. The table of contents and list of tables and illustrations precede the other materials.

Introduction to the Study

An introduction to a study is analagous to a preface of a book. It should include such items as the researcher's interest in the topic researched, the salient points stressed in the exposition to follow, and a general overview of the area of research. This should be brief and serve as a perceptual set for the reader.

Need for the Study

This section of the thesis, if it is included, should support the practical or theoretical importance of the research. If the study is a necessary replication of a former project, this should be stated. If it is another step in advancing knowledge in an area that has enjoyed much prior attention, or if it is a study that serves to break the barriers in a hitherto unresearched area, this, too, should be noted. This section serves to direct the reader's attention to important considerations. If such a section is not included, the information it would normally contain is discussed in the introduction.

Related Literature

Writings and studies in the area of the completed research should be dealt with in the writer's proposal, but not in the depth that is demanded by the final work. While the proposal describes studies related to the projected research, the final writing of this section must be critical and analytical, not just a chronology of events. A pedestrian account, such as the following, would be inadequate: "Johnson and Aniwiddy (15) in 1915 reported a significant difference between hod-carriers and mailmen in their ability to lift 10 lb weights over a protracted period; Metcalfe and Bannon (22) replicated the Johnson-Aniwiddy Study in 1923 and reported differing results." It would be more informative if the writer stated that, "Johnson and Aniwiddy (15) in 1915 reported a significant difference between hod-carriers and mailmen in their ability to lift 10 lb weights over a protracted period, but Metcalfe and Bannon (22) replicated the Johnson-Aniwiddy Study in 1923 with a slight change in the procedures and reported differing results." This statement reveals that the difference found in the Johnson-Aniwiddy study may have been caused by the procedures and not the difference in the subjects' performance.

Related literature is not only an indication to the reader that the researcher has combed the library for pertinent materials, but that he has read these materials critically and that he rejects some studies and accepts others on tenable grounds.

When one reports related literature he must analyze it in terms of its credibility. Are the conclusions of the reported research based on logic and/or experimental evidence or are they only speculations and opinions?

Chapter 4 (pp. 57-74) deals with searching the literature, and the author suggests appropriate methods for coding and organizing the materials discovered. But, as a precaution, we must suggest (at the cost of redundancy) that one establish a card file for related literature. This method of recording is far superior to running accounts of articles written in a notebook. A card file that consists of a face card for each article or book with the author's name, title of the article or book, title of the journal in which the article appears, journal volume and number, month and year, and pages on which the article appears, or the city, publisher, date, and total number of pages of a book to be cited, is far superior and more timesaving than other methods of recording. If a verbatim quote is recorded from an article or book, the pages on which the material appears should be recorded also. This type of recordkeeping saves much time and energy when the final draft of the thesis or dissertation is written. The summary of the related literature section should be such that the writer, in his own words, draws pertinent conclusions from the reported literature. This serves to build the rationale for his own work and contributions to his chosen area of research.

Definitions, Basic Assumptions, Hypotheses, Methods and Procedures

These four sections of the thesis or dissertation have been described above in the discussion on the writing of the proposal. If the proposal is adequate, these sections will need little rewriting. The only change, other than substantive changes, is that the methods and procedures are to be written in the past tense rather than the future tense. As has been suggested, clarity and attention to detail are most important in this section. If someone wishes to replicate your study he must be able to do so down to the last, minute procedure.

Results

The section of the thesis or dissertation that presents the results of the data collection is fairly cut-and-dried. When statistical procedures have been used the results are reported straightforwardly in the form of tables. The writing is also straightforward and merely serves to expand and clarify the information presented in the tables. At this point no attempt is made to speculate on the results.

Conclusions

The researcher involved in an experimental investigation is limited by his statistical results to stating whether or not his hypotheses are supported or rejected. Thus, the reader should be able to reread the hypotheses and turn immediately to the conclusions to determine whether or not the researcher's hunches were supported.

Discussion

This section of the work is one that is most free from the restrictions imposed on the researcher by the design of the study. It is the part of the thesis that allows the investigator to "let down his scientific hair." Pertinent discussion, speculation, or mini-theory may be set forth. Hunches that occurred because of various responses by subjects during testing or comments made during or after the test period may be discussed in this section. "Bugs" in the methodology or procedures employed should be delineated and pertinent; creative analyses of conditions that may have affected the results are permissible. Often this section may be of greatest interest to the reader.

Implications for Further Study

After the researcher has perused his results, conclusions, and discussion he has many suggestions for further research in the area. These implications may include 1) replication of the study with certain procedural changes, 2) replication with a different age group, 3) a change in method that may result in different findings, or 4) any related work that might be done to expand knowledge in the specific area of investigation.

RESEARCH ARTICLE

All of the foregoing suggestions may be followed when one is about to write an article for a scientific journal. However, each journal has its own requirements for the writing of manuscripts, and before the writer launches himself into the task of writing for a journal he should consult the editorial offices of that journal for the format and particulars required.

An article written in the style acceptable to the *Research Quarterly*, for instance, may not be acceptable to the editors of *Perceptual and Motor Skills*. There are many journals in psychology to which one might wish to submit his work, but each journal requests its own format. Journals in physiology or work physiology also have their particular requirements. Before submitting articles to a journal be sure you adhere to its standards and format so that your article will get the attention it merits. If you don't, it may be returned to you—unread! Most articles written for journals are considerably shorter than theses or dissertations because of publishing costs and also the publication lag that is prevalent for most scientific periodicals. Graphs, charts, and illustrations should be kept to a minimum because of extra typesetting and plate costs. You should be highly selective about what goes into the articles because your message must be clear and complete in very few words.

Whether you are writing a proposal, thesis, dissertation, research article, or a request for research funds, the requirements are the same—be concise, clear, explicit, and thorough.

REFERENCES

1. Campbell, William C. *Form and Style in Thesis Writing.* New York: Houghton Mifflin Co., 1954.
2. Hurt, Peyton. *Bibliography and Footnotes, A Style Manual.* Berkeley, Calif.: University of California Press, 1963.
3. Roget, Peter M. *Roget's University Thesaurus.* Edited by C.O.S. Mawson. New York: Thomas Y. Crowell Co., 1963.
4. Turabian, Kate. *A Manual for Writers of Term Papers, Theses, and Dissertations.* Chicago: University of Chicago Press, 1955.
5. *Webster's Seventh New Collegiate Dictionary.* Springfield, Mass.: G. & C. Merriam Co., 1963.

CHAPTER 15 ORAL RESEARCH REPORTS

Perry B. Johnson
University of Toledo
Toledo, Ohio

ALTHOUGH THERE MAY BE DIFFERENT PERSONAL motivations which lead one to submit a research paper for consideration as a part of a state, regional, or national research program, there is clearly and simply but one purpose for any research paper — *to inform*. It is imperative that a research paper accomplish this purpose. A research presentation can be many other things, ranging from interesting to entertaining, depending upon the particular personality traits and speaking skills of the speaker, but in the final analysis a research paper must be judged on whether or not it was completely and thoroughly informative. The audience must *understand*; it is not your purpose to persuade or entertain. If most of the audience understands why the study was done, what the process was, what your conclusions and interpretations are, then the presentation has succeeded. They may not endorse your interpretations, but they know what you have done. The particular things about which the paper must inform the listener vary somewhat according to the type of paper; these will be outlined and discussed subsequently.

TYPES OF ORAL RESEARCH REPORTS

There are basically only two major types of research papers, those which review and synthesize the literature relating to a particular area of scientific investigation, and those which simply report the results of some specific research study. One might argue that a third type exists—one in which the author presents a new or modified theory. But this seldom can be done a priori, since any theory or hypothesis must almost without exception be based on some prior evidence; thus, such papers really fall under the general category of review and synthesis of research.

By far the more prevalent of the two types of research papers is the presentation of a specific research study. The reason for this is obscure, but is apparently related to the importance attached to the "scholarliness" of original research as contrasted with reviewing and synthesizing the research produced by others. This may be a most unfortunate stigma we have attached to the review paper. A thorough and carefully prepared synthesis of existing research may contribute considerably more to a profession or discipline than any number of poorly designed or inadequately presented original research papers. A good synthesis may also do a great deal to stimulate needed research. This in no way subordinates the value of reporting skillfully the results of carefully conducted original research. It is simply an effort to call attention to the need for systematic review and synthesis of research. Perhaps one reason that very few synthesis papers are presented at research section meetings is simply that the time usually allotted for papers is insufficient for effective presentation of review and synthesis papers.

Regardless of the reason, most research papers fall into the "specific research study" category and most of our attention will be directed to this type of report. However, most of the principles to be discussed are applicable to either type of research report.

GENERAL CONSIDERATIONS

In any kind of public oral presentation, there are certain factors that must be taken into account by the speaker. The research report is no exception. First, the speaker should have his objective clearly fixed in his mind. In the case of the research paper, the objective has already been identified—to inform.

Second, he must consider the audience to which the research will be reported. What is their level of knowledge (general knowledge and knowledge related to the specific research under consideration)? Will they be a "captive" or volunteer audience? What will they most probably be looking for; that is, what will they want to get from your presentation? Will they want to go away with something practical that they can use in their personal lives or in their work? How many will be there? One may wish to consider other audience characteristics, depending upon the special nature of the situation, but those mentioned are almost always of importance; they are factors which will help determine certain directions for the research paper.

A third factor to consider is one's speaking ability and characteristics. The speaker must be heard by all of the audience; he may or may not need to use an amplification system. He must consider the maximum speed with which he can speak effectively. He should try to capitalize on his particular personality traits as a speaker.

Finally, it should be obvious that the speaker must consider the particular occasion of the presentation. Is his paper a small part of a long session of unrelated research papers or part of a symposium of related papers? How much time will be available? Will there be time for questions? Are abstracts to be provided to the audience well in advance of the program? Will abstracts be provided at the meeting? What kind of visual aid equipment will be available? Will a visual aids operator be available? All of these factors will need to be considered in one way or another in order to prepare the best possible paper.

THE REPORT—ITS COMPOSITION AND TECHNICAL ASPECTS

The report of a specific research study should usually be composed of three major parts: an introduction, a description of the process, and a discussion of the product. The review and synthesis report obviously does not include the description of process, unless it is germane to include such a description for one or more of the studies reviewed.

The Introduction

There are two vital missions which a good introduction should carry out. It should set the stage for the report and catch the attention of the audience. Technically speaking, it includes all material prior to the description of the specific study. Though one or more of the following components are often left out, they are all essential to a good introduction and should help to arouse audience interest if included with some imagination and perhaps with the reinforcement offered by visual aids or even audience participation of some sort.

1. Why was the study conducted? Why was it deemed important? In other words, at the very personal level, why did you do the study? What caught *your* interest? Perhaps the same aspect will catch the interest of the listeners. Examples are: "As I watched the wrestlers weighing in, apparently drawn and dehydrated after four days of starvation, I wondered what this was doing to their health;" or "Because I had noticed that members of a class from one particular socioeconomic group seemed to excel in most physical activities where competition was involved, I became curious as to whether the socioeconomic situation might in some way affect motivation, competitive drive, and so on;" or "Epidemiological data strongly suggest that those who are engaged in sedentary occupations suffer heart attacks and have more severe attacks than those in more

active occupations; I became interested in studying the possibility that this was related *not* to the physical activity involved but to the emotional involvement in the job."

2. What was the status of knowledge about the phenomenon of interest before you initiated your study? This is commonly referred to as the "review of literature" or "review of related studies." It can be (in fact, often *is*) the least useful and most interest-destroying part of the oral research report. The purpose should be to bring the audience up-to-date concerning the status of knowledge in as few succinct statements as possible. Methods and procedures in other studies are usually, though not always, unimportant at this point. Each and every related study need not be cited. The purpose is best served by briefly summarizing what was known and/or what was *not* known at the time your study was initiated. There are obvious exceptions to this rule. If one's study is a direct repeat of an earlier study and the comparison is important, or if one's study was the same as an earlier investigation except for one critical variable, then it may be essential to be a little more explicit and detailed in describing that study. It should be obvious that a report which is primarily a review and synthesis of research will not be bound by the same restrictions concerning the length of the review.

3. What was the specific purpose of the study? After mentioning your interest in the study and providing a statement of the status of knowledge prior to the study, it is essential to state the specific purpose clearly and unequivocally. It does not suffice to say "to gain further insight into . . ." This is quite obvious. The statement must be specific enough so that when you have completed the paper the audience can determine whether or not the purpose was fulfilled. For example: "The purpose of this study was to determine the effect, if any, of regular and vigorous exercise on the collateral circulation of the heart of the guinea pig," or " . . . therefore the present study was undertaken to determine whether a cause and effect relationship exists between core body temperature and motor skill learning readiness."

The Process

Having gained attention and set the stage via the introduction, the next step is to describe as clearly and succinctly as possible the essential details of the design of the study and the procedures and methods employed. Although the technique has seldom been used in the past, it is often most helpful to the audience to provide a visual aid which clearly portrays the design of the investigation. (See Figure 1.)

If the procedures are particularly complicated or confusing, a visual aid may minimize the confusion for the audience. In describing methods utilized, provide only those details which are essential to understanding the paper. It is obviously not possible to provide such a detailed description that the methods themselves can be evaluated and analyzed by the audience. If there are inconsistencies or possible errors in method, this will have to be determined during the question period or even by personal communication after the meeting. Take advantage wherever possible of any well-known names of methods (for example, the "closed circuit method for determining basal metabolism"). The knowledge level of the audience will affect this decision, but remember that time is usually limited and even if the audience is *not* knowledgable about the method, not much will be gained from a detailed description of the technical aspects of methodology.

Although the description of design, procedure, and methods should not occupy any more time than absolutely necessary, it is important to keep in mind that the product or results you will describe will take on greater meaning to the audience if the process has been clearly presented in an understandable manner.

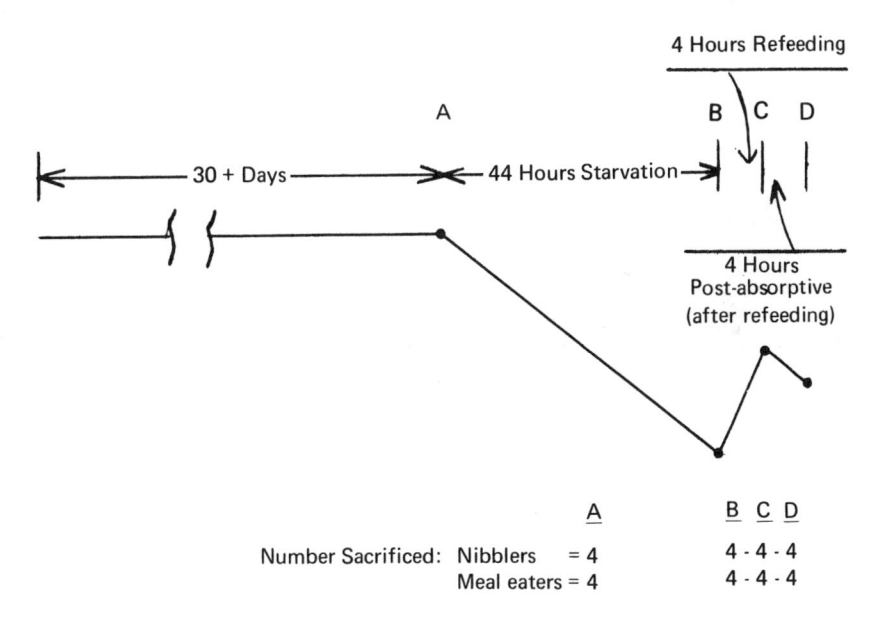

Figure 1. Design of starvation-refeeding experiment. Example of a diagrammatic representation of the basic design of an experiment. With a little explanation, the speaker could show that 32 animals were sacrificed as follows: 4 from each group (nibblers and meal-eaters) (A) after 30 days acclimatization and before starvation; (B) immediately following 44 hours starvation; (C) after 4 hours refeeding; and (D) 4 hours post-absorptive (after refeeding).

The Product

There is no universal formula for putting together the best presentation of the research product in an oral presentation. It is generally agreed that the results should be presented and that a clear-cut statement of conclusions should be offered. Although some studies lend themselves more to certain of the following ingredients than others, these should be considered as essential parts of the presentation of the research product. (Incidentally, this phase of the report is quite often the point at which the very excellent and scholarly research paper stands out above the more ordinary and inferior papers.)

1. Results. The data should be presented in a straightforward and unbiased manner; there should be no interpretation at this point. Statistical treatment which enables you to make decisions about any inferential significance of the results, if utilized in the study, can be added as the results are presented. Care must be taken to make only appropriate inferences and significant statements. It is most essential that some form of visual aids be employed to enable the audience to assimilate the information more quickly and thoroughly. *Graphs are usually much more comprehensible than tables* (Figure 2). They must be large enough to be seen from the rear of the room and should be as simple as possible. There should be a minimum of information portrayed on one graph.

Because there are more important aspects of the report than the presentation of results, when there are too many different results of the study to present all of them and to add adequate discussion and implications, it may be best to eliminate some of the results and focus on only the most important ones.

2. Discussion of results. It is at this point that the results begin to take on real meaning. Here you may shed the cloak of scientific formality. Here you have an opportunity to interpret your findings, to attempt to theorize about your results, to explain underlying mechanisms. Of course you want to be as objective and scientific as possible, to draw upon known facts and prior research wherever possible; but you may also be imaginative and may make use of extrapolation and liberal hypothesizing. Remember at this point that you are now permitted to put some of yourself into the research presentation. This is where it begins to live, this is where new research ideas can be born. You do not have to be correct in your interpretations or explanations. Naturally you hope that your interpretations and explanations are correct, but you must be willing to reexamine your hypotheses and explanations in the light of different viewpoints and new information. The possibility that you may be wrong in your interpretation should make you work diligently to avoid such error, but should not deter you from an honest effort! Interpretations and explanations are essential to the good research report. It is essential

ORAL RESEARCH REPORTS   337

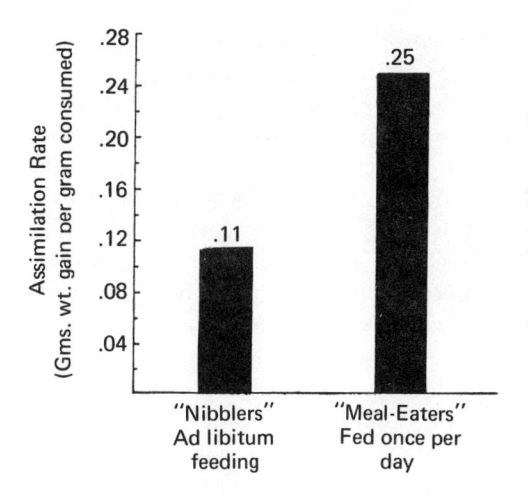

(a). Comparison of assimilation rate of consumed food in "nibblers" and "meal eaters." Ration of weight gained to food eaten. Number was 16 in each group of male albino rats. Data from Johnson and Cooper.

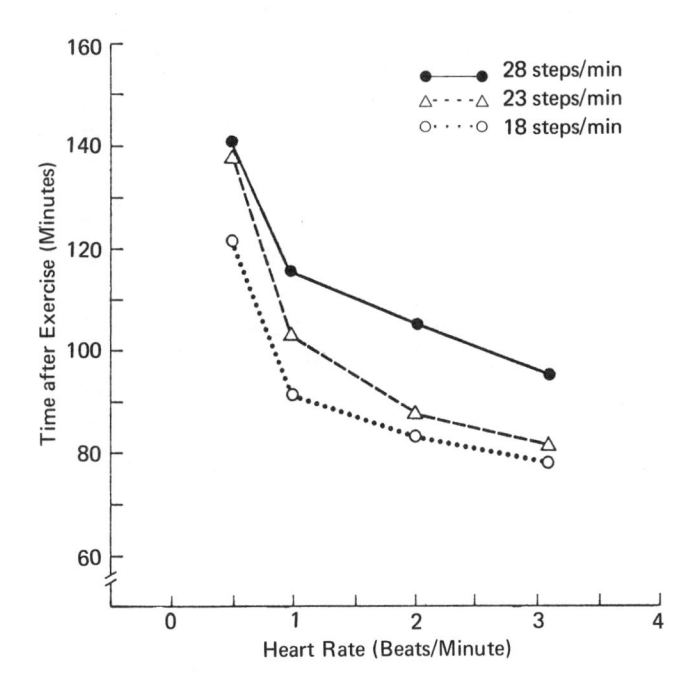

(b). Effect of varying rate of stepping on heart rate recovery. A 21 in. bench was used; the test was 2 minutes in length. Source: Physiology of Exercise Laboratory, University of Toledo.

Figure 2. Graphs are usually more helpful to the viewer than tables. Two types are commonly employed: (a) bar graph (b) line graph.

that your interpretations and explanations be *understood* by the audience, for they cannot accept or reject the position you have adopted if they cannot understand it!

The discussion of results is the ideal time to work in any important related research. It makes a great deal more sense to mention specific studies at this time than during the introductory phase of the paper. Other studies may be questioned or corroborated by your results; other studies may provide a missing link in an interpretation of your results. The presentation can become much more interesting and meaningful with effective use of related literature during the discussion phase.

3. Conclusions. In order to leave the audience with a clear picture of your study, it is necessary to tie the loose ends together. After all, you may have just completed several minutes of some interpretations and theoretical explanations which have taken you and your audience far afield from the facts supported by your study. It would be a mistake to leave them with a false impression about the specific results of the study you are reporting. As a final expression of unbiased research reporting, you should state in a clear and concise manner the conclusions warranted by your study. At this time you should make no statement that cannot be supported by your data and their statistical treatment.

Implications

If your study lends itself to any kind of important implications, either for further research or for practical use in the profession, these most certainly should be passed on to the audience. The nature of these implications will depend upon the audience to a great deal. A gathering of practitioners will benefit most from implications for teaching, while a group of researchers most likely will be more interested in implications for further research. Implications are probably best discussed just prior to the conclusions since they are usually personal reflections not necessarily based on the facts alone. From the audience point of view, implications can be the most important and most useful aspect of the research report.

Time Allotments

It is not possible to prescribe the exact time to be allotted to each part of the paper. In the case of the review and synthesis paper, most of the time should be devoted to the review with only a minimum of time allowed for the introduction.

The nature of the study, the data to be reported, the discussion to which the data lend themselves, whether or not there are important implications—all of these factors affect the time allotment for the various parts of the paper. It is possible, however, to think in terms of general principles of time allotment. This will provide a point of departure and modifications can be made with objectives and consequences clearly in focus. The following is suggested as a rough guideline based on the most common time module currently in use at scientific conferences and meetings (12 min plus 3 min for questions).

Introduction	1–2 min
Design, procedures, and methods	2–3 min
Results and treatment of data	2–2½ min
Discussion (implications, if in order)	3½–6 min
Conclusions	1 min
	12 min total time

It is quite obvious that time is usually not abundant. This means that the efficiency of presentation (technical aspects) must be *maximal* and that time spent on meaningless words is time foolishly spent!

COMMON ERRORS

Any person who has spent much time listening to research papers could easily make up a list of the most common errors and distractions. That these errors are so familiar and yet so seldom avoided is indeed incongruous. Yet one can attend any research meeting and be almost assured of finding at least several distracting errors repeated time and again, paper after paper. It is in the interest of positive and helpful criticism that these common errors are mentioned and in the hope that some attention to the avoidance and correction of such common errors will motivate our researchers, neophytes and veterans alike, to initiate a new era in research reporting. It can be an era where research reporting becomes more meaningful, useful, stimulating, and, most important, more informative and understandable.

The most common errors in oral research reporting are:

1. Too much review of literature, leaving little time for the study being reported.

2. Failure to state clearly and precisely the purposes of the study.

3. Too much material to cover in the allotted time, causing the speaker to rush through the results, discussion, and conclusions.

4. Extemporaneous speaking which, though possibly more pleasing in style, often leads to wandering and problems with finishing on time which may mean rushing through or cutting out the most important material.

5. Failure to discuss results, to make implications, to tie in results with related literature.

6. A tendency to "overkill," that is, to imply certain conclusions not fully warranted by the data (there is apparently a greater tendency to do this in an oral report).

7. Poor visual aids. The most common errors are:

   a. Using tables instead of graphs.

   b. Too many lines on one line graph. (See Figure 3.)

   c. Figures on tables or graphs too small to read from all parts of the room.

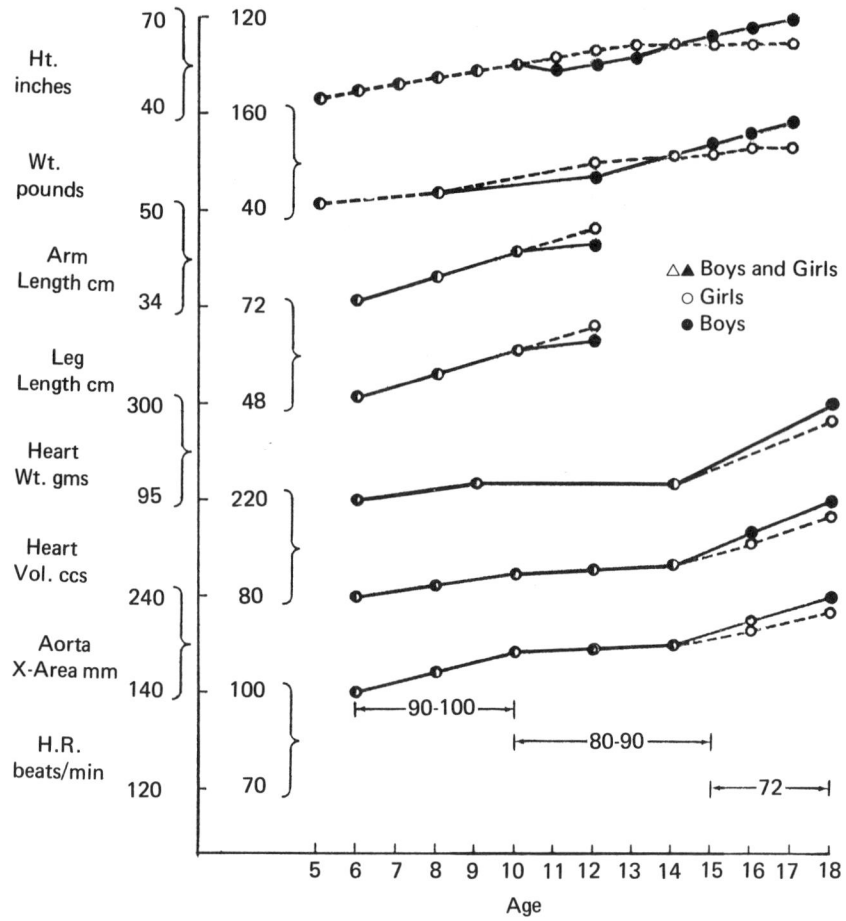

Figure 3. Various growth and circulo-respiratory measures, ages 5-18. A line graph or bar graph that includes too much data can be distracting and ineffective. Compare this with the line graph in Figure 2(b).

d. Using too many figures on one table (if tables must be used) as demonstrated in Figure 4.

TABLE A. Selected Causes of Death in the United States, 1900-1965
(Deaths per 100,000 Population)

CAUSE OF DEATH	1900	1910	1920	1930	1940	1950	1960	1965
Major cu-r[a] diseases	345	372	365	414	486	511	522	516
Heart	132	159	159	206	295	357	369	367
Arteriosclerotic heart disease	–	–	–	–	–	213	276	287
Cancer	63	76	83	97	120	140	149	154
Influenza and pneumonia	203	162	208	103	80	33	37	32
Diabetes	10	15	16	19	27	16	17	17
Cirrhosis of the liver	13	14	7	7	8	9	11	13
Ulcer	3	4	4	6	7	6	6	5
Tuberculosis	194	154	113	71	46	23	6	4

[a]Cardiovascular renal. Source: U.S. Bureau of the Census.

TABLE B. Average Prevalence of Selected Chronic Conditions,
Number per 1000 Population

CONDITION	1957-1959	1959-1961
Heart disease	29.5	30.2
High blood pressure	30.8	32.3
Ulcer	14.4	15.9
Arth.-rheumatoid	63.9	65.6

Source: U.S. Bureau of the Census.

TABLE C. Selected Causes of Death in the United States, 1900-1965
(Deaths per 100,000 Population)

CAUSE OF DEATH	1900	1910	1920	1930	1940	1950	1960	1965
Major cu-r[a]	345	372	365	414	486	511	522	516
Heart	132	159	159	206	295	357	369	367
Arteriosclerotic heart disease	–	–	–	–	–	213	276	287
Cancer	63	76	83	97	120	140	149	154
Influenza and pneumonia	203	162	208	103	80	33	37	32
Diabetes	10	15	16	19	27	16	17	17
Cirrhosis of the liver	13	14	7	7	8	9	11	13
Ulcer	3	4	4	6	7	6	6	5
Tuberculosis	194	154	113	71	46	23	6	4

[a]Cardiovascular renal. Source: U.S. Bureau of the Census.

Figure 4. Too many numbers in a table can be distracting to the viewer. Note the difference between Tables A and B. If Table A must be used, its effectiveness can be improved by circling the numbers to which you wish to draw attention (as in Table C).

8. Failure to "rehearse" adequately to determine whether time permits the entire paper to be delivered. Actual oral presentation almost always consumes more time than reading a paper to oneself, especially if it is delivered at a proper pace and not too hurriedly. Speakers are often surprised and chagrined to hear the 2-min warning signal and find that they are only half-way through the paper. Rehearsal is time well spent. One might well employ a tape recorder to evaluate the presentation before making final modifications.

9. Too much time wasted on projection of slides. This may be the fault of the projectionist, the equipment, or the speaker who has given incomplete instructions to the projectionist. In any case, several minutes can be lost and visual aid problems can be extremely distracting to the audience.

10. Speaking too hurriedly.

11. Reading paper with little or no apparent interest. While it is best to prepare the paper and "read" it (for timing purposes), it *can* be assimilated well enough in advance to prevent a dry and uninteresting presentation.

SUMMARY

1. The primary purpose of the oral research report is to inform, to have the audience *understand* your purpose, what you have done, and what you have concluded.

2. There are two basic types of oral research reports: 1) the review and synthesis of research, and 2) the report of the specific research project.

3. In putting together the final research paper, the speaker must consider the objective of the paper, the audience characteristics, his ability as a speaker, and the occasion for the report.

4. The parts of the oral report of a specific research study are: the introduction, description of the process, and discussion of the product.

5. The introduction usually includes a statement about the stimulus for the study, a summary of the status of knowledge (or lack of it) prior to the study, and a clear statement of the purpose of the study.

6. The description of the process includes any of the following that are applicable: design of the study, procedures involved, methods utilized.

7. Discussion of the product includes: a straightforward presentation of the results and any statistical treatment, a discussion of the results as related to previous studies, an effort to explain and interpret

the results, and to make implications where warranted, and, finally, a clear statement of conclusions based on the data.

8. A time allotment based on the most common time module for research papers has been suggested. It gives primary emphasis to results and discussion of results and implications, and it minimizes time for the introduction.

9. Common errors have been listed. Of these, the most critical probably are: excessive review of literature when supposedly reporting a specific original research study; too much material for the time allotted; failure to discuss the results and implications adequately; failure to assess realistically the time allotment with respect to normal speed of delivery; poor visual aids.

PART V

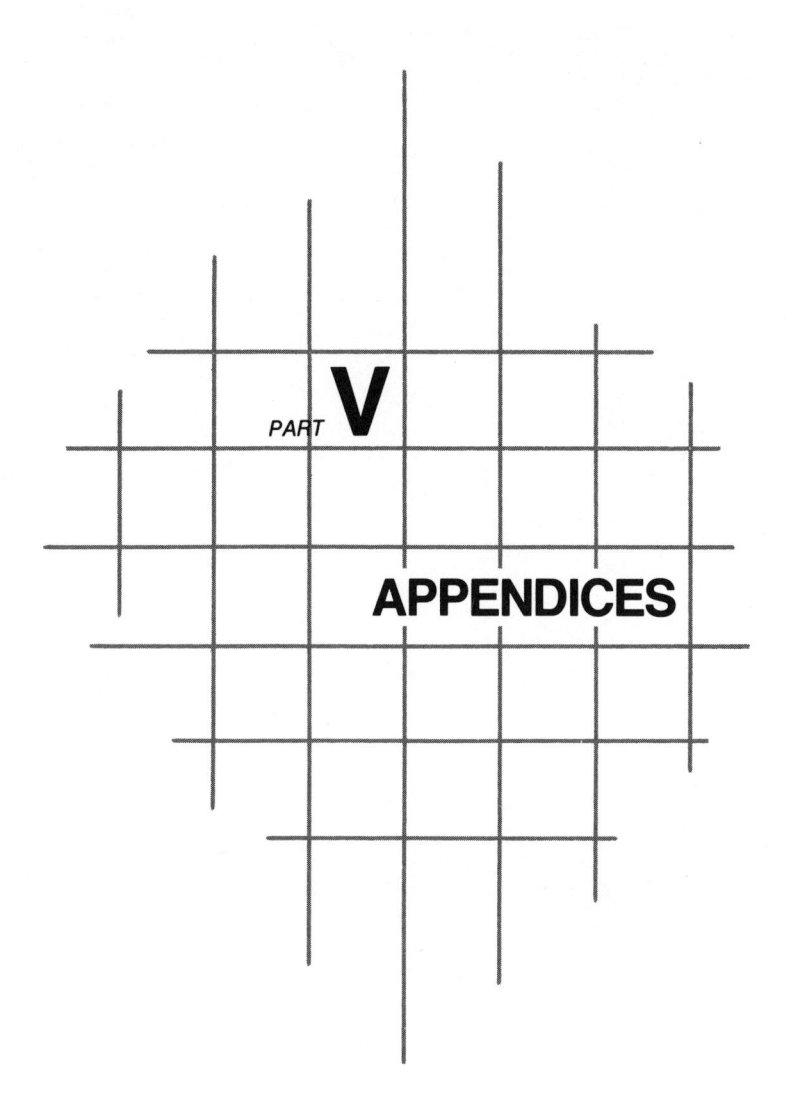

APPENDICES

APPENDIX A

SELECTED LIST OF ABSTRACTS, BIBLIOGRAPHIES, DIGESTS, AND INDICES

Vern Seefeldt

Abstracts

Abstracts of Mycology
Covers the relationship of fungi to biochemistry, cytology, genetics, microbiology, and pathology. Contains a collection of brief abstracts with author index, subject index, and cross index. A list of new books and periodicals is recorded in the front of each issue. Published monthly.

Abstracts of Regional Statistics
Abstracts compiled in order to bring together the main economic and social statistics available for regions of the United Kingdom. Consists of numerical statistical tables. Has index of sources. Published yearly with supplements which contain explanatory notes and definitions.

Abstracts of Scientific Literature
Contains selected abstracts from journals of medicine, pharmacy, chemistry, biochemistry, etc. from 1935 to present.

Abstracts of Soviet Medicine
Covers abstracts of general and specific medical topics. Aim is to make available to international medical science the significant content of medical literature published in the Soviet Union. Contains subject and author index. Published monthly.

Abstracts on Hygiene
Contains selective and critical abstracts and reviews of the world literature on all aspects of public health including: community medicine, environmental hygiene, occupational hygiene, food and food poisoning, noncommunicable diseases, communicable diseases, mycoses, microbiology, and immunity. Also contains book reviews. Published monthly in standard and single-sided editions to form one annual volume.

Biological Abstracts

An abstracting journal of theoretical and applied biology. Titles are given in original language with an English translation. Each issue contains abstracts arranged by section and subsection with subject, author, and cross indices with annual cumulations of each. New lists of books and periodicals appear in each issue. Published semimonthly.

British Abstracts of Medicine (also listed as International Abstracts of Biological Sciences)

Provides abstracts on the following topics: anatomy, animal behavior, biochemistry, cytology, experimental botany, experimental zoology, genetics, immunology and experimental pathology, odontology, pharmacology, and physiology. Attempts to cover important papers in experimental biology. Contains short abstracts and reviews of symposia and society proceedings. Contains an author index. Published monthly.

Chemical Abstracts

A comprehensive publication of abstracts from a worldwide list of journals. Contains an author index, an annual author index, and a subject and formula index from 1920. From 1960 the subject and formula indices are issued semiannually. Published weekly by American Chemical Society. The aim is to publish adequate and accurate abstracts of all scientific and technical papers containing new information of chemical and chemical engineering.

Child Development Abstracts and Bibliography

Publication of the Committee on Child Development, National Research Council, V 1–9. Contains abstracts of articles from some 125 American and foreign periodicals and book reviews. Arrangement is by subject. Author and subject indices cumulate annually. Issued three times yearly from June 1927 to present.

Dental Abstracts

Contains a selection of abstracts from periodicals of the world literature in dentistry. Includes lists of doctoral and master's theses. Annual subject and author indices. Published monthly.

Dissertation Abstracts

Contains the abstracts of doctoral dissertations submitted to University Microfilms, Inc. by various universities. Includes abstracts of dissertations and monographs in microfilm. Provides subject and author indices. Issued monthly.

Education Abstracts

Published quarterly, but now defunct. Published as *Fundamental Education Abstracts*, 1949–1951. *Education Abstracts*, 1952–1965. Not an abstract journal in the usual sense. Beginning with volume six each issue is devoted to a particular topic including bibliographies on special subjects, education in various countries, etc.

Excerpta Medica
Monthly issues are published for each section with annual author and subject indices. Section titles are general-medical. Contains short abstracts. It is the international medical abstracting service.

Health Ed Journal
Includes selected articles and editorials in health. Contains table of contents, but no index. Published bimonthly since 1938.

International Aerospace Abstracts
Covers published literature in periodicals and books, meeting papers and conference proceedings issued by professional and academic organizations, and translations of journals and articles. Has a subject index. Published semimonthly.

Medical Abstracts
Ceased publication in 1957. Three volumes of book reviews covering internal medicine, pediatrics, surgery, neurology, and obstetrics and gynecology. Included a table of contents but no indices. Was published monthly.

Nutritional Abstracts and Reviews
Contains a collection of abstracts and reviews of interpretive material covering subjects such as diseases of deficiency, metabolism and physiology, and therapeutic studies. Issued under the direction of the Commonwealth Agricultural Bureaux Council and Medical Research Council of Aberdeen, Scotland. Contains annual table of contents and author and subject indices. Published quarterly.

Physiological Abstracts
Contains a collection of abstracts on general physiological topics. Subject and author index.

Social Science Abstracts
Comprehensive abstracting and indexing journal of the world's periodical literature in the social sciences. Ceased publication in 1933. An extensive bibliography with abstracts written by specialists.

Sociological Abstracts
A classified abstract journal covering a broad range of sociological articles in periodicals of various languages. Published nine times a year since 1952; cumulated index appears in December.

Zoological Record
Comprehensive abstracting and indexing journal to zoological literature published in all parts of the world. Particularly useful for systematic

zoology. Detailed subject index, author index, and list of new generic and subgeneric names. Literature is related in sections of a phylum or class of animal kingdom. Published annually.

Bibliographies

Bibliography of the American Journal of Nursing
Under *American Journal of Nursing* (Indices). Subject headings based on medical subject headings beginning with the 1966 yearly volume. Indexed by subject and author.

Bibliography of Developmental Medicine and Child Neurology
Contains a list of books and articles received during the current year. Lists journals covered and provides author and subject indices. Published annually.

Bibliography of Philosophy
Reprinted from *Journal of Philosophy*. Ceased publication in 1937. Intended to include all the scholarly philosophical literature published during the year in English, French, German, and Italian with some items in other languages. Annual classified lists with alphabetized author indices.

Bibliography of Research Studies in Education
Lists doctoral dissertations, master's essays, and other research studies. A classed list with institutions and author and subject indices. Ceased publication.

Bibliography of Social Science Periodicals and Monographs
In progress. When complete, will cover 22 countries in the Communist bloc or other areas using "difficult" languages. Each number is a classified listing of titles available in the Library of Congress. Annotations (or table of contents) and indices by subject, title, and issuing agency are supplied. Thus far the countries covered are Rumania, Mainland China, Republic of China, Greece, Albania, Hong Kong, North Korea, Republic of Korea, Iceland, Denmark, Finland, Hungary, Turkey, Norway, Poland, and the USSR.

Indices

Art Index
Provides an author and subject index to a selected list of fine arts periodicals. Fields covered include: archaeology, architecture, art history, arts and crafts, fine arts, graphic arts, industrial design, interior decoration, photography and films, and landscaping. Published in January, April, July, and October.

Bibliography of Medical Reviews

Each volume includes references to review articles in thousands of journals in many languages. Contains subject and author index. Cumulation of citations to review articles indexed in the *Index Medicus* from 1966–1970. Since 1967 it has appeared in each monthly issue of *Index Medicus* and as a separate production called *Monthly Bibliography of Medical Reviews*.

Biography Index

Cumulative index to biographical material in books and magazines. Comprehensive and intended to serve general and scholarly reference needs. Indices of name, profession, or occupation. Americans, unless otherwise noted. Published yearly.

British Education Index

Indexes some 50 British periodicals by subject. Includes an author index. Cumulates biennially. Published three times a year.

Completed Research in Health, Physical Education and Recreation

Printed annually. Covers the research completed during the previous year in health, physical education, recreation, and allied areas. Includes abstracts of master's and doctoral theses and an index of citations from selected published sources.

Cumulative Book Index

World list of books in the English language. In dictionary catalog form with entries under author, title, and subjects. Each volume includes a list of publishers with addresses. Published monthly since 1898.

Cumulative Index to Nursing Literature

A guide to book reviews, pamphlets, illustrated material, films, and recordings. Lists all auxiliary journals scanned, giving publication dates for the issues from which articles have been selected. Has subject-author reference to broad selection of subject matter of importance to nurse and related health scientists. Issued quarterly with annual indices.

Current Contents

Available for life, physical, and chemical sciences. Provides a tri-annual cumulation of pertinent international journals. Includes author index. Contains divisions of agricultural, food and veterinary sciences (1970-); behavioral, social, and educational sciences (1969-); engineering and technology (1970-); life sciences (1958-); and physical and chemical sciences (1961-).

Current Index to Journals in Education

Provides detailed indexing for articles in over 500 education and education-related journals. Contains subject index, author index, journal contents index, and main entry section. Published monthly.

Current List of Medical Literature
Published 1945–1959 semiannually, then became *Index Medicus*. International listing of all journals and periodicals with author and article in sequence of appearance. No indices.

Dancing Encyclopedia
Includes long, encyclopedic articles on various forms of dance written by specialists. Briefer articles cover biography, special ballets, types of dances, terms used in dancing, etc. Appendices include a bibliography of books on dance in English and a discography of dance music used in the theater.

Education Index
Has undergone several changes in format and content as follows: 1929–1931, cumulative subject index to a selected list of educational periodicals, proceedings, and yearbooks. 1932–1960, published monthly, cumulating throughout the year with annual and bienniel cumulations. Indices of more than 200 periodicals covering all phases of education. Included many references to books, pamphlets, and analytics in books and society transactions. 1961 to present, subject index only with coverage restricted to periodical literature.

Guidance Index
Published as *Vocational Index*, 1941–1946. *Guidance Index*, 1947–1953. Ceased publication. Contained scholarly material in guidance and related fields. Divided into material for counselor, teacher, administrator, and professional worker and student. Abstracts were published monthly.

Guide to Microfilms in Print
An annual publication which provides a comprehensive guide, in alphabetical order, to materials which are available on microfilms from U.S. publishers. Theses and dissertations are not listed. Published 1961 to present.

Index and Abstracts of Foreign Physical Education Literature
Collection of abstracts on foreign physical education literature. Index for each volume. Published yearly.

Index Medicus
Published monthly, cumulates into *Cumulated Index Medicus*. Issued in two sections—subjects and authors. Has appeared in the following format: 1879–1927, was a standard current bibliography of medicine—a classified list with annual author and subject index. 1927–1956, was published as a quarterly cumulative index medicus with an author and subject index to some 1,200 periodicals forming a general index to journal literature. 1956–1959—included a medical biography, a current list of medical literature, journals listed alphabetically, and author and

subject indices and cumulative indices to each volume. Currently a list of journals is indexed in the January issue, with supplements in the February through November monthly issues. Also included in each monthly issue are a list of U.S. publications and a bibliography of medical reviews.

An Index of Periodical Literature on Testing
Ceased publication in 1936. Literature dealt with psychological tests and results. Bibliography listed by author alphabetically. Contained subject index and cross index.

Index of Printers, Publishers and Booksellers
Index of printers, publishers, and booksellers in A. W. Pollard and G. R. Redgrave. A short title catalogue of books.

Index to American Doctoral Dissertations
Issued annually as number 13 of *Dissertation Abstracts*. Consolidates into one list the dissertations for which doctoral degrees were granted in the United States and Canada during the academic year covered. Arranged by subject classification with author indices.

Index to Current Periodicals
Lists periodicals of recent and past holdings by alphabet. Contains place of publication, call number, language, location, holdings, and cross-references. Computerized. Frequency of publication varies, with supplements.

Index to Dental Literature
Contains author and subject index to dental periodical literature. Lists dental subject headings by alphabet, and dissertations and theses by institution and author. Contains a current list of books. Published quarterly with annual cumulations.

Index to Finnish Periodicals
Index in Finnish. Contains author index, contents, and list of periodicals.

An Index to Indexes
Subject bibliography of published indices. Contains appendix, frequency table, and author-title index. Listed by subject titles. First and only edition published in 1942.

Index to Latin American Periodical Literature
Includes approximately 250,000 entries of authors, subjects, and other secondary entries. Photo reproduced from card catalogs. Indexing is on a broad selective basis from an estimated 3,000 different periodical titles. Began annual cumulation in 1962.

Index to Scientists of the World
Indexes 338 collections in the English language, covering all phases of science with listings for world scientists from ancient to modern times. Gives full name, years of birth and death, and distinguishing identification.

Index to Selected Outdoor Recreation Literature
Compilation of abstracts of articles, books, conference proceedings, directories, documents, reports, speeches, yearbooks, and bibliographies of outdoor recreation literature. Subject index, name, and biographic index. Appendices of periodicals indexed and books cited. Published yearly since 1967.

Index to Selected Periodicals
Published as *Index to Selected Negro Periodicals*, 1950–Spring 1959. Covers Negro periodicals not indexed elsewhere. Contains an author and subject index and book reviews.

Index to South African Periodicals
Indexes some 300 South African periodicals. Covers scientific and scholarly journals fully, others selectively. Combined author and subject entries are in alphabetical sequence. Issued annually with 10-year cumulations.

Index to 35mm Education Films
Gives educators a bibliographic resource guide to 35 mm educational filmstrips. Enables organizations to identify their holdings with titles listed in the National Information Center for Educational Media master file for the purpose of checking local listings. Allows producers and distributors to compare materials relative to curriculum and subject areas. It is divided into three principle sections: (1) subject guide to filmstrips, (2) alphabetical guide, and (3) directory of producers and distributors. First published in 1967. Second edition, 1970. Currently planning to publish supplements.

Music Index
A guide to current music periodical literature. Contains indices by author and subject. It represents various aspects of the music field ranging from musicology to the retailing of music. Includes complete indexing for musical periodicals. Indexes all articles pertinent to music and some of a general nature, all first performances, and all obituaries. Music reviews are listed under composer, title, and medium. Issued monthly, cumulating annually.

Population Index
An annotated bibliography of books and periodical literature in all phases of population problems. Arranged by class with annual

cumulated indices by author and country. Includes special articles and current items. Issued quarterly.

Psychological Index
Published 1894–1935. An annual bibliography of the literature of psychology and cognate subjects. Contains a classified subject list with an alphabetical author index. Lists both books and periodicals. Continued by *Psychological Abstracts*.

Readers' Guide to Periodical Literature
Indexes U.S. periodicals of broad, general, and popular character. Complete set to date consists of all permanent cumulated volumes, all annuals since the last cumulated, and the subsequent numbers for the current year. Contains full dictionary cataloging of all articles, a catalog by subject heading, and full indexing of book reviews.

Research in Education
Consists of articles and book reviews on all types of empirical research in education, whether sociological, psychological, economic, or organizational. Contains no indices, but does have a table of contents. Published semiannually in May and November.

Research Studies in Education
A subject and author index of doctoral dissertations, reports, and field studies. Includes a research methods bibliography. Annual publication.

Social Sciences and Humanities Index
Formerly *International Index to Periodicals*. It is a cumulative index made up of three forms: (1) permanent cumulated volumes covering four, three, or two years, (2) annual volumes, and (3) current numbers issued quarterly in June, September, December, and March. Important for large or scholarly library on same plan as *Readers Guide*, but covering periodicals of a different type, i.e. more scholarly journals in the humanities and social sciences.

Subject Index to Periodicals
An annual English index, 1915–1961. 1915–1916, author-subject arrangement. 1917–1919, general author index. 1920–1922, no author index. 1926 to present, alphabetical subject list to articles on definite subjects. British and American periodicals indexed. After 1940 only British material was included. Regional lists including entries of local interest were collected. Continued by the following indices: British Humanities Index, British Education Index, British Technology Index. Subject and author index with list of periodicals.

APPENDIX B

SELECTED BIBLIOGRAPHY:
Laboratory Instrumentation

W. D. Van Huss

The following are for readers interested in in-depth coverage of specific phenomena or a broader coverage of the field of laboratory instrumentation.

Instrumentation, General

Donaldson, P. E. K. *Electronic Apparatus for Biological Research.* London: Butterworth & Co., 1958.

Jackson, Herbert W. *Introduction of Electrical Circuits.* 3d ed. Englewood Cliffs, N.J.: Prentice-Hall, 1970.

Jones, E. B. *Instrument Technology.* 2d ed. New York: Plenum Publishing Corp., 1965.

Lion, Kurt S. *Instrumentation in Scientific Research: Electrical Input Transducers.* New York: McGraw-Hill Book Co., 1959.

O'Higgins, Patrick J. *Basic Instrumentation, Industrial Measurement.* New York: McGraw-Hill Book Co., 1966.

Prensky, Sol D. *Electronic Instrumentation.* 2d ed. Englewood Cliffs, N.J.: Prentice-Hall, 1971.

Reid, M. H. and Mackay, R. S. *Medical and Biological Engineering.* New York: John Wiley & Sons, 1968.

Smyth, C. N., ed. *Medical Electronics. Proceedings of the Second Conference, Paris, June 24–27, 1959.* London: Iliffe, 1960. 614 pp.

Bioelectric Potentials

Burch, George E. and Winsor, Travis. *Primer of Electrocardiography.* 6th ed. Philadelphia: Lea & Febiger, 1972.

Electrocardiographic Text Book. New York: American Heart Association, 1956. (Out of print)

Marinacci, Alberto A. *Applied Electromyography.* Philadelphia: Lea & Febiger, 1968.

Seyffarth, Henrik. *The Behaviour of Motor-Units in Voluntary Contractions.* Oslo: Skrifter Norske Videnskaps Akademie, Matematisk-Naturvidenskapelig Klasse, Nr 4, 1940. 63 pp.

Whitfield, Ian C. *Manual of Experimental Electrophysiology.* Elmsford, N.Y.: Pergamon Press, 1964.

Telemetry

Caceres, Cesar A., ed. *Biomedical Telemetry.* New York: Academic Press, 1965.

Foster, Leroy E. *Telemetry Systems.* New York: John Wiley & Sons, 1965.

Mackay, R. Stuart. *Biomedical Telemetry.* 2d ed. New York: John Wiley & Sons, 1970.

Rose, K. D. and Dunn, F. L. Telemeter electrocardiography: A study of heart function in athletes. *Nebraska Medical Journal* 49:447–456, 1964.

Slater, Lloyd, ed. *Bio-Telemetry.* New York: Pergamon Press, 1963.

Exercise Metabolism

Consolazio, Frank C.; Johnson, R. E.; and Pecora, L. J. *Physiological Measurements of Metabolic Functions in Man.* New York: McGraw-Hill Book Co., 1963.

Kleiber, Max. *The Fire of Life: An Introduction to Animal Energetics.* New York: John Wiley & Sons, 1961.

Pauling, L.; Wood, R. E.; and Sturdivant, J. H. An instrument for determining the partial pressure of oxygen in a gas. *Journal of the American Chemical Society* 68:795–798, 1946.

Spoor, H. J. Application of infra-red analyzer to study of human energy metabolism. *Journal of Applied Physiology* 1:369–384, 1948.

Van Huss, W. D. and Heusner, W. W. *The Respiratory Burden of the Field Protective Mask.* Edgewood Arsenal, Chemical Research and Development Laboratories, 1965.

W. Collins Company, Boston, Mass. (Resistance values for respiratory valves and tubing are published in the catalog for metabolic equipment).

Index of Manufacturers

1972–1973 guide to scientific instruments. *Science* 178A, no. 4063A: Nov. 1972. (This fine index is published annually by the American Association for the Advancement of Science).

Thomas' Register of American Manufacturers. New York: Thomas Publishing Co. Published annually.

Wolf, J. G., University of Wisconsin. Periodically as a function of the Research Council, a listing of manufacturers of research equipment is published in mimeograph form. Dr. Wolf has chaired this committee since its inception.

Anthropometric Measures

Bayer, Leona and Bayley, Nancy. *Growth and Diagnosis: Selected Methods for Interpreting and Predicting Physical Development from One Year to Maturity.* Chicago: University of Chicago Press, 1959.

Brozek, Josef M., ed. Body composition. *Annals of the New York Academy of Science* 110:1–1018, 1963.

———, ed. *Body Measurements and Human Nutrition. Proceedings of the Committee on Nutritional Anthropometry Food and Nutrition Board, National Research Council, Harvard University, June 17–18, 1955.* Detroit: Wayne University Press, 1956. 167 pp.

Brozek, Josef M. and Henschel, A., eds. *Techniques for Measuring Body Composition.* Washington, D.C.: U.S. Government Research Report AD286560, 1963.

Cureton, Thomas K., Jr. and Wickens, J. Stuart. The center of gravity of the human body in the antero-posterior plane and its relation to posture, physical fitness and athletic ability. *Research Quarterly Supplement* 6, no. 2:93–105, May 1935.

Howland, I. S. *Body Alignment in Fundamental Motor Skills.* New York: Exposition Press, 1953. 192 pp.

Krogman, W. M. *A Handbook for the Measurement of Height and Weight in the Growing Child.* New York: Kraus Reprint Co., 1948.

Leighton, J. An instrument and technique for the measurement of range of joint motion. *Archives of Physical Medicine and Rehabilitation,* Sept. 1955.

McCloy, C. H. *Appraising Physical Status: The Selection of Measurements.* University of Iowa Studies in Child Welfare, 12. Iowa City: State University of Iowa, 1936.

Montague, A. *A Handbook of Anthropometry.* Springfield, Ill.: Charles C. Thomas, Publisher, 1960.

Respiratory Measures

Comroe, Julius H., Jr. et al. *The Lung: Clinical Physiology and Pulmonary Function Tests.* 2d ed. Chicago: Year Book Medical Publishers, 1962.

Cotes, J. E. *Lung Function: Assessment and Application in Medicine.* 2d ed. Philadelphia: F. A. Davis Co., 1968.

Lim, Thomas P. *Cardiopulmonary Function Tests in Clinical Medicine.* Springfield, Ill.: Charles C. Thomas, Publisher, 1966.

McHardy, George J.; Shirling, D.; and Passmore, R. *Basic Techniques in Human Metabolism and Respiration.* Oxford: Blackwell Scientific Publications, 1967. 64 pp. Reprint. Philadelphia: F. A. Davis Co., 1968.

Transducers

Lion, Kurt S. *Instrumentation in Scientific Research: Electrical Input Transducers.* New York: McGraw-Hill Book Co., 1959.

Neubest, H. K. *Instrument Transducers: An Introduction to their Performance and Design.* Oxford: Clarendon Press, 1963.

Slemon, Gordon R. *Magneto-Electric Devices.* New York: John Wiley & Sons, 1966.

Computers

Advances in biomedical computer applications. *Annals of the New York Academy of Sciences* 128: Article 3, 1966.

Alt, Franz L. *Electronic Digital Computers: Their Uses in Science and Engineering.* New York: Academic Press, 1958.

Arden, Bruce W. *An Introduction to Digital Computing.* Reading, Mass.: Addison-Wesley Publishing Co., 1963.

Braun, Edward L. *Digital Computer Design: Logic, Circuitry and Synthesis.* New York: Academic Press, 1963.

Davis, Gordon B. *An Introduction to Electronic Computers.* New York: McGraw-Hill Book Co., 1965.

Fifer, Stanley. *Analogue Computation: Theory, Techniques and Applications.* 4 vols. New York: McGraw-Hill Book Co., 1961.

Hartley, Michael G. *An Introduction to Electronic Analogue Computers.* New York: Barnes & Noble, 1962.

Hoeschele, D. F. *Analog to Digital: Digital to Analog Conversion Techniques.* New York: John Wiley & Sons, 1968.

Introduction to Analog Computation. New York: American Institute of Chemical Engineers, 1965.

Jenness, Roger R. *Analog Computation and Simulation: Laboratory Approach.* Boston: Allyn & Bacon, 1965. 304 pp.

Richards, Richard K. *Electronic Digital Systems.* New York: John Wiley & Sons, 1966.

Scott, N. R. *Electronic Computer Technology.* New York: McGraw-Hill Book Co., 1970.

The use of data mechanization and computers in clinical medicine. *Annals of the New York Academy of Sciences* 161: Article 2, 1969.

INDEX

Andrews, T. G., 214
assumptions, 31-32, 225
   in philosophic research, 309-312
      definition of, 310
      examples of, 311
   in research process, 31-32
   in scientific method, 31
   in selecting research problem, 52
   statistical, 210-211, 218
   within a study, 32
axioms
   definition of, 22

Bacon, Francis, 26
Ballou, Ralph B., 311
bibliography
   (see library research)
Bloom, Benjamin S., 99
Bravais, A., 213-214

Campbell, D., 260
card catalogue
   (see library research)
case studies, 275-280
causal-comparative studies, 275
cause, 30, 180, 213-215
   analysis of, 9
   definition of, 30
comparative studies, 274-275
Council of the American Physiological Society, 74
Cureton, Thomas K., Jr., 277

data
   analysis, 144-145
      collection and, 250-251
      in case study, 278-279

      interpretation and, 256-257
      treatment in research proposal and, 326
   collecting, 143-177
      analysis and, 144-145
      controls in, 161
         environmental, 161
      identification of subjects in, 160-161
      mechanics of, 153-164
         observations, 153-154
         procedure manual, 162
         records, 154-159
         rehearsal, 163
      problems in, 169-171
      procedure for processing and, 326
      quality control in, 169
      recording and, in developmental studies, 283
   definition of, 180
   errors, in measurement, 164-172
      psychological bias, 168-169
      random errors, 164-166
      systematic errors, 167-168
   hypotheses, 244-245
      directional, 224
   interpretation of, 256-257
   longitudinal, 283-284
   population, 143-144, 247
   processing statistical, 179-180
   recording, 39, 154-159, 162
      analysis of, 39
      collecting and, 283
   reliability
      proof of, 37
      validity versus, 37-38
   storing, 162
Descartes, Rene, 39

descriptive research, 271-285
  studies, types of
    case, 275-280
      analysis of data, 278-279
      appraising effectiveness, 279
      determining value, 277
      making recommendations, 279
      obtaining relevant data, 278
      values and limitations, 280
    causal-comparative, 275
    comparative, 274-275
    developmental, 280-285
      cross-sectional method, 280-281
      difficulties in, 284-285
      interpretation of findings, 284
      longitudinal method, 281-282
        data collecting and recording, 283
        initial planning, 282-283
      need in physical education, 285
    documentary, 273-274
    interrelationship, 275
    normative, 274
    opinion polls, 273
    status, 272-273
    surveys, 272-273
developmental studies, 280-285
diary, 92-93
dissertations
  conclusions, 329
  definitions, 325-326
  discussion, 329
  format, 327
  introduction, 327
  problem solving, 326
  related literature, 328-329
  results, 329
documentary research, 273-274
Doubleday, Abner, 298-299

Ebel, Robert L., 104
Eddington, Arthur Stanley, 28
education, 3-4
  approaches to, 6-7
  purpose of, 3-4
experimental research, 10, 239-268
  biases in, 251-252
    experimenter, 252
    instrument, 252
    subject, 251-252

control in, 249-250
data
  analysis and interpretation, 256-257
  collection and analysis, 250-251
  population, 246-247
definition of, 242
designs
  adjusting with covariance, 264-265
  factorial, 265-266
  matched group, 260-261
  randomized, 261-262
    blocks, 262
  repeated measures, 261
  rotational, 262-264
  single variable, 259-260
experiment, 240-243
field, 242-243
hypotheses in, 244-245
  null, 245
laboratory, 242-243
level of significance, 253-254
  errors, 254-255
  probability, 254
nature of, 239-243
principles of, 244-252
problem, 244
rehearsal, 163
reproducability of, 251
results, application of, 266-268
statistics in, 252-257
subjects, 89-98
  intact group, 248
  manipulation of, 249
  selection of, 246-248
  stratification of, 247
  volunteers, 248
tests, items in, 106
validity, 250-251
variables
  dependent, 245-246
  environmental, 249-250
  extraneous, 246
  independent, 245
  organismic, 246
  selection of, 245-246
variance in, 256

fact, 25
  and theory, 12-16

factor analysis
  computations of, 228
  definition of, 9
Fisher, R. A., 196, 210

Galton, F., 213
Garrett, Richard E., 85
Good, Carter V., 46
Graves, Abner, 298-299
Guilford, J. P., 103-104

Hayman, John L., 46
Henderson, Robert, 298-299
historical research, 7-8, 289-303
  findings, 303
  hypotheses in, 301-303
  interpretation of data in, 301-303
  procedures in, 291-303
  purpose of, 289-291
  as a science, 290
  source materials, 292-300
    criticism of, 295-300
      examples of, 298-300
      external, 295-296
      internal, 296-297
      principles of, 300
    primary, 292-295
    secondary, 293
Huelster, Laura J., 316
hypothesis, 33-39, 51-52, 325
  conclusion and, 39
  definition of, 33
  in experimental research, 244-245
  formulation of, 33-34, 301-303
  null, 200, 212, 245
  tenability of, 39
  testing of, 35-39
  (see theory)

instrumentation, 77-141
  accuracy, 81-83, 115-116
  calibration, 38, 115-121
    accuracy as percent of scale range, 116
    accuracy in relation to true value, 116
    hysteresis loop, 117-118
    multiple instrument, 118
    point accuracy, 116-117
    standards, 118-121

  design construction, 84-85
    guidelines for, 84-85
  evaluation, 81
    criteria for, 81-84
  experiment biases and, 251-252
  hardware, 77, 113-141
    computers, 137-140
    electrical
      bio-electrical potentials, 124-129
        electrocardiography, 124-129
        electromyography, 124-126
      measuring circuits, 129-135
        potentiometer circuit, 132-134
        transducers, 134-135
        Wheatstone bridge, 131
      recording techniques, 135-137
        telemetry, 137-138
      users, 113-114
        guidelines for, 114
  precision, 83, 121
  principles for operation of, 86
  purpose of, in research, 79
  rangeability, 84, 124
  responsiveness, 122-123
  selection of instruments, 79-84
  sensitivity, 83, 122
  software, 77, 89-110
    indirect measurement, 107-110
    interview, 91-92
    questionnaire, 90-91
    subject evaluation, 93-98
    tests
      motor performance, 104-107
      written, 98-104
  standards, 118-121
  systems
    approach to, 79
    simulation of, 85-86
    subsystems, 78-79
interrelationship studies, 275
interviews, 91-92
investigator
  (see research worker)

Kaiser, H. F., 232
Kenyon, Gerald S., 311
Kerlinger, Fredrick N., 248

library research, 57-74
  automated information retrieval, 70-74

(library research, cont.)
  microfiche, 72
  microfilm, 72
  retrospective searching methods, 71-74
    Educational Resources Information Center (ERIC), 71-72
    Medical Literature Analysis and Retrieval System (MEDLARS), 71
    special indices, 72-73
      Key-Word-in-Context (KWIC), 72
      Key-Word-out-of-Context (KWOC), 72
  bibliographic cards, 64-69
    arrangement of, 64-65
    example of, 65
    information on, 65
  bibliography
    card catalog and, 59-61
    construction of, 70
    formation of, 59-63
  card catalogs, 59-61
    arrangement of cards in, 61
    bibliography and, 59-69
    classification systems, 60
      Dewey Decimal system, example of, 60
      Library of Congress system, example of, 60
    filing of cards, 61
      interfiling, example of, 63
    types of cards, 61, 62, 63
      author card, example of, 62, 63
      cross-reference cards, example of, 63
      subject card, example of, 63
      title card, example of, 63
  collation of sources, 69-70
  literature
    relevance of, 64
    review methods of, 64-69
      brief abstract, 67
        example of, 66
      comprehensive abstract, 67
        example of, 68
        writing of, 68
      reproduction of documents, 69
  methodology, 57-73
    planning, 58-59

    reference lists, 61
      abstracts, 61, 64
      bibliographies, 61
      digests, 61
      indices, 61, 72
      key words in, 58, 61
    role of, 58
    scope of, 58-59
logic, 22, 23-24, 27-28, 308

measurement
  attitude scales and inventories, 108
  of circuits, 129-135
  errors in, 164-172
  indirect, 107-110
  moment, 190
  point, formula for, 190
  projective methods, 108-109
  sociometric, 109-110
  of statistical scores, 192
  of statistical units, 191-192
Metheny, Eleanor, 311

normative studies, 274

observation, 37, 93-98
  controlled, 37
  errors in, 37
  identification of phenomena, 35
  judgment of, 94-96
  methods of, 96-98
  probability and, 29
  selection of methods, 36
  of subject, 93-98
  validity of, 37-38
opinion polls, 273
oral reports, 331-343
  common errors in, 339-342
  composition and technical aspects of, 333-339
    introduction, 333-334
    presentation, 334-335
    product, 336-338
      conclusions, 338
      implications, 338
      results, discussion of, 336
  factors involved in, 332-333
  purpose of, 331
  time allotments, 338-339
  types of, 331-332

visual aids, 334-338
  common errors with, 340, 341

Pearson, K., 210, 211, 213
phenomena
  fragmenting of, 23
  identification of, in testing hypothesis, 35
philosophic research
  assumptions, 309-311
  curriculum problems, 317-318
  definition of, 8, 307-309
  difficulties in, 318-319
  elements included in, 312
  hypothetical problem and, 312-313
  legitimacy of, 305-307
  limits of, 308-309
  physical education and, 316
  problems in, 308
  theory of instruction, 315
Poincaré, Henri, 24
population
  data, 143-144
  problem, 143-144
postulate
  (see assumption)
predictability, as measure of science, 10-12
prediction equations, 221, 222-223
probability, 28-29, 39, 193-196
  certainty and, 28-29
  definition of, 29
  degrees of freedom and, 195-196
  experiment significance and, 254
  level of, 29, 34
  normal curve and, 193-195, 210-211

questionnaires
  determination of content, 90-91
  format, 91
  timing of, 91

Ray, William S., 260
reasoning, 26-28
  deduction, 22, 27, 267
  induction, 27, 267-268
Reed, Walter S., 85
references
  (see library research)

research
  article
    writing of, 323-324, 330
  assumptions, 31-32, 52
  certainty and probability in, 28-29
  communication in, 30-31
  criteria for, 40-42, 47-51
  definition of, 21, 35
  delimitations of, 52-53
  descriptive
    (see descriptive research)
  documentary, 273-274
  errors, 164-172, 254-255
  ethics, 172-177
    between scientist and nonscientist, 175-176
    between scientist and student, 176-177
    Declaration of Helsinki, 173-174
    guidelines to, 173-175
  experimental
    (see experimental research)
  field, 242-243
  funding, sources of, 55
  historical
    (see historical research)
  instrumentation in, 79-80
    objective of, 79-80
  laboratory, 242-243
  library
    (see library research)
  limitations, 53-54
  observational, 8-9
    (see observation)
  oral reports
    (see oral reports)
  orderliness in, 23-24
  philosophic
    (see philosophic research)
  problem
    criteria for acceptance of, 47-48
    definition of, 21, 45, 49-54, 58
    duplication of, 46
    extension of, 46
    identification of, 45-47
    location of, 46-47
    selection of, 26, 45-49, 291-292
    understanding, 244
  proposal
    (see research proposal)

purpose of, 4, 18, 50
question, 32-33
rationale of, 22-23
significant, 25-26
sources, 160
statistical
  (see statistics)
steps in, 7
successful, 42
terminology, 54
title, 49
worker
  (see researcher)
researcher
  qualities of, 18-19, 24-25, 26, 48-49, 243
  role of, 4-6, 24-25
  qualifications of, 243
research proposal, 54-55, 324-326
  data analysis and treatment, 326
  data collecting and processing, 326
  definitions, 325-326
  problem solving, 326
  problem statement, 324
  related literature, 325
  subproblems, 324-325
Rosenthal, Robert, 252

sample, size of, 152-153
sampling distribution for frequencies, 210-211
sampling methods
  cluster, 150-151
  random, 146-148
  stratified, 149-150
  systematic, 148
sampling theory, 145-146
scientific method, 22-42
Seyffarth, Henrik, 126
Sheets, Maxine, 311
Sheldon, William H., 276-277
sources
  in historical research, 292-295
  original, 160, 292-295
Spaulding, A. G., 298
Spearman, C., 224
Stanley, Julian C., 260
statistics, 179-233, 252-253
  ANCOVA, 207-209, 214

  cross-products and, 208
  definition of, 207
ANOVA, 201-207
  chi square and, 211
  computations of, 204-205
  definition of, 201-202
  formula for one-way (table), 203
  purpose of, 204
assumptions, 211-212
  r and, 218-219
bifurcation, 213
calculus, infintesimal, 184-186
causal relations, 180, 213-215
  bases for, 221
centiles, 190
chi square, 210-211
  definition of, 210
  formula for, 210
classification and measurement, 180-186
communality, 228
computations, 188-189
confidence interval, 198
constants, 186
conversion formulae, 186-187
  from mean, 188
  symbols, 187-188
correlation
  definition of, 9
  matrices and reflection, 228-229
  matrix, 224
    tetrad deviation and (table), 225
  multiple, 220-222
  paired scores and, 215
  partial, 219-220
    first order, formula for, 220
    higher order, 220
  r, 215-219
    product-moment, 215
    regression and (table), 217
    significance of, 219
    standard error of, 219
    two-factor, 224-226
covariability, 213-215
  analysis of, 207-209, 214
covariance
  correction, 208-209
  in experimental research, 264-265

final means corrected for (table),
209
(see ANCOVA)
critical ratio and t distribution
correction for sample size, 199-201
definitions of, 199
curve, normal
definition of, 210
formula for height of ordinance of,
193-194
probability and, 210-211
as random error curve, 194
deciles, 190
definition of, 180-196
differential, 214
differentiation
algebra and, 185
coefficients and, 186
in infintesimal calculus
integration and, 184
distributions
platykurtic, 195
small sample, 195-196
t, 199-201
errors
computational, 188
of origin, correction for (table), 189
standard, 196-198
Type I, 200, 212, 255
Type II, 200, 255
of variance, estimate of, 201
experimentation, 212-213
research and, 253
factor analysis
computation of, 228
extracting meaning from, 231-233
fiducial limits, 198
formulae, 186-188
definitions and, 188
four-treatment design, 205-206
intercorrelation matrix, 226-228
isomorphic operations (table), 181
explanation of, 181-182
mathematical models, 181-182
purpose of, 182
McCall's T scores, 192
mean, 188
final, corrected for covariance
(table), 209

random variation of, formula for,
199-200
as reference point, 190
standard error of, 197
difference, formula for, 200
formula for, 197-198
variability of successive samples of,
formula for, 197
measurements, 191-192
moment, 215
moment measures, 190
multiple correlations: $R_{a \cdot bc}$, 220-222
multiple prediction, 222-223
equations, 222
formula for, 222
nonparametric tests, 211-212
null hypothesis, 200, 212, 245
paired scores, 200-201
parameters
best estimate of, 197
definition of, 196
as limiting factors, 211-212
point measures, 190
population and random sampling,
196-197
prediction equations
multiple, 222-223
R and, formula for, 221-222
probability, 195-196
degrees of freedom and, 195
normal curve and, 193, 210
product-moment correlation, 215
proof, 184
proportionate reference point, 152-
153
proportions, 190
bases of, 191-192
quartiles, 190
r, 215-219
raw scores, 192
reflection, 228-229
regression
coefficient, 216-218
correlation and (table), 217
formula for, 213-214
residual matrix, 229
significance, 201-202
(table), 202
standard errors, 196-198
standard scores, 192

sum of squared deviations, 203
sums of squares, 203
t statistic
   distribution and critical ratio
      correcting for sample size, 199-201
      definitions of, 199
      Student's model for, 195-196
   test variances, 228-230
   tetrad derivation and correlation matrix (table), 225
   tetrad difference, 224-226
   trend analysis, 205
   two-factor correlations, 224-226
   variability, 193
      best estimate of, 197
   variance, 203
      analysis of, 201-207
   zero
      infinity and, 182-184
      operations with (table), 183
status studies, 272-273
Student (pseud. for Gosset, William Sealy), 195-196
subjects
   behavior evaluation, 93-98
   direct approach to, 89-93
   identification of, 160-161
   selection in experimental research, 246-251
   (see also population)
surveys, 272-273

terminology, 30-31
testing
   direct, 98-107
   knowledge and understanding, 99-100
tests
   item analysis, 102-104
      difficulty rating, 102
      nonfunctioning foils, 102
      validity, 102
   motor performance, 104-105
      battery construction, 107
      criterion selection, 105-106
      experimental items, 106
      norms, 107
      objectivity, reliability, 106
      validity of, 106-107
   steps in constructing, 99-100
   written, 98-104
theory, 25-26, 27
   definition of, 25
   fact and, 12-16
   sampling, 145-146
   (see hypothesis)
Thompson, G. H., 226
thought, 24, 26-27
   (see logic, reasoning)
Thurstone, L. L., 226

Van Dalen, Deobold B., 46-47

Watson, James D., 24
Welch, Edmond, 311
Whitehead, Alfred North, 31
Whitney, Frederick L., 47
Wilson, Ruth M. 311

Zeigler, Earle F., 316

The American Association for Health, Physical Education, and Recreation is the voluntary professional organization which brings together teachers, administrators, leaders, and students in these related fields. The AAHPER membership, now more than 40,000, is concerned with the present condition and future progress of physical education and dance, health education and school nursing, athletics, safety education, recreation, outdoor education, and programs of professional preparation for leadership in these areas. The AAHPER serves members at all levels —elementary and secondary school, college and university, and community. The AAHPER is a national affiliate of the National Education Association and is housed in the NEA Center in Washington, D.C.

The Association publishes books and pamphlets to meet the varied needs of its members and the general public, averaging about 30 new titles each year. The list includes conference proceedings, position papers, sports guides and rules, reports of research, teaching manuals, and explanations of HPER intended for the general educator and public. AAHPER's publications list, giving a complete listing of materials in print, may be obtained by writing to AAHPER Publications-Sales, 1201 Sixteenth St., N.W., Washington, D.C. 20036.